THE
INTERNATIONAL
DIRECTORY OF
Voluntary
Work

THE
INTERNATIONAL
DIRECTORY OF
Voluntary Work

Edited by
DAVID WOODWORTH

Assisted by
Giles Smart

Distributed in the U.S.A. by
Peterson's Guides, Inc.
202 Carnegie Center
Princeton, N.J. 08543-2123

Published by Vacation Work, 9 Park End Street, Oxford

First published 1979
Second Edition 1982
Third Edition 1985
Fourth Edition 1989
Fifth Edition 1993

THE INTERNATIONAL DIRECTORY OF
VOLUNTARY WORK

ISBN 1 85458 085 X (softback)
ISBN 1 85458 086 8 (hardback)
ISSN 0143 — 3474

Printed by Wm Gibbons & Sons Ltd.,
Willenhall, West Midlands

Contents

Non-Residential Work in the United Kingdom 171

Introduction

It is sad to report that these are boom years for voluntary work; this fifth edition of *The International Directory of Voluntary Work* contains its widest ever range of opportunities around the world. This is not simply because we are now living in the 'caring nineties' and showing more concern for our fellow man as a reaction against the greed-dominated eighties. The reason is not philosophical, but economic; as economies around the world teeter on the edge of recession there is less government money available to be spent on non-essential services, and so more is left to be done by volunteers in making up for official cutbacks whether domestically, as they affect social services, or internationally in compensating for reductions in foreign aid. For example, at the time of going to press, cuts of up to 15% are threatened to the UK's Overseas Development Agency Budget. There is therefore more to be done: and, thanks to increasing unemployment in most western countries, there are more people available to do it.

Voluntary work can, of course, involve far more than just helping to meet basic human needs at home or abroad: tackling human deprivation is just one of its most conspicuous manifestations. The volunteer is more than a human sticking plaster to apply to the wounds that the state does not bandage. To volunteer means simply to give one's time and energies freely to help some project or cause, and volunteers may be active in any area that people feel strongly enough about to motivate themselves into action. This may be fighting starvation in Africa, or helping the campaign against smoking in Britain; acting as an unpaid labourer to assist an organic farmer in Belgium, or improving the standard of housing for the poor in Latin America.

This book sets out to cover the full range of voluntary work. At one extreme are the long-term positions away from home lasting for over a year, in which the participant may almost lose contact with their old way of life; at the other are opportunities such as helping a charity with a door-to-door collection that may require only an occasional commitment and can be done even by most people with full-time jobs and families to look after. In between the two are those placements lasting for a few weeks or months that can be done by those such as students who have a few spare months to fill during their year, or working people with generous holiday entitlements or lenient employers, who are able to make temporary interruptions into their normal ways of life.

We also have looked for opportunities to suit all types of people, from those with some highly specialised skill or qualification to those with none. Different types of work call for volunteers of different abilities, sometimes on the same premises: for example, a Romanian orphanage may need people with experience of child care, fully-qualified medical personnel and experienced decorators. No one type of voluntary work is 'better' than another. When you mention voluntary work many people will conjure a mental image of a volunteer for Oxfam riding in the back of a Land Rover laden with sacks of food aid across the African scrubland. Nothing could be less accurate than this glamorous image, as Oxfam does not send volunteers abroad: the real heroes of its aid work are the approximately 26,000 volunteers who devote part of their spare time every week to helping in Oxfam charity shops across the UK and without whom it could not raise the money needed for its work.

Another misconception about voluntary work is that volunteers are not paid. This is not necessarily true, especially in the case of long term voluntary work. No organization could expect someone to spend perhaps two years of their life totally without an income, however dedicated they may be: even the most self-denying of volunteers may wear out their last pair of socks, or need to pay to have their spectacles mended. In practice, pocket money is often paid to volunteers who commit themselves to working for more than a few weeks on any project. Long-term volunteers in developing countries will often receive what is in local terms an average wage, although it might seem a pittance by western standards.

In order to keep this book to a reasonable length we have had to follow a few principles. Political parties employ large numbers of volunteers especially during election time, but it has been assumed that anyone who is motivated strongly enough to help the local branch of their party will know how to find it. Similarly, we have excluded a number of associations and societies such as Rotary Clubs or the Variety Club of Great Britain, even though they perform many invaluable voluntary services, because they only want help from their members. We have had to be particularly selective with the section on fund-raising, as there is hardly a charity in the country that would turn down an offer to help raising money.

Few volunteers end up better off in material terms as a result of their donation of time, but they can benefit in many other ways beyond the obvious one of knowing that they have done something useful. For an unemployed person, working on a local community project can provide a constructive way of passing the time as well as a means of gaining self-confidence in a working environment and adding to a curriculum vitae to show to a future employer. For a student, helping on an archaeological dig in Israel might, in addition to providing a unique experience, add depth to studies of history. A dentist could gain a new perspective on his profession by practising in India, as might a bank manager by working with the homeless. Whatever your background, we hope that you too can find something to suit you in this book.

The International Directory of Voluntary Work is revised regularly, and any new information that you think should be included should be sent to David Woodworth at Vacation Work, 9 Park End Street, Oxford OX1 1HJ

Residential Work Throughout the World

This section of the Directory examines the different types of voluntary work for which the volunteer is required to live and work away from home. This usually means a full time commitment, ranging from a weekend to several years.

For the purposes of classification, organizations requiring resident volunteers have been divided between long term and short term. The organizations classed as 'long term' require volunteers for periods of a year or more; 'short term' denotes residential work for anything up to a year. The short term organizations are further sub-divided geographically.

Obviously the dividing line between short and long term is indistinct and arbitrary and there are many organizations which fall into both categories. In such cases these organizations will be fully described under the category in which they are most active. Cross references will then be found at the end of the chapter on the other relevant category.

Applicants for voluntary work outside their own country are reminded that visas and work permits are sometimes necessary. The fact that voluntary work is unpaid does not always exempt them from these requirements. Regulations around the world change frequently, so volunteers going abroad are advised to check with the appropriate embassy before departure.

Long Term

A dividing line has to be drawn between short term residential voluntary work, which many people can take part in without unduly disturbing the flow of their lives, and long term voluntary work, which involves a clear break with normal routine. Most working people could go on a two week voluntary placement as part of their annual holiday allowance, and many students, teachers and academics could manage to spare a couple of months or more during the long summer vacation for a slightly longer stay: some students also take a year off before or after going to, or while studying at, college.

Even now, at a time when many people feel that their jobs are less than totally secure, there can be found sympathetic employers who will allow their workers to go on sabbatical for six months or up to a year; over a year, however, and even the most generous employer may begin to have doubts about the worker's loyalty to his job. In many cases, therefore, long term volunteers must face the possibility of their job not being held open for them when they return from their placement; even where this does not happen, they risk losing the chance of climbing a rung or two on the career ladder while away.

It is, of course, not only the volunteer who is placing a lot at stake by taking up a long-term post; the organization that recruits him or her is also taking a chance. Sending a volunteer abroad for a period of a year or more involves a major investment of both time and money: in the initial screening of applicants to make sure they are suitable, in training them, which may well involve teaching them a new language, and finally in all the direct costs involved in a placement, such as air fares, insurance etc. Even when the organization or government that actually is making use of the volunteer covers the cost of housing and living allowances as, for example, happens with VSO, this still comes to a considerable sum. And a glance through this section will reveal that the type of people that recruiters are looking for to invest all this time and money in are, in most cases, people with some definite profession, skill or qualification to offer.

For the long term volunteer is, in general, no longer someone who goes to work in a developing country for a year or two with nothing specific to offer except energy and a wish to help. The emphasis with most of the large placement organizations now is to help developing countries to help themselves by sending experienced professionals abroad not only to do a specific job, but also to train a local worker to take over the job from them when the placement finishes. The range of skills needed is wide and includes people with a background in education at almost any level, mechanics, trained doctors, dentists, opticians and nursing staff, engineers, horticulturalists, foresters, builders, librarians, and administrators, among many others.

By sending professionals of these types voluntary organizations can provide a country with a level of expertise that it would never be able to afford by paying the going commercial wage. There are several reasons why it is best that people with these skills should be placed for periods of one or two years, or even longer: the first is to spread the investment over as long a period as possible. It costs the same to fly a surgeon to the Sudan whether they stay for a week or a year, but obviously it makes more economic sense to keep them there for the longer period. When they reach their placement the volunteer will need time to adjust to the new way of life, perhaps to become familiar with a new language or dialect, and to come to terms with the job they have been sent to do: then, once they have become familiar with their task, they may well have to help select the local worker who they will in due course train to replace them.

Volunteers who devote a year or more of their lives to helping others require a considerable amount of dedication to the particular cause for which they are working. It is hardly surprising therefore, that many of the organizations requiring long term volunteers are religious foundations. Some of these, like the Missions to Seamen are overtly Christian and evangelistic in outlook, and their need is therefore for committed Christians. Other Christian organizations, like the Catholic Medical Mission Board, are less interested in the evangelical side of missionary work, and more interested in providing practical help (in this case, medical) to the third world.

Not all long term work is in the developing countries, and not all projects are concerned with long-term development programmes. For example ATD Fourth World Voluntariat specialises in the developed nations of the 'first world', and the Tear Fund is an organization that handles disaster relief programmes rather than the mainstream of development.

Long term volunteers stand to gain more from their period of service than their short term counterparts. To begin with, they are likely to have had all their travel and living expenses paid. More significantly, the deeper involvement gives a greater insight into both the project and the country in which the work is done, and it may be found that abilities may be stretched further than they would be when working back home. Thus a recently qualified teacher may find him or herself confronting a whole class of adults in a teacher training college, or a young staff nurse may be appointed chief nursing officer in a brand new hospital. Anyone who survives such challenges is likely to return more confident, more skilled, and with a completely new outlook on life. But not everyone is capable of bearing such pressure, and so applicants for long term voluntary work must be prepared to undergo a rigorous selection process by the recruiting organization.

The main organizations needing long term volunteers are described in the following pages. A number of the organizations concentrating on short term opportunities also offer varying amounts of long term work. These organizations are listed at the end of this chapter, but are described in full in the various subsections of the *Short Term* chapter, which follows.

Annunciation House
1003 East San Antonio, El Paso, Texas 79901, USA (tel 915 545-4509).

Annunciation House sponsors shelters, known as houses of hospitality, for the homeless poor, intended in particular for the those without documentation, who are largely immigrants from Mexico and refugees from Central America. About 30 volunteers, who must all be over 19 years of age and in good health, are required annually; all must make a minimum commitment of one year. Jobs expected of volunteers include almost every duty and task associated with the staffing and operation of shelters for homeless people. This includes meal organization and preparation, social service casework, building maintenance, one-to-one counselling, office work and administration, lots of cleaning and painting etc., organization of guest activities, immigration counselling, duty shifts and English classes.

For the volunteer, service at Anunciation House is a way of being and living. It is essential that applicants can speak both English and Spanish, as the population with whom the House works is 100% monolingual Spanish. Since, however, the houses are located on the border, English is also necessary. It must also be emphasised that service at the houses is totally voluntary, and no pocket money is provided. After one complete year of service, a transportation stipend is provided to assist with travel back home. Board and lodging is provided and there is access to laundry facilities.

Applications should be made to the Director, Ruben Garcia, at the above address.

ATD Fourth World Voluntariat
48 Addington Square, London SE5 7LB (tel 071-703 3231).

ATD Fourth World is an international movement working in eight European countries, the USA, Canada, Asia, Africa and Central America. The movement is concerned with the 'Fourth World', a term referring to the part of any national population at the bottom of the social scale which is excluded from social, economic, and political life. Through long-term involvement with the most disadvantaged communities, the purpose of ATD Fourth World's work is to demonstrate the will and capacity of the very poorest individuals and families to fulfill their role as parents and citizens. Practical projects established with the poor include family centres, children's street libraries and learning clubs, youth clubs, literacy programmes, training workshops, family holidays and community programmes that reinforce co-operation between very disadvantaged families and the community they live in. Fourth World families are involved in the planning, implementation, and evaluation of these projects.

The core of the movement is formed by an international voluntariat, whose members are full time workers from different professions and backgrounds who are concerned by the suffering of persistently disadvantaged families. Applicants wishing to stay for a minimum of two years enter into the voluntariat training programme, which begins with a period of service in his or her country of origin. The minimum age for participation in the voluntariat is 18. Good health and references are required and previous work experience is desirable, but no specific qualifications are needed. Food and accommodation are provided and pocket money is given after three months' sevice. National Insurance contributions are paid on the same basis, but general insurance should be obtained by the volunteers themselves for the first three months except for cover for accidents while at work. Normal visa requirements apply.

The movement also organizes working weekends from its national centre in London, a three month Short Term Volunteer Scheme, and summer workcamps in the UK and France. They provide an opportunity to contribute practically to the development of ATD Fourth World and to discover how people can work together to change the situation of these families.

Agency for Personal Service Overseas
30 Fitzwilliam Square, Dublin 2, Ireland (tel 01-614411; fax 01-614202).

APSO is a state body established in 1974 to aid the transfer of skills to developing countries by qualified Irish people. Volunteers must be qualified in their particular field and be over 21.

Assignments are usually for two years. Return fares, accident and sickness insurance, board, lodging, pocket money and a resettlement allowance are normally provided.

Applications should be made to the Overseas Register at the above address.

Associate Missionaries of the Assumption
914 South 49th Street, Philadelphia, PA 19143, USA (tel 215-724 1504).

A lay missionary association, Associate Missionaries of the Assumption operate religious communities in Third World countries or their equivalent, which help the local people through education and self-development programmes. Communities currently exist in Africa, the United States, Japan and countries in Europe. Around 15 volunteers a year are required for one to two years service as parish ministry workers, health or child care workers or teachers.

Volunteers must be single Catholics aged 23 to 40 who have a college degree and are fluent in the language of the country they intend to visit. Training consists of a one week orientation course in Philadelphia. Board and lodging within the religious community and a monthly stipend are provided. The volunteer pays for medical expenses and insurance, and must obtain a visa for their period of stay as a lay missionary.

British applicants should apply to Sister Aquinas, 23 Kensington Square, London W8 before March of each year.

Benedictine Lay Volunteers
Mother of God Monastery, RR 3, Box 254, Watertown, SD 57201, USA. (tel 605-886 6777).

Sponsored by the Mother of God Benedictine Monastery this programme provides

Volunteers with the opportunity to serve American people. Volunteers provide the community with whatever skills they have — teaching, cooking, gardening, nursing, etc.

Approximately ten one year placements are available every year to single people or married couples with no dependants provided they are at least 21 years old, in good health and speak English. Appropriate qualifications are required for holding professional positions within the community. Board, lodging, liability, an allowance, local transportation and other benefits are provided. Depending on the site, short term placements of from one week to two months are also possible. The above restrictions for volunteers apply but only board, lodging, and local educational outings are provided.

Apply to the Director at the above address for further information.

Boys Hope

4200 Ripa Avenue, St. Louis, MO 63125 USA (tel 314 544-1250; fax 314 544-2789).

Founded in St. Louis, Missouri in 1977, Boys Hope's mission is to serve abused, abandoned and neglected youths. Boys Hope provides a stable home environment and a college preparatory education to capable but needy youths. Every year about 20 volunteers are needed to work in their 21 US homes, national office and summer camp in the USA. Boys Hope also has two homes in Brazil and one home in Guatemala.

Volunteers who can make a one year commitment are asked to live in the boys' homes to act as 'big brothers' or 'big sisters' and to provide a positive role model. As education is emphasized in the program, the volunteer may also contribute by acting as a tutor for the boys.

Volunteers are also needed for a summer camp in Canada; this runs from the first week in June to the first of August. The camp offers fishing, swimming, boating, archery, shooting, a ropes course and an assortment of athletics courses. The boys are offered this chance to experience the wilderness as well as learn something about themselves. Applicants must have a University degree, but there are no other restrictions as personal situations are considered individually.

For both short and long term volunteers health insurance, board and lodging, and a small allowance are provided. Applications should be made at any time of the year to Mr. John Ryan, National Program Director, at the above address.

Brethren Service

150 Route de Ferney, 1211 Geneva, Switzerland (tel 791-6330).

Brethren service is an American based organization, sponsored by the Church of the Brethren, whose primary activity relates to the exchange of personnel between America and other countries. After a brief period of orientation volunteers are assigned to a project related to social work, community development, youth leadership in churches etc. Most of those taking part in the scheme are American, but Brethren Service in Geneva does also send Europeans to projects in America. The number of participants from each European country is kept to a quota in order to maintain a balance.

Most volunteers are in their twenties, but the scheme is open to anyone over

18 who is in good health. Although Brethren service is a church sponsored agency, as are most of their projects, applicants need not be Christian in the orthodox sense but they must be motivated primarily by spiritual and humanitarian concern. The more skills the applicant has the better, although none are essential. However, most projects request persons with some training, experience or interest in 'social-type' work. A knowledge of foreign languages, for example, may increase the applicant's chances of being accepted. Volunteers going to the USA must pay for their own travel, but once there room, board and pocket money are provided. The normal term of service is one year.

Those interested should write to the Co-ordinator at the above address for further details.

Brethren Volunteer Service

1451 Dundee Avenue, Elgin, Illinois 60120, USA (tel 708 742-5100).

The goals of the BVS programme are making peace, advocating social justice, meeting human needs and maintaining the integrity of the environment. Volunteers serve in community-based organizations or national offices working on grass-roots needs as well as on systemic structural changes leading towards these goals. Projects include counselling delinquent youth, community development work, care of the elderly and people with AIDS, office work and refugee work. Volunteers serve a minimum of one year in the USA or two years abroad.

Volunteers must be at least 18 and in good health. Specific requirements may apply to some placements. The volunteers' experience begins with three weeks of orientation in preparation for service. Participants receive living expenses and $45.00 per month pocket money, as well as medical and accidental death insurance.

Contact the Recruitment Officer at the above address for further information.

Catholic Medical Mission Board (CMMB)

10 West 17th Street, New York 10011-5765, USA (tel 212 242-7757; fax 212 807-9161).

The Placement Services Department of the CMMB facilitates the placement of health care volunteers in independent medical missions in Latin America, the Caribbean, Africa, India, and Papua New Guinea. The Board reviews the credentials, licences, registration and letters of recommendation of prospective licensed physicians, surgeons, nurses, dentists, optometrists and other registered ancillary health care workers who are seeking placement as volunteers. Applicants must be fully qualified as CMMB does not accept students or residents in training.

Each mission has its own requirements, and makes its own contract with the applicant. Many missions seek one to two years (with allowance) service commitment. Some short term tours of duty lasting from two weeks are also available. Missions provide room and board. Applicants must pay their own travel costs to the mission.

Applicants should contact the Co-ordinator, Program Services, at the above address.

Christians Abroad

1 Stockwell Green, London SW9 9HP (tel 071-737 7811).

Christians Abroad is an ecumenical body which exists to help those who are thinking about long or short term work overseas. They provide an information service about opportunities abroad for different occupations and ages, and for people of any faith or none. Their individual information leaflets include several on voluntary work. Individual leaflets are available free of charge (cost of postage is appreciated). They also recruit teachers, health workers and occasionally other skills on behalf of overseas employers. Christians who will be working or travelling abroad are invited to contact them if they would like an introduction sent ahead of them to the church abroad or help in preparation.

Further information and a list of publications can be obtained from the Information Secretary.

Christian Appalachian Project
235 Lexington Street, Lancaster, KY 40444, USA (tel 1-800 755 5322; fax 1- 606 792 2219)

The Project is a Christian service organization founded to assist people in the Appalachian region of Kentucky. Volunteer opportunities are available in programmes ranging from child development centres to residential programmes. The Volunteers Program focuses on a life of prayer, family-style living and service. Volunteers must be over 21 years of age, but no special qualifications or skills are needed. The minimum length of placement is one year. Volunteers must pay for their own travel to the Project, but once there, they receive a monthly allowance and health benefits. Accommodation is provided.

Applications should be sent to Ken Kinley at the above address.

Christian Foundation for Children and Ageing
1 Elmwood Avenue, Kansas City, KS 66103, USA (tel 913 384-6500; fax 913 384-2211).

The Foundation is an organization founded and directed by Catholic lay people to work with poor and abandoned children and ageing people through person-to-person assistance programmes. Volunteers are a vital link in their service as they form part of a local mission team. Motivated by love, their goal is to embrace the poor and to serve, recognizing their dignity, and work with them towards self-sufficiency. At present the Foundation has teams working in Central and South America, India, Africa and the Philippines.

Project co-ordinators request 90 long and short term volunteers every year of varying skills and backgrounds, from agriculturalists to child care workers, nurses, building tradesmen, social workers etc. The Foundation cannot place medical doctors in a clinical or surgical setting, but there is a need for health care professionals who wish to provide more basic health care. Short-term summer placements in Venezuela are for three months. The longer term of service is one year or more. Fluency in Spanish is required for Latin American placements.

All volunteers must fund themselves, but room and board is provided at the project sites. Applicants need not be US citizens but all applicants must come to Kansas City for a four day orientation, although this does not mean that a commitment to service has been made by either party. Due to travel expenses this may be difficult for applicants outside the US. The minimum age limit is 21 years. Those interested should contact Victoria L. Hoffman at the above address.

Christian Outreach
1 New Street, Leamington Spa, Warwickshire (tel 0926-315301).

Christian Outreach functions chiefly as a child care agency working in the Far East and Africa. Its current projects include: running mother and child health clinics in refugee camps and villages in Thailand, Sudan and Cambodia; business and community development programmes in Sudan and Cambodia; working in a home for handicapped children in Bangkok; and supporting a children's home in the Philippines and a school in India. At any one time approximately 50 skilled volunteers help Christian Outreach with its work abroad for periods of between one and two years. They are needed mainly to work abroad as either midwives or paediatric nurses, but there are occasional needs for engineers, nursery nurses, community workers and administrators.

All volunteers must be at least temporarily resident in Britain, aged over 21, usually unmarried, and qualified for the job they have applied for. They should also be regular attenders of a church of some Christian denomination and be prepared to live and work as part of a team. All expenses are paid, including air fares, accommodation,· food, some pocket money and a resettlement allowance on return to the UK.

Those interested should contact the Director at the above address.

Christian Welfare and Social Relief Organization
Box 981, 39 Soldier Street, Freetown, Sierra Leone, West Africa (tel 224096/224781; fax 232 22 224439).

The Organization provides an array of much-needed services in Sierra Leone including adult literacy programmes, camp programmes, agricultural and relief work, community health programmes, rural water projects, tree planting, environmental programmes and work with the handicapped.

About 700 volunteers of any nationality are needed every year to help with teaching, construction, voluntary relief work and agricultural work. Volunteers can be aged between nine and 45, and no special qualifications or skills are needed. Short-term volunteers can stay for one month, others can stay for up to three years. Accommodation is provided, but there is no pocket money. Volunteers pay registration and orientation fees.

All applications to Rudolph Hill, the Director, at the above adress.

Church Missionary Society
Partnership House, 157 Waterloo Road, London SE1 8UU (tel 071-928 8681).

The Society sends mission partners to 26 countries in Africa and Asia. Such people go in response to requests from churches overseas for assistance in particular areas. A wide range of ages and occupations is represented by mission partners and all have a particular skill or occupation. There is a particular need for people to offer themselves for long service of six years or more. There are also some openings for short-term service; these too require a professional qualification or practical skill. All mission partners must be practising Christians though not neccessarily Anglican. All should have technical or professional training and be qualified in their field. Mission partners receive an allowance related to the cost of living in the country they work in, fares are paid and there is a pension scheme. Visa and work permit requirements vary from country to country.

The Society also organizes Experience Placements, which are opportunities for young Christians to gain cross-cultural experience of mission through being placed in an appropriate location for a couple of months. These placements are either overseas or in Britain and are task-based. Applicants are responsible for most of their own costs.

For further information about any of these schemes write to the Overseas Service Department at the above address.

Concern

1 Upper Camden Street, Dublin 2, Eire (tel 681-237/754-163; fax 757362)/47 Frederick Street, Belfast, Northern Ireland (tel 084-231056; fax 084-330839)/248-250 Lavender Hill, Clapham Junction, London SW11 1LJ (tel 071-7381033; fax 071-7381032).

Concern is an Irish non-denominational organization devoted to the relief, assistance and advancement of people in need in less developed areas of the world; it is now working in Bangladesh, Thailand, Ethiopia, Mozambique, Uganda, Sudan and Tanzania. There are currently over 100 volunteers passing on their skills to locally employed staff. The type of professionals that Concern recruit include: nurses, civil engineers, agriculturalists, horticulturalists, foresters, primary school teachers, social workers, accountants, home economics teachers and nutritionists.

Assignments are for two years and all living expenses, including return airfare, are covered by Concern. There is a lower age limit of 21 years.

For further information contact the Personnel Division at the nearest of the addresses above to you.

Covenant House

690 8th Avenue, New York, NY10036, USA.

Covenant House in New York works with homeless and hungry people under the age of 21, providing them with food, clothes, shelter, medical care, vocation training and counselling. Volunteers are needed to make a long-term commitment of at least 13 months to Covenant House and to act as counsellors and intake and assessment workers. Applicants of all nationalities can apply, but they must speak English. They should also be at least 22 years of age and in good health. Board and lodging, and insurance are provided. An allowance is offered after the first 13 months.

Applicants are invited to apply for the 30-50 places available at any time of year. Those interested should contact 'Community Orientation' at the above address.

CUSO

135 Rideau Street, Ottawa, Ontario, Canada K1N 9K7 (tel 613 563-1264).

CUSO, an independent, non-profit-making organization, has since 1961 sent more than 10,000 volunteers to fill needsfor personnel in developing countries. Originally, recruitment was aimed at young graduates for teaching positions, but the needs have expanded to include health personnel and people of all ages skilled in trades, technology, business, community development and agriculture. At any one time CUSO has about 200 volunteers in the field, and is at present operating in 26 countries in Asia, Africa, Latin America, the Carribean and the South Pacific. The annual intake of volunteers is about 100 and contracts are for two years.

Recruitment is carried out within Canada and is aimed at Canadian citizens and landed immigrants. There are no age limits (except where dictated by host countries), but all applicants must be suitably qualified and in good health. For business or agricultural posts, experience may be a more valuable asset than formal qualifications. CUSO pays tracel costs to and from the posting, also medical, dental and life insurance, and for any language training or orientation that may be necessary. Housing is either subsidised or provided free, and volunteers are also paid settlement and resettlement allowances. In principle, the employer is the overseas government or agency requesting CUSO's services, so volunteers are in most cases paid the same wage as local employees.

Enquiries should be sent to the Ottawa office, above, or to one of the 32 local or regional committies across the country. CUSO also holds regular recruitment and information meetings within Canada.

The Daneford Trust
18 Cheverell House, Pritchards Road, London E2 9BN (tel 071 729-1928).

The Trust organizes group and individual exchanges between young people in inner-city areas of the UK, particularly inner London, and young people in Africa, Asia and the Caribbean; the main placement areas overseas are Botswana, Zimbabwe and Bangladesh.

The Trust needs about nine volunteers per year to work as student/assistant teachers in schools or education centres with the Commonwealth Youth Exchange Council in London. Applicants of any nationality may apply, but applicants must live within the above areas. Applicants must be aged between 17 and 21 years, keen to do much work themselves, and willing to maintain interest and do follow-up work in the wider community after placement. Any skills, such as typing, experience of work with children, driving licence etc., would be very useful. Placements last between three months and one year. Accommodation is provided, but most participants have to share full costs (with help from Trust).

Applications should be sent to to Anthony Stevens at the above address.

East European Partnership
15, Princeton Court, 53-55 Felsham Road, London SW15 1AZ (tel: 081-780 2841; fax 081-780 9592).

The East European Partnership (EEP) was started by Voluntary Service Overseas with the objective of posting skilled volunteers to countries in eastern Europe in response to requests from these countries. It currently sends around 150 volunteers a year to Poland, Czechoslovakia, Hungary, Bulgaria, Romania and Albania.

Volunteers are needed to work as teachers of English and humanities in schools and colleges. There are also requirements for specialist childcare staff in Romania, including nursery, paediatric, sick children's and mental handicap nurses to work as in-service trainers in children's homes; social workers with experience in residential childcare and fostering are also needed. In Albania there is demand for mental handicap nurses, special needs teachers, and social workers with experience of working with mentally handicapped people.

Volunteers must have qualifications and work experience appropriate to the posts on offer, and should be aged between 22 and 70 and native speakers of English. The teaching placements last for two years; childcare and social positions in Romania and the posts in Albania are for one year. Placements begin in September and January.   For full details contact the above address.

Eirene, International Christian Service for Peace
Engerser Strasse 74b, 5450 Neuwied 1, Germany.

Eirene organizes three voluntary programmes which are complementary to each other: the north programme is operating in Europe and USA, the south programme in Nicaragua, Nigeria, Chad and Morocco and the solidarity and learning programme in Africa, Latin America and Asia. In the north programme young and older volunteers, especially conscientious objectors, work together with minority groups such as migrant workers and handicapped people: in the south programme professionally qualified and experienced volunteers collaborate with projects in agriculture, irrigation, handicrafts, community development, co-operatives, health and vocational training: and in the solidarity and learning programme volunteers are invited to propose to Eirene a project in the Third World in which they want to collaborate. This scheme is financially and morally supported by basis groups in Europe: it provides a real link on the grassroot level between the Third World and Europe.

Approximately 30 volunteers are needed each year; most of them are recruited from Germany. Those wishing to work in Europe and the USA must be at least 20 and those going to Africa or Latin America must be at least 21. All volunteers are expected to know the language of the country to which they are being sent, and to have some previous involvement in social and non-violent activities. In the north programme the minimum duration of service is one year, in the south programme it is from one to three years. Board, lodging, a monthly allowance, insurance and travel costs are all paid for, although volunteers are asked to find a support group to give some financial contribution as well as to support the service of the volunteer.

Applications should be made to the above address.

Escuela De Enfermeria — Stella Maris
Apartado Postal 28, Zacapu, Michoacan, Mexico CP 58670 (tel 436 3-1300).

Escuela De Enfermeria — Stella Maris is a private nursing school whose student body is made up of many students from very poor areas. Between one and six volunteers per year are needed to help with general school maintenance and act as secretaries or, if qualified, to be teaching nurses or doctors.   Applicants of all nationalities are welcome but a knowledge of Spanish would be helpful. It is preferable that volunteers should possess a driver's licence, the ability to type, good organizational skills and a good attitude. Placements vary from six months to a year. Accommodation is provided, as is a small monthly allowance. However, volunteers must pay their own travel expenses to and from Mexico.

Applications to Christine Wilson at the above address.

Food for the Hungry — Hunger Corps Program
7729 East Greenway Road, Scottsdale, Arizona 85260 USA (tel 602 998-3100).

The Hunger Corps Ministry of Food for the Hungry offers overseas opportunities for Christians who desire to help meet the two hungers — physical and spiritual. The Hunger Corps offers invaluable experience which can open the door to a lifetime of cross-cultural ministry or employment. For people who are just beginning, as well as those with prior overseas experience, Hunger Corps offers assignments of two to three years' commitment, as well as opportunities to serve as a career.

Volunteers must be committed Christians and able to raise their own personal financial support. At present, 50-60 volunteers are working for the Program, but there is room for many more. Volunteers work in a huge range of countries throughout Asia and Africa.

Most overseas positions currently involve skills in agriculture/animal husbandry, primary health care/nutrition, engineering/water resources, physical or occupational therapy, community development or administrative/logistics/office skills. No special linguistic knowledge or previous overseas experience are required. The minimum age limit is 18 years. Benefits include a cost of living allowance, transportation, training, pension, health/life insurance, and a return from field allowance. However, each volunteer must raise funds to cover the benefits package. It must be emphasised that applicants must be willing to make a long term commitment of at least two years.

Those interested should contact Scott D. Allen, Recruitment Co-ordinator, at the above address.

Frontier Apostolate
PO Box 7000, Prince George, BC, V2N 3Z2, Canada (tel 604 964 4424).

Frontier Apostolate aims to promote Catholic education in the Diocese of Prince George in British Columbia, Canada. Around 50 volunteers are needed annually to staff 13 elementary and two secondary Catholic schools in this region. The greatest need is for elementary and secondary school teachers but Frontier Apostolate also recruits secretaries, houseparents, bus drivers, kitchen staff, maintenance workers and Parish workers. Placements are for two years.

Canadian, American, Irish and English volunteers are accepted. Teachers need to be qualified and secretaries need general secretarial skills. It is desirable to have a driving licence. Medical coverage, room, board and a stipend of around £75 for first year volunteers and about £100 for those beyond their first year are provided but there is only limited accommodation for married couples with children. Applicants are interviewed in their home country before being accepted for a position, but once accepted will be given the necessary employment authorization.

Those interested should apply to the Director at the above address.

GOAL

PO Box 19, Dun Laoire, Co. Dublin, Ireland/9 Northumberland Ave, Dun Laiore, Co. Dublin, Ireland (tel 2809779; fax 2809215).

GOAL is primarily a Health Care Organization which focusses on primary health care, specifically mother and child health care. Their volunteers (30 at any one time) work in Sudan, Ethiopia, Liberia, Swaziland, Mozambique, Zaire, Phillipines and Cambodia.

Volunteers are required to offer their services as nurses, doctors, administrators or accountants. Many volunteers are involved in training and education in local health communities in the above areas. Applicants of all nationalities are welcome to apply, but overseas volunteers must be available for pre-departure training courses. A full driving licence is essential, as is excellent health. The minimum length of placement is one year. GOAL covers expenses, apart from the cost of travel, and accommodation (usually shared with at least one other GOAL volunteer) is provided. The minimum age limit is 21 years of age.

Applicants should write to the above address at any time of the year.

Habitat for Humanity

12 Habitat Street, Americus, GA 31709, USA (tel 912 924 6935).

Habitat for Humanity is an ecumenical Christian housing ministry whose objective is to eliminate sub-standard housing from the world. Habitat has 700 house building projects in North America and 100 projects at third world sites including Africa, Asia, the Pacifia Islands and Latin America. Thousands of volunteers are needed for the North American programmes, 300 at the International office in Americus, Georgia and 75 for third world programmes. In North America there are openings in accounting, child care, administration, book keeping, construction, clerical work, graphic arts, shipping, maintenance, photography and public relations, while in third world countries volunteers are responsible for construction, administration, and community development.

Volunteers are needed year round for periods of three months or longer for all jobs in North America but volunteers for overseas projects must be prepared to serve for three years.Volunteers to work in North America must be at least 18 years old and English speaking while volunteers for overseas projects need to be flexible and non-judgmental of other cultures, English speaking, and at least 23 years old. Construction and office skills are desirable.

Volunteers working in the US receive accommodation and pocket money to cover basic expenses but they must pay for their own transport and support and organize their own visas, etc. Volunteers for overseas projects receive six weeks of training in Americus, work permits for the assigned country, and once abroad housing, health insurance and a monthly stipend.

Contact the Director of Recruitment at the above address for more details.

Happy Acres Educational Field Centre
PO Box 65, Magaliesburg 2805, South Africa (tel 01382 ext. 31).

The Centre runs residential and day courses in practical biology to enhance schoolchildren's understanding of their prescribed biology syllabus. Many of these children come from the under-privileged section of the community. The Centre engages about four volunteers per year to supervise the children who study with prepared work-sheets in the live animal and plant displays. The more able-bodied children take guided ecology walks. Voluntary staff are also responsible for the maintenance of the live animal and plant displays and many other small sections of the Centre's work. Applicants from overseas are welcome but they must have at least an O Level standard qualification in Biology. A driving licence will make their stay more fruitful, and it is desirable that applicants should have good English, without a strong accent. The ability to get on with young people and live in a community is essential. Volunteers must be physically capable and under 25 years of age.

The minimum length of placement is one year; volunteers are required either from February to November of the year following or August to the October of the following year. Full board and accommodation, including a laundry service, are provided and the Centre pays volunteers a modest salary.

Those interested should contact Jigs Rinsma, Director, at the above address; all applicants will be asked to complete a postal interview.

House of Hospitality Ltd
Grace and Compassion Convent, Paddockhurst Road, Turners Hill, Crawley, West Sussex RH10 4GZ (tel 0342-751672; fax 0342-718157).

The House of Hospitality is an interdenominational charity running homes for the elderly based in a Catholic religious insitution. It has six residential homes, a nursing unit and sheltered flats. Volunteers are invited to join the life of prayer and charity work of this lay community of Sisters (Shalom). In an average year, the community welcomes about 20 volunteers. Shalom members are usually aged between 18 and 65, but age limits are flexible; a satisfactory medical report is normally required, however.

Members of the lay community work full-time hours, with one free day per week. They must have a desire to share in the work and prayer life of the community of Sisters. The minimum length of placement is one year. Full board and lodging are provided, together with pocket money of approximately £26 per week.

Those interested in joining Shalom should contact Sister Patricia at the above address.

Innisfree Village
Route 2, Box 506, Crozet, Va. 22932, USA.

Approximately 18 volunteers who are experienced in working with mentally handicapped adults are required every year to act both as houseparents and co-workers in the bakery, weavery, woodshop and garden at the village in Crozet, Virginia.

Volunteers of all nationalities are welcome provided that they are fluent in English, over 21 and in excellent health. The only other requirements are patience, an interest in community living, and an ability to cook. Board and lodging are provided as are medical expenses and $150 a month pocket money. Volunteers are required to stay for one year and are given three weeks holiday with $30 per day spending money. They also accumulate $45 a month for severance. Those interested should apply to the above address.

International Co-operation for Development (ICD)
Unit 3, Canonbury Yard, 190a New North Road, London N1 7BJ (tel 071-354 0883).

ICD, a department of the Catholic Institute for International Relations, recruits professionally qualified people with a minimum of two years work experience to share their skills with communities in developing countries. ICD has development workers in south and central America, Namibia, Yemen and Zimbabwe who are working to implement programmes that challenge poverty and promote development.

ICD recruits people in response to requests from partners overseas. These partners are either community organizations such as peasant federations, women's groups and co-operatives or are local development associations or government minstries. ICD development workers are employed in various capacities; as advisers in agricultural co-operatives, as health workers in urban and rural health care programmes, as trainers in peasant-run education programmes or as teacher trainers and university lecturers. ICD offers a minimum two year contract, a salary based on local rates, a UK allowance, accommodation and essential household equipment, return flights, a pre-departure grant, comprehensive insurance cover, language training and extensive briefings.

Write to the Recruitment Officer at the above address for a copy of the current vacancy list.

International Health Exchange
Africa Centre, 38 King Street, London WC2E 8JT (tel 071-836 5833).

IHE maintains a register for experienced health workers who wish to work in developing countries and acts as a co-ordinating body for the sending agencies it services. IHE also provides a health development magazine which lists posts available and conducts short training courses to prepare health workers for work in Third World countries.

For further information contact the Information Worker at the above address.

International Liaison of Lay Volunteers in Mission (Catholic Network of Lay Mission Programs)
4121 Harewood Road N.E., Washington, D.C. 20017, USA (tel 202-527 1100).

International Liaison acts as a reference centre for various agencies and programmes and potential volunteer personnel. Lay volunteers from all walks of life with many different skills and qualifications are referred to organizations which then send them on programmes which take place all over the world. Volunteers are usually aged between 25 and 65, but some are younger. Most programmes last for one to three years, but a few are for the summer only.

Those interested should contact International Liaison at the above address, who will refer them to an agency that seems to suit their interests, qualifications, etc.

International Office for Asia-YMCA of the USA
909 4th Avenue, Seattle, WA, 98104, USA (tel 206 382-5008).

Volunteers are required to teach conversational English in community-based YMCAs throughout Japan and Taiwan. The OSCY program is more than a language program, it is a cultural learning opportunity for both the teacher and the student. Approximately 60 people are placed annually. Due to visa restrictions, teachers must be US or Canadian citizens, or have successfully completed twelve years of teaching English language classes.

In Japan, teachers work a forty hour week, spending up to 21 hours in the classroom. In Taiwan, teachers are expected to work a thirty hour week, with up to 20 of these spent in the classroom. Applicants must speak English fluently, be flexible in adjusting to new situations and be interested in participating in extra-curricular activities that strengthen personal relationships and a sense of community. It must be emphasised that the length of placement for teaching in Japan is two years, while the length of placement for Taiwan is one year. Applicants must have a four-year degree. Teaching experience and training are desirable.

For Japan, the application deadlines are October 5 for spring placement (approximately 20-25 people) and March 15 for the autumn placement (approximately 5-10 people). For Taiwan, the deadline is April 15 for the autumn placement (approximately 20-25 people). Accommodation is provided on both programs. On the Japan program volunteers receive the round-trip airfare (from the US), salary, health insurance, an allowance to study Japanese for the first year, commuting expenses and paid vacation. On the Taiwan program volunteers receive return airfare (from the US), monthly allowance, health insurance, allowance to study Mandarin Chinese, paid vacation and financial bonuses.

Write to Bonnie Main at the above address for brochures and application forms.

Interns For Peace
270 West 89th Street, New York, NY 10024 (tel 212 580-0540; fax 212 580-0693)/ Rehov Geula 35, Tel Aviv 6304 (tel 03 656-525; fax 03 657-995).

IFP is an independent, non-political community sponsored program dedicated to building trust and respect among the Jewish and Arab citizens of Israel. Guided by IFP's Jewish and Arab field staff, volunteer community workers carry out the bulk of the program, while receiving in-depth work experience designed to help them become human relations professionals.

Volunteers are trained and placed to live and work in Arab and Jewish communities in Israel, where they develop projects in education, sports, health, the arts, community and workplace relations and adult interest groups. Volunteers are Jews and Arabs from Israel and abroad. Volunteers are needed every year and the usual length of placement for volunteers is two years. Applicants must have a BA, BS or equivalent degree and intermediate to advanced proficiency in Hebrew or Arabic. They must have stayed previously in Israel for at least six months, and have had experience in community or human relations work. They should also have a background in or more of the following areas: sports, business, teaching, healthcare, youth work, art, music or community organization; professional work experience is an advantage. Applicants must also possess the ability to work with staff, co-workers and people from two different cultures, as well as a high tolerance of ambiguity in confronting constantly changing situations which challenge a young, pioneering organization. IFP occasionally needs short-term volunteers during the month of July.

For further information and/or an application form, contact Interns For Peace at either of the above addresses.

Irish Missionary Union

IMU, Orwell Park, Rathgar, Dublin 6, Ireland (tel 965433/071770; fax 965029).

The IMU was founded to promote co-operation between missionary, mission-sending and mission-aid organizations, thereby helping them to make the best and most efficient use of their personnel and other resources. Its principal aim is to assist the Bishops in the task of spreading the Gospel and therefore the IMU works in close collaboration with the Irish Hierarchy. It also acts as a liaison between missionary bodies and national or international organizations involved in evangelization and development.

The IMU recruits volunteers to work in the following areas in African and Latin American countries; medicine, education, trade, agriculture and pastoral and community development. Qualified and experienced doctors, nurses, laboratory tecnicians, teachers, paramedics, builders, plumbers and social workers are all needed. It is essential that all volunteers should derive their motivation from Christian values, and be in good health and at least 21 years of age. The minimum length of placement is two years. A monthly allowance, accommodation, resettlement allowance, insurance and return airfare are all provided.

Those interested should contact the Laity Department at the above address at any time of the year.

Jesuit Volunteer Corps: California-Southwest

PO Box 23404, Oakland, California 94623, USA (tel 510 465 5016).

The Jesuit Volunteer Corps is a service organization which offers women and men an opportunity to work full time for justice and peace. Jesuit Volunteers work in the United States by serving the poor directly and working for structural change. The challenge for the volunteer is to integrate Christian faith by working and living among the poor and those on the margins of society by living simply and in community with other Jesuit Volunteers and by examining the causes of social injustice. Since 1956 Volunteers have worked in collaboration with Jesuits whose spirituality they incorporate in their work, community lives, and prayer. The JVC seeks to develop persons whose year or more of service challenges them to live always conscious of the poor, devoted to the promotion of justice and service of faith.

Applicants should be 21 years or older, or have a college education and have a firm Christian outlook, be in good physical condition, adaptable and have a good sense of humour. A one year commitment beginning in August is expected; room and board are provided, plus a small monthly stipend.

Applications should be made to the above address.

JVC Britain

Union Chapel, Wellington Road, Fallowfield, Manchester M14 6EB (tel 061 224-3411).

The Jesuit Volunteer Community offers young adults the opportunity to develop themselves through living in the community while working in areas of social need. The volunteers live together in small groups of five or six and work as full-time volunteers in a variety of placements. JVC has communities in Glasgow, Liverpool, Birmingham and Manchester. JVC offers a structured development programme which consists of a series of workshops/retreats during the course of the year. Approximately 24 to 30 volunteers are taken on each year.

Current placements include work with the homeless, with refugees, with people with learning difficulties, with victims of crime, with people with drug and alcohol addictions and at advice centres. New placements are being developed on a regular basis. The emphasis is on working with people who are marginalized or discriminated against by society. Each work placement provides any necessary training and each volunteer has regular supervision. Applicants of any nationality are accepted, but applicants must be fluent in English and must be able to pay for travel to and from Britain for interviews, and start and end of placement. Only three or four applicants from overseas can be accepted at any one time. Final acceptance is dependent on being accepted by a work placement.

Volunteers must be aged between 18 and 35, in good health, available for a full year and have Christian motivation. The usual length of a placement is one year. The JVC year begins in late August and interviews take place from January onwards. Accommodation is provided, and each work placement provides the rent, bills and food allowance, pocket money and travel expenses to and from work.

Those interested should contact Chiara Mallia at the above address.

Lalmba Association

7685 Quartz Street, Golden, CO 80403, USA (tel 303 420 1810).

The Lalmba Association operates medical clinics and other health programmes in Sudan, Kenya and Mexico. Between 20 and 40 volunteers are needed annually to staff these projects. Most opportunities are for medical staff, (physicians, nurses, and midwives), but occasionally volunteers with managerial or administrative skills are needed to act as project directors. Placements in Sudan are for one year while placements in Kenya and Mexico are for two years.

Applicants must be at least 25 years old, qualified in either the USA or certain European countries, and have some experience in their field. Round trip transportation, board, lodging, health and life insurance and pocket money are provided.

Contact the Medical Director at the above address for more information.

Lay Volunteers International Association
Corso 4 Novembre, 28 — 12100 Cuneo, Italy (tel 0171-696975; fax 0171-602558).

The Association organizes rural development, primary health care and technical training projects in the following African countries: Ethiopia, Kenya, Tanzania, Burundi, Senegal, Ivory Coast, Guinea Bissau, Mali and Burkina Faso. Each year around 20 suitably qualified volunteers are needed to undertake various technical jobs related to these projects. Placements are normally for 30 months.

Volunteers should be over 20 years old, in good health both physically and mentally, speak French, English or Portuguese according to the country of destination and have a driving licence. Accommodation within the local community and pocket money are provided.   Write to the General Secretary at the above address for more information on specific projects.

Lutheran Volunteer Corps
1226 Vermont Ave, NW Washington, DC 20005 USA (tel 202 387-3222).

The Lutheran Volunteer Corps operates a one to two-year volunteer service programme. 60-70 volunteers per year work for social justice full-time in agencies ranging from shelters and health clinics to environmental and public policy agencies. Volunteers live simply in Christian communities of four to seven volunteers, located in six different urban areas in the United States. The areas in which help is needed include community organizing, environmental work, hunger relief, emergency social services, health care, housing, legal assistance, neighbourhood centres, public policy advocacy, shelters, youth/education and women's issues.

Applicants must be US citizens, at least 21 years of age and without dependents. Skills needed vary depending on the placement agency; for all volunteers, flexibility, dependability and commitment are essential. The usual length of placement is one year. The application process runs from January to June; the placements begin at the end of August.Volunteers receive room and board plus $85 per month personal allowance. Travel to the placement, health insurance and two weeks of vacation are also provided.

Those interested should contact Don Billen at the above address.

Mansfield Outdoor Centre
Manor Road, Lambourne End, Essex RM4 1NB (tel 081 500-3047).

This Outdoor Centre and Farm in Essex is a charity catering for able-bodied and handicapped children and young people from Newham and surrounding areas. The Centre provides a range of activities including archery, climbing, canoeing, orienteering and also a small farm unit for 'hands-on' experience. The Centre aims to help young people in their personal development using outdoor activities. Six volunteers per year work at the centre as trainee activity instructors and/or farm assistants. The Centre sometimes accepts volunteers from abroad. Applicants must have some previous experience of outdoor activities and/or farming knowledge. Volunteers are needed all the year round; long-term volunteers stay for a year, while short-term volunteers are needed in the summer for one month or more. Volunteers receive an allowance of £40 per week; accommodation is provided

in caravans.
Those interested should contact Mrs Irene Lock or the Centre Manager at the above address.

Marianist Voluntary Service Communities (MUSC)
PO Box 9224, Wright Bros. Branch, Dayton, OH 45409 USA (tel 513 229-4630; 513 229-4000).

MUSC is a lay volunteer program dedicated to service among disadvantaged people in urban areas of the United States. Volunteers provide services through existing social agencies. MUSC offers the opportunity for mature Christian men and women, single or married but without dependents, to develop personally and spiritually through experiences of service, a simple lifestyle and Christian community. Volunteers share household expenses, meals and group prayer. 15 to 20 volunteers are engaged by MUSC every year to participate in a wide variety of activities including business, clerical, building or child-care work, healthcare, law and legal advice, group home-work, youth advocacy, counselling, social work and senior citizen outreach.

Applicants of any nationality are welcome to apply but they must be able to speak English fluently. Applicants must not be using the program as a way to get into the USA, and it is preferable that applicants have had some cultural understanding of the USA and/or previous service or volunteer experience, particularly in cities or urban areas. A driving licence and a knowledge of Spanish are useful. Those who have had a secondary education are preferred. The ability to live with others is essential. Applicants should between 20 and 70, with no pre-existing health problems; please note that MUSC is not able or equipped to handle severe disability. Minimum length of placement is one year with an option for renewal for a second year (if approved).

Accommodation is provided and volunteers receive a monthly allowance which adequately covers food, rent and other expenses, but MUSC does not pay for travel to and from the mission site in the USA.

Applicants should contact Laura Libertore at the above address; the deadline for applications is June 1st each year.

The Medical Missionary Association
244 Camden Road, London, NW1 9HE (tel 081-485 2672).

The MMA acts as an agent channelling young doctors, nurses, dentists and paramedical workers to various mission and church organizations in many countries of the world. Apart from its Oyster Scheme (see separate entry), it does not have any voluntary work of its own overseas but recruits for most of the Protestant missionary societies of the UK.

As the MMA acts only as a channel, it is prepared to deal with requests from qualified Christian personnel of any nationality. The conditions of service vary, according to the usual practice of the society concerned. A quarterly magazine, *Saving Health*, is published depicting medical mission work in the world, and listing present openings in the various Protestant mission and church hospitals.

Applicants should apply to the Secretary at the above address for information on openings.

Mennonite Central Committee
21 South 12th Street, Akron, Pennsylvania 17501-0500, USA. (tel 717-859 1151)

The Mennonite Central Committee is a voluntary relief and development agency supported by the Mennonite and Brethren in Christ churches of North America. They work in 50 countries in Asia, Africa, Latin America and North America, usually in conjunction with other agencies to which they often second personnel.

About 1,000 volunteers are engaged each year, and special skills, experience and qualifications are required in the following areas of recruitment: agriculture, economic and technical assistance, education, health and social services. Language training is provided for work in non-English speaking areas. A small monthly allowance is paid, and all expenses, including round trip transportation, are met in full. Accomodation is also provided.

Applicants must be members of the Christian church. Positions in North America are usually held for two years; elsewhere three years is the normal period of service. There are no nationality restrictions, although most applications come from within the North American continent.

Enquiries and applications should be sent to the Personnel Office at the address given above.

Mercy Corps
Gwynned Mercy College,Gwynned Valley, PA 19437, USA (tel 215 641-5535; fax 215 641-5596).

Mercy Corps' members serve the poor, the sick and the uneducated throughout the USA. Members serve in schools, hospitals, social service agencies, shelters, housing redevelopment, adult literacy programs, etc. 25 volunteers work with the Mercy Corps every year in a wide range of activities including nursing, social work, physical and occupational therapy, secretarial work and education at all levels.

Applicants need not be US citizens and the minimum age limit is 21 years. Volunteers must also be in good health and possess flexibility, a sense of humour and the ability to get along with others. They should also be in relatively good health. The usual length of placement is one year, and there is a possibility of some two-year placements. Volunteers receive a small allowance, board and accommodation, medical insurance and transportation. Volunteers must pay their own travel costs to and from the USA.

Those interested should contact Sister Kathleen Lyons, the Director, at the above address at any time of the year.

Mission Aviation Fellowship
Ingles Manor, Castle Hill Avenue, Folkestone, Kent CT20 2TN (tel 0303-41356).

Mission Aviation Fellowship is a Christian organization which provides an air service for churches, missions and development agencies working in remote areas. The United Kingdom branch currently has bases in Chad, Ethiopia, Kenya,

Madagascar, Namibia, Tanzania and Uganda and also flies into other neighbouring countries. Commercially qualified pilots and engineers are needed, as well as administrators, builders and teachers. Terms of service are normally for a minimum of three years.

MAF workers must be committed Christians, fit, in good health and have appropriate experience. MAF staff usually raise their own support, which includes cost of accommodation and other relevant expenses. MAF obtains any visas or work permits and provides pre-field training.

Further information can be obtained from the Manager at the above address.

Missions to Seamen

St. Michael Paternoster Royal, College Hill, London EC4R 2RL (tel 071-248 5202).

Each year some 25 young men and women are needed to assist port chaplains in their work of looking after seamen of all nations. During their time with the mission, these volunteers visit sailors on board ship and in hospital, welcome visitors to the mission's club, take a share in the daily worship, and help to man the telephone, the shop and the canteen. Mission Stations exist in the UK, the USA, Asia, Australia and Europe. The length of service is one year and usually coincides with the academic year. Occasionally there is a vacancy at a different time or for a shorter period.

Applicants must be over 18, possess a driving licence, and be committed Christians. Travelling expenses are met, and board and lodging and weekly pocket money provided.

Enquiries should be sent to the Deputy General Secretary at the above address.

Oyster Scheme

The Medical Missionary Association, 244 Camden Road, London NW1 9HE, UK. (tel 071-485 2672)

The Medical Missionary Association runs a scheme called 'Oyster', which is an acronym standing for 'One Year's Service To Encourage Recruiting'. Under this scheme arrangements are made for British doctors to be appointed by a missionary society to a mission hospital in Africa or Asia for a period of one year, to bring the enthusiasm and encouragment of outsiders to the existing medical staff, as well as to broaden the volunteers own horizons and make them keen supporters of missionary work when they return to their practices in Britain or Eire. It is also hoped that following the one year of service, some candidates will choose to continue a career in the mission field.

The scheme is for registered medical practitioners from the United Kingdon and Eire. It is preferable that they have the mobility of the unmarried. The candidate must satisfy the recruiting missionary society in respect of his or her character, doctrine and health. Candidates must be willing to accept the authority of the permanent mission hospital staff as they will always be stationed along with one or two other experienced doctors.

Applications must be made in good time since the decision and fare bookings are made months in advance. Enquiries may be sent to the Secretary at the above address.

Paradise House Community

Paradise House, Painswick, Stroud, Glos. GL6 6TN (tel 0452-813276).

Paradise House is a long-term home for 32 adults suffering from a wide range of mental handicaps who are in need of special care. Its activities are based on the work of Rudolf Steiner. The residents' time is divided into training, work, adult education and recreation. Between 12 and 15 volunteers work as full members of staff for periods of at least a year helping to organize the activities, which include teaching the basics of housekeeping, gardening, farming, craft work etc.

Although specific skills in crafts, cooking, gardening or farming would be useful, it is more important that the volunteers should be enthusiastic and genuinely interested in this demanding work. There are no strict age limits, but applicants aged over 20 are preferred. Volunteers are provided with free board and lodging and pocket money of around £22 per week, and are also given £330 a year to pay for holidays.   Applications should be made to the Principal at the above address.

Peace Brigades International

c/o Greenleaf Bookshop, Box 35, 82 Coston Street, Avon BS1 5BB (tel 0272 411146).

Peace Brigades International sends unarmed peace teams when invited into areas of violent repression or conflict; these teams can flexibly pursue avenues not open to governments or political groups. Their work is to reduce the violence and support local social injustice initiatives through protective accompaniment of those whose lives are threatened, fostering reconciliation and dialogue for peace among conflicting parties, and educating and training in non-violence and human rights. The organization has its main international office in London, but has support groups which liase with potential volunteers in 14 countries.

50 volunteers of all nationalities work with PBI every year; they can join the peace teams in Central America or Sri Lanka, or assist with administrative work in PBI offices in Britain and Canada, or work with the regional support groups — of which there are ten in Europe, two in North America and two in the South Pacific. The projects use the official languages of the states in which they are based; volunteers must have knowledge of these.

The minimum age for volunteers is 25 years, but younger applicants will be considered depending on experience and suitability. The minimum length of placement for projects is six months, but longer is desirable; for the office work this varies. Accommodation is provided; the peace team members have their living costs covered and receive some pocket money. They usually have to pay their own travel costs but PBI groups are able to advise on possible sources of bursary aid for this.

There are PBI groups in New Zealand, Germany, Spain, France, Italy, the Netherlands, Austria, Switzerland and Sweden. Their addresses may be obtained from Steve Graham at the above address.

Applicants in the USA, Australia or Canada should write to the relevant address below;

PBI-USA, C/O Mary MacArthur & Randy Divinsky, Box 1233, Harvard Square, Station, Cambridge MA 02238, USA.

PBI-Australia, PO Box A243, 2000 Sydney South, New South Wales, Australia. PBI-Canada, 192 Spadina Avenue, Suite 304, Toronto Ont. M5T 2C2, Canada. British volunteers wanting more information should contact Steve Graham at the Bristol address above.

Peace Corps of the United States
1990 K Street, NW, Washington, DC 20526, USA (tel 1800-924 8580 x. 2293).

The goals of the Peace Corps are to help promote world peace and friendship, assist developing countries to meet their needs for skilled personnel and to promote mutual understanding between people of the United States and those of developing countries. There are close to 6,000 Peace Corps volunteers and trainees in 90 nations in Latin America, Africa, Asia, the Pacific and Eastern Europe. Placements normally last for two years plus three months training time.

Volunteers must be US citizens and at least 18 years old. The volunteers receive a monthly allowance for rent, food, travel and medical costs, transportation to and from training sites and overseas placements and a readjustment allowance of US$200 per month, paid on completion of service.

Those interested should contact the above address.

Pestalozzi Children's Village Trust
Sedlescombe, Battle, East Sussex TN33 0RR (tel 0424-87044; fax 0424-870655).

The Village is devoted to the education and training of more than 120 poor children from developing countries, who all live within the Village community. Between five and ten volunteers of different nationalities are engaged annually to help in many areas. These volunteers can work as research assistants, or in public relations and marketing, or on the farm and estate. They can also assist with holiday activities with the children or sports and hobbies. Volunteers are also required to work as EFL teachers and as assistant/trainer houseparents.

Volunteers must be aged between 25 and 65. There is no fixed duration for a placement; some people stay for three months, some for three years. Food, single accommodation and some pocket money are provided.

Those interested should contact Colin Wagstaff, Director, at the above address.

Ponape Agriculture and Trade School
PO Box 39, Pohnpei, Federated States of Micronesia 96941.

Ponape Agriculture and Trade School (PATS) is a four-year vocational High School run as a a residential boarding school for young men from all over Micronesia. Volunteer teachers, especially specialists in agriculture, mechanics and construction are always needed. There is also a need for high school-standard teachers to teach academic subjects. Students work in the classrooms in the mornings and work at their trades under supervision in the afternoons. Volunteers are also needed to give secretarial help, and to act as administration personnel. The School usually has about 15 volunteers on its staff.

Applicants of any nationality are welcome but they should note that the School is in a remote area on a very isolated island. The School has a strong Christian focus, in which all volunteers are expected to share. Volunteers are only taken on for two or three year commitments. Other qualities necessary include an ability to live in a very close-knit community, respect for others and Christian commitment. The desire to quietly pass this sense of commitment on to others is also required. Applicants should be in fairly good health, as the Micronesian Health Services are not particularly good. For this reason, it is very difficult for the School to accept handicapped people. The School needs help all the year round. Two weeks vacation per year are granted to volunteers, as well as an allowance of 50 US Dollars per month. Room and board are provided along with some other modest perks. Volunteers must pay for their own travel costs to and from Pohnpei, although help can sometimes be given.

Those interested should contact Fr. Joseph A Cavanagh, the Director, at the above address.

Project Trust
Breacachadh Castle, Isle of Coll, Scotland, PA78 6TB (tel 08793-444).

Project aims to further the education of school leavers who have taken A Levels or Highers, by sending them to work overseas for a year. The work projects take place in Australia, Botswana, Brazil, China, Egypt, Honduras, Hong Kong, Indonesia, Jamaica, Japan, Namibia, Pakistan,South Africa/Transkei,Thailand and Zimbabwe. Volunteers are mainly involved in social service, farming or teaching. Individuals must raise a portion of the total costs. 200 volunteers a year take this opportunity. Conditions which must be met by the applicants include; being a UK national, being aged between 17 and 19, and being in full time education up to the time that they go abroad. They must also raise 3/4 of the cost of their placement. Once abroad, they receive free board and lodging, and pocket money.

Those interested should apply to the Director at the above address. Applications normally close on January 1st in the year of departure

Quaker Peace and Service
Friends House, Euston Road, London NW1 2BJ, UK. (tel 071-387 3601)

This organization is engaged in a variety of activities around the world, all of which are committed to practical peacemaking. QPS supports long term (ie. at least two year) projects for trained workers in the fields of health, agricultural and rural development, community development, education and refugee counselling. There are QPS workers in Africa, Asia and the Middle East. A small number also work in Northern Ireland and at the Quaker UN office in Geneva.

Formal membership of the Society of Friends is not essential, but understanding of and sympathy with Quaker objectives is. Food and accommodation are always provided and pension rights, etc, are safeguarded. All transportation expenses are paid.

Applications and enquiries should be sent to the Service Projects Secretary at the above address.

Queen Louise Home for Children/Lutheran Social Services
PO Box 866, Frederiksted, St. Croix, US Virgin Islands 00841.

The Home provides temporary care for abused, abandoned, neglected and developmentally retarded children, regardless of race, religion or national origin, while permanent placement plans for them are processed. The Virgin Islands Department of Human Services relies heavily upon the Home to meet a large part of the evergrowing need for institutional childcare. The Home takes in approximately ten volunteers annually to work as cottage parents. Cottage parents serve as live-in caretakers for eight to ten children, aged between three and twelve. Responsibilities include caring for each child's emotional, physical, educational and spiritual needs; developing creative, social, educational, recreational and cultural programs for them; and maintaining the cottages, grounds, clothes and vehicles. Applicants may either be married with no dependents or two single people who work as a team. They must have experience with children, flexibility, patience and be culturally adaptable, as well as professional and objective judgement and attitude. They must be team workers and willing to work under supervision.

Applicants of any nationality are welcome, but they must have had two years of college training (preferably in child development but this is not essential). They must possess a strong personal Christian commitment and have had experience of childcare in or out of a job setting. A valid driving licence is essential. The Home is wheelchair-accessible, but disabled applicants should note that the role of cottage parent demands a high level of energy and physical capabilities. Cottage parents applying as a couple are contracted to spend a total of 18 months at the home;single cottage parents are contracted to spend one year. Volunteers are entitled to $2,912 per person and living quarters are provided along with meals for the period of employment. They are also entitled to the price of the ticket for the flight to St. Croix. Return fare is paid contingent upon completion of contract.

Enquiries should be sent to the Director at the above address.

Returned Volunteer Action
1 Amwell Street, London EC1R 1UL (tel 071-278 0804).

RVA does not send volunteers to work abroad but does give advice and information to people considering working overseas. It is an independent organization of individuals who have worked overseas as project workers or volunteers in development projects. It works to ensure that the experience of volunteers is put to good use after their return, both through contacts with British community groups and through feedback to overseas development agencies and sending societies regarding the appropriateness of their programmes and methods.

There is an RVA network of local groups and contacts across the country who organize weekends for newly recruited project workers, 'Questioning Development' days for prospective volunteers, and conferences, as well as providing a focus for those who want to participate in relevant activities at a local level.

RVA publishes a number of books on volunteering and development, and urges anyone considering working overseas to write for a copy of their pamphlet *Thinking about Volunteering?*; for a copy send £1 and a stamped addressed envelope to the above address.

Richmond Fellowship International
The Coach House, 8 Addison Road, Kensington, London W14 8DL (tel 071-603 2442; fax 071-602 0199).

The Richmond Fellowship International exists to help its sister organizations in countries overseas to improve the condition of the mentally ill, generally by helping them to set up therapeutic communities to be used as a model for the future extension of mental health work in each country, and by providing training courses for practitioners. RFI recruits about 30 volunteers per year; they are given placements in one of its therapeutic communities around the world where they work alongside the regular staff. One of their main tasks is to help people to take their place in society after a breakdown; this might include home-making, administrative work and public relations. Applicants are required to have qualifications in social work, psychology, nursing or previous volunteer experience.

Applicants may be of any nationality, but they should be at least 23 years of age, able to speak fluent English and to deal with stress and have a mature outlook. A driving licence is an advantage. Special ethnic and language preferences depend on overseas placements but within the UK RFI is committed to equal opportunities. Ex-drug users are accepted to work on drug rehabilitation projects. The usual length of placement is one year; the minimum is six months and volunteers are required all the year round. Board, lodging, insurance and a weekly allowance of £27.00 (or equivalent in other currencies) are all provided.

Those interested should contact Leela Joseet at the above address.

Skillshare Africa
3 Belvoir Street, Leicester LE1 6SL (tel 0533-540517).

Skillshare Africa sends skilled and qualified personnel to work in support of development in Botswana, Lesotho, Mozambique and Swaziland. Its objective is to tackle the causes of deprivation and underdevelopment by promoting self-reliance and reducing dependency. Volunteers are recruited in response to specific requests from the governments, NGOs and local communities of the countries.

Placements are very diverse and have included dress designing, boat building, public relations, tropical agriculture, business advice, community development and many other skill areas. Placements are for two years and flights, national insurance payments, modest living allowance/salary, small home savings allowance, rent-free accommodation, health insurance and equipment grants are all provided. Applicants should have relevant qualifications and at least two years' post-qualification experience. It is also essential that volunteers are flexible, mature, able to perform under stress and respond to a challenge.

Information packs and application forms are available by phoning the above number and leaving your name and address quoting reference VW/93.

St. Ebba's
Hook Road, Epsom, Surrey KT19 8JQ (tel 0372-722212 ext. 251).

St. Ebba's is an NHS hospital for 360 mentally and/or physically handicapped adults. Thirty volunteers per year help in the hospital's physiotherapy department and with extended education, sports, day services and all areas of work that require the training of residents. Applicants may be of any nationality but must be able-bodied, interested in working with the handicapped and able to speak good English. The minimum age limit is 18 years, and volunteers must be in good health. The length of placement is one year. No pocket money is provided, but a room and all meals are free.

Those interested should contact E M Kerslake at the above address.

Tear Fund (Evangelical Alliance Relief Fund)
1OO Church Road, Teddington, Middlesex TW1 8QE (tel 081-977 9144).

Tear Fund is a Christian charity which supports Christian development work in developing countries. The Fund is also involved in emergency relief programmes following natural disasters. All personnel must be fully qualified in their profession, should hold a driving licence, and will be required to undertake language study at the start of their assignments. Tear Fund workers are at present operating in about 20 countries, mostly in Africa, Asia and Latin America.

About 40 volunteers are recruited annually, usually for assignments of three to four years: all should be committed Christians and resident in the UK, preferably as British citizens. No age limits are applied, but a high standard of medical fitness is necessary. Full expenses are paid, and workers receive accommodation and a regular monthly allowance.

Enquiries should be sent to Miss Anthea Fisher, Overseas Personnel Department, at the above address.

United Nations Association International Service
Suite 3a, Hunter House, 57 Goodramgate, York YO1 2L5 (tel 0904-647799).

UNAIS recruits skilled and motivated people to work in West Africa, Latin America and the Middle East. With them it helps selected organizations which aim to strengthen local groups struggling to improve their situation, and to gain a fairer share of resources. UNAIS recruit volunteers in the three main fields of health, agriculture and water engineering. The countries in which they work are: Bolivia, Brazil, Mali, Burkina Faso, the West Bank and Gaza.

Volunteers are paid a monthly allowance calculated in relation to the local cost of living which is very adequate for a single person. Their accommodation is also covered and there are a variety of grants paid during the period of service. Flights and insurance are also provided.

For further information contact the Recruitment Administrator at the above address.

United Nations Volunteers Programme (UNV)
Palais des Nations, 1211 Geneva 10, Switzerland (tel 022-788-25-01).

The United Nations Volunteers (UNV) programme was created in recognition of the need for trained professionals for development activities and of the role volunteer service can play in this field. It currently has over 2,000 volunteers working in over 110 developing countries. These volunteers are sent to countries only at the request of and/or with the approval of their governments. The purpose of the UNVP programme is to channel professionally qualified men and women on a volunteer basis into development assistance calling for middle and upper level operational expertise: to promote effective participation of youth in development activities; and to assist and cooperate with domestic development service (DDS) organizations on both national and regional levels. The DDS organizations promote self-reliant economic and social development at the grass-roots level through participatory initiatives.

UN Volunteers are agronomists, doctors, economists, engineers, entomologists, geologists, graphic designers, technicians, librarians, mechanics, midwives, youth workers and representatives of 140 other professions. All are professionals and technicians who possess the requisite educational qualifications, at least two years of professional experience, and meet the linguistic requirements which include proficiency in one or more of the working languages of the UN. Although there are obviously exceptions, UNVs on average bring ten years' working experience to their assignments, and their average age is 39. The minimum acceptable age is 21, but very few UNVs are in their twenties; the oldest serving UNVs are in their seventies. UNV assignments are for a minimum period of two years, although an assignment may be extended beyound this length of time.

Additional information may be obtained from the Executive Co-ordinator at the above address.

Viatores Christi
39 Upper Gardiner Street, Dublin 1, Eire (tel Dublin 749346/728027).

A lay missionary association founded in Dublin in 1960, Viatores Christi has its headquarters and training programme in Ireland. It recruits, trains and helps place volunteers overseas wherever there is need for them. Besides offering their own skills in such fields as medicine, teaching, carpentry, mechanical engineering, secretarial work, etc. volunteers, as lay missionaries, should be prepared to participate actively in the work of the local Church.

Volunteers must undertake a part-time training course in Ireland for a minimum period of nine months. To be assigned overseas they should be practising Catholics, at least 21, in good health and possess some professional qualification or skill. All assignments are for a minimum period of one year but most volunteers stay for at least two years. Return air fare, insurance, living allowance and accommodation are normally provided by the receiving agent.

Applications should be made to the Secretary at the above address. Since it is necessary to be in Ireland in order to undertake the part-time training course, residents in the UK may prefer to contact the Volunteer Missionary Movement.

Visions in Action
3637 Fulton Street, NW, Washington, DC 20007, USA (tel 202-625 7403; fax 202-625 2353).

Visions in Action is an international non-profit making organization founded in 1988 out of the conviction that there is much that individuals can learn from — and contribute to - the developing world by working as part of a community of volunteers committed to achieving social justice in an urban setting. Visions Interns work side-by-side with host country nationals, allowing a genuine understanding of the country's needs to emerge. The Urban Development Internship program aims to work towards social and economic justice in the urban areas of the developing world by providing overseas volunteer opportunities with non-profit making organizations, working as partners in the development process.

40-60 volunteers per year work in indigenous or expatriate organizations as development journalists, community workers, project managers, low-income housing facilitators and healthcare assistants, etc. Placements are available in the following sectors; women's issues, education, housing, small business and appropriate technology: they take place in South Africa, Zimbabwe, Kenya, Uganda and Burkina Faso. All programs last for one year, with the exception of South Africa, which lasts for six months. Applicants may be of any nationality, but they must have two years' college experience or equivalent. Programs begin in January and July. The total cost of participating in a program is $5,000. Volunteers must pay for all their costs. The program fee includes accommodation.

Those interested should apply to Majken Ryherd at the above address.

Volunteer Missionary Movement
Shenley Lane, London Colney, Herts AL2 1AR (tel 0727-824853).

VMM recruits and sends skilled Christian volunteers to work for a minimum of two years in development projects linked with local churches in Africa. People of the following professions are needed to pass them on to the local communities: midwives, RGN nurses, tutors, doctors, pharmacists, qualified teachers for secondary schools, lay chaplains, pastoral and community development workers, secretaries able and willing to teach, qualified agriculturalists, and diploma holders in mechanics, carpentry, building and other technical skills.

Volunteers must be committed Christians aged between 21 and 65 and can be either married or single. The selection procedure includes an initial interview and four day introduction course, and all volunteers attend a five week residential preparation course before going overseas.

Those interested should contact the Director at the above address.

VSO
317 Putney Bridge Road, London SW15 2PN (tel 081-780 1331).

VSO is a registered charity committed to sharing skills with the peoples of developing countries. Over 800 volunteers are posted overseas each year to contribute to improvements in education, health and food production as well as in the use of appropriate technology, social development and the growth of business.

Posts are for a minimum of two years. Volunteers aged between 20 and 70 must all have qualifications and usually relevant work experience in their respective fields, although VSO does post some people soon after qualifying if they have studied sciences and/or languages and are prepared to teach.

VSO pays air fares, national insurance contributions, grants towards equipment and re-settlement and arranges language courses where necessary. Accommodation and salary, which is paid at the local rate for the job, are provided by the overseas employer.

For further details contact the Enquiries Unit's 24 hours ansaphone on the above number.

Volunteers in Mission
The Presbyterian Church (USA), 100 Witherspoon, Louisville, Kentucky 40202, USA.

VIM is a programme offering opportunities for people of all ages who are willing to live at subsistence level while helping to meet social needs around the world. All volunteers must be church members and most are required to have some specialized training such as medicine or teaching. Some assignments are for at least a year but summer camps are also arranged.

Further information can be obtained from the above address.

WorldTeach, Inc.

Harvard Institute for International Development, One Eliot Street, Cambridge, MA 02138-5705, USA (tel 617 495-5527; fax 617 495-1239).

WorldTeach is a small, private, non-profit making organization whose purpose is to recruit about 200 volunteers per year and place them as teachers in countries that request assistance. Volunteers admitted to the programme teach English on one year contracts in Costa Rica, Ecuador, Namibia, Poland and Thailand. WorldTeach volunteers serve as full-time teachers at elementary and secondary schools, training colleges and universities. Most teach English, though volunteers in Namibia also teach maths and science and volunteers in South Africa coach sports.

Volunteers may be of any nationality but they must speak English with native fluency. Volunteers must have accquired at least 25 hours of training or experience in Teaching English as a Foreign Language before they depart. Participants in full-year programmes require a university degree. There are no age limits. Volunteers must be in good health and able to live and work under rigorous conditions.

Volunteers must pay a participation fee, which covers round-trip airfare (from the USA), health insurance, orientation, placement, field support and administrative costs. Current fees range from $3,300 to $4,360. While the volunteers are teaching they receive either room and board or housing and a living allowance from the host school, community or government. Payments on student loans can be deferred during the term of service. WorldTeach offers fundraising advice and encourages volunteers to raise money for the participation fee in their own communities.

For further information write to Sydney Rosen at the above address.

Youth With a Mission (YWAM)

13 Highfield Oval, Ambrose Lane, Harpenden, Herts AL5 4BX (tel 0582-765481; fax 0582-768048).

YWAM is an international charitable organization which is interdenominational in character and undertakes evangelical, training and relief ministries in around 100 countries. All tasks are undertaken by volunteers and are financially supported by their home church, fellowship, friends or family.

Volunteers are needed in whatever field they wish to offer their service, and they can serve from two weeks to a lifetime. Those wishing to serve for a long term must be willing to attend a basic training course with YWAM. Volunteers must be committed Christians with their own financial support (£200 per month is a rough average, depending on the location).

For more information apply to the Director of Personnel Services at the above address.

Other Long Term Opportunities

The following organizations have been included in the various sub sections of the *Short Term* chapter, but also require a number of volunteers for periods of a year or longer.

Worldwide
Action Health 2000
Christian Medical Fellowship
Global Outreach UK
Institute of Cultural Affairs
WEC International

United Kingdom
Camphill Rudolph Steiner School
Flysheet Camps Scotland

Israel
UNIPAL

North, Central and South America
Los Ninos

Europe
Aktionsgemeinschaftsdienst den Frieden
Discovery '80' Share Ltd
France Mission Trust
Operation Mobilisation

Short Term

There is a far wider range of short rather than long term opportunities available to the volunteer; there are also far more people who may be free to leave home to volunteer for a few weeks or months than could spare a period to be measured in years. Some of the schemes described in the next few chapters could be fitted into a worker's or student's holiday entitlement, and there are others that could be fitted into a pre-arranged short-term leave of absence.

It is not possible to make the same broad generalisations about short term voluntary work as can be made about its long term counterpart. Some of the organizations below have needs for professional workers that are every bit as specific as those in the long term section: for example, HCJB UK is looking for, among others, audio and broadcasting engineers, scriptwriters and announcers for work in Ecuador and South America for periods of from one to three months: but to spend the same length of time working on a Kibbutz in Israel you need just be able-bodied and aged between 18 and 30.

Some of the schemes below require dedication from the volunteer as great as any in the long term section , but others require little more than enthusiasm. The latter applies in particular to many of the large number of workcamps that are are organized every year; they are aimed primarily at volunteers aged under thirty, but some organizers will consider older applicants if asked. While most of the short term opportunities described below are pretty self-explanatory, a note of introduction is advisable about workcamps.

A workcamp is a project that sets out to accomplish some specific goal over the course of one or more seasons with the help of groups of volunteers who arrive to help for periods of perhaps two or three weeks. This project may involve conservation work, forestry, restoring an ancient monument, building some community amenity, or one of many other types of job that would not be done if volunteers were not prepared to undertake it. Workcamps take place all over east and west Europe, North America, North Africa and sometimes further afield. While each camp will have some specific objective, such as clearing a derelict pond and the surrounding woodland and converting it into public parkland or restoring an ancient building, they also achieve something by their very existence. Many organizations select the participants on a camp to represent as many nationalities as possible, in order to give those taking part the opportunity to meet and work alongside people from different cultures and backgrounds.

Many volunteers on short term assignments — and this applies particularly to students on workcamps, archaeological digs and kibbutzim — see their involvement principally as a working holiday or a means of staying somewhere rather more cheaply than would otherwise be possible. Indeed in some Eastern European countries short term voluntary work may be the only way of getting more than a tourists view of the way of life. And, although English is the standard language in most international workcamps, the environment can provide invaluable practise for students of other languages. The hours of work expected of volunteers on a workcamp can be light, perhaps just involving working in the mornings: at least part of the remainder of the time may be filled with organised' educational' activities such as outings, lectures etc., intended to give participants a taste of the local culture.   ,

It is not possible to generalize about the financial arrangements for short-term voluntary work. In some cases pocket money is paid in addition to travel expenses and free accommodation. In other cases no money changes hands at all, or volunteers may find themselves making a contribution towards the cost of food and accommodation. It all depends on the source and extent of available funds. Officially sponsored organisations, like Community Service Volunteers, usually have the funds to provide at least the bare necessities. As another example, kibbutzim, by their very nature, are expected to provide volunteers with free board and accomodation, but could not reasonably be expected to meet everyone's travel expenses, particularly when applicants literally come from all over the globe. Stays on kibbutzim therefore tend to be marketed as 'working holidays', as do many archaeological digs for the same reason — no funds are available to cover all costs. Indeed, participants in many archaeological digs have to pay for their own board and lodging as well.

Because of the great number of organisations requiring short term volunteers, it has been necessary to sub-divide them geographically. One or two organizations thus fall into more than one classification and will therfore be listed more than once. However, the organizations which are truely international in their recruitment policies and activities have been listed separately under the heading Worldwide.

As there is a heavy preponderance of British and European organizations, the sections on the United Kingdom and Europe have been further subdivided, the UK by types of work, and Europe by country. These divisions are far from clear cut, especially in the UK chapter. Many of the entries under Religious Projects, for instance, cut across several of the other classifications: and there is a great deal of overlap between Child Care and Work with the Sick and Disabled, as jobs involving sick and disabled children tend to be listed in the former category. The subheadings are therefore to be considered as a rough guide only. Entries are otherwise listed in simple alphabetical order within their respective sections or sub-divisions.

Worldwide

Action Health 2000
Unit 10, The Gate House, 25 Gwydir Street, Cambridge CB1 2LG.

Action Health 2000 is an international charitable association concerned with the promotion of appropriate health care in developing countries: current projects operate in India, Bangladesh, Tanzania, Zimbabwe, Zambia and China. Every year 20-25 health workers are sent abroad to help for periods ranging from six months to two years and more.

Most placements are in rural, semi-rural and deprived urban areas and will involve many areas of primary health care, although some positions may be available in general or specialist hospitals teaching local health staff and passing on specific health skills. Applicants should be fully qualified and registered doctors, midwives, nurses or other health workers. The payment of expenses depends on the length of service: those staying for two years or more have all their expenses covered and receive a small allowance.

A number of medical students are also taken on during their training as electives for periods of six to eight weeks. They are attached to an existing health team, often following a special programme including clinical work, tutorials and visits to other institutions. An elective fee of £72 covers selection, placement, an orientation course, and practical help with travel and support while abroad: a membership fee of £10 and approximately £150 to cover board, lodging and health insurance must also be paid.

Applications will be considered at any time of the year, but should be sent at least six and preferably twelve, months before the desired date of starting work. For further information contact the Director at the above address.

Archaeology Abroad
31-34 Gordon Square, London WC1H OPY.

This organization provides three information bulletins annually about forthcoming opportunities for archaeological fieldwork and excavations abroad. Publications are available by subscription. Enquiries should be sent to the Secretary at the above address enclosing a stamped self-addressed envelope.

British Executive Service Overseas (BESO)
164 Vauxhall Bridge Road, London SW1V 2RB (tel 071-630 0644).

BESO recruits retired volunteer business executives with professional, technical or specialized management skills for short term assignments in developing countries. Such countries receive financial aid from various international sources, including the United Kingdom, but remain in urgent need of assistance to overcome their shortages of experts with technical, financial and managerial skills. The duration of an assignment averages two to three months. Executives receive neither fee nor salary.

BESO makes air travel arrangements and meets the full cost for both executive and spouse if accompanying (this includes cost of innoculations, travel and medical insurance and other incidental charges). An initial clothing allowance is normally paid to the executive, as is a small local overseas allowance. The host organization is required to provide suitable accommodation, subsistence and transport during the term of the assignment. Further information is available on request to BESO.

Enquiries should be sent to the Director at the above address.

Canadian Crossroads International
31 Madison Avenue, Toronto, Ontario, M5R 2S2, Canada (tel 416 967 0801).

Canadian Crossroads International is a non-profit making organization of volunteers in Canada and 31 other countries in Africa, the South Pacific, South and Central America and the Caribbean. Volunteers take part in short term work placements: about 200 Canadians are sent overseas, about 60 Third World volunteers are brought to Canada and over 800 volunteers help run the programmes. Volunteers live and work with host families and agencies. The work undertaken varies but could include community development, health care, education, agriculture, construction, etc. Placements are from four or six months to one year long.

All volunteers must be at least 19 years old. Volunteers are accepted from all countries in which Canadian Crossroads International operates but to qualify for placements in a Third World country applicants must be Canadian citizens or landed immigrants.

Further information can be obtained from the Administrative Assistant at the above address.

Christian Medical Fellowship
157 Waterloo Road, London SE1 8XN (tel 071-928 4694; fax 071-620 2453)

The Fellowship offers advice for Christian doctors and medical students. There is a list of about 40 medical misssionary organizations with vacancies for doctors to work in the developing world, for periods of six months and longer. There is a similar list for medical student electives of two to three months.

For further information contact the General Secretary at the above address.

Christian Movement for Peace
186 St. Paul's Road, Balsall Heath, Birmingham B12 8LZ (tel 021-440 3000; fax 021-446 4060).

The main activity of the CMP is the placement of volunteers on voluntary projects throughout East and West Europe, the USA, Canada and North Africa. They seek short term volunteers for summer projects abroad, usually for two to six weeks with between 10 and 20 volunteers on each project. There is an enormous variety of work available. In France, for instance, it may be conservation work, working on the land or social work in deprived urban areas.

CMP also organizes a series of seminars on contemporary social issues each year that are held in various European countries. Travel subsidies are available for these seminars. In addition there are occasional opportunities to work for six months as a volunteer giving administrative support in one of CMP's offices in Europe.

For further details about any of these activities send an SAE to CMP at the above address.

Concordia (Youth Service Volunteers) Ltd.

8 Brunswick Place, Hove, East Sussex BN3 1ET (tel 0273-772086).

Concordia is a charitable organization which organizes the placement of volunteers from the UK on international voluntary work camps in the following countries; Czechoslovakia, Latvia, France, Germany, Italy, Turkey, Tunisia, Spain and Portugal. Camps last only from two to three weeks and take place between June and September. However, Concordia is hoping to arrange longer term placements as from the summer of 1993, possibly for from six to nine months.

The projects on offer vary enormously and include archaeological digs, building work, restoration of monuments and castles, ground maintenance in parks and gardens, nature conservation, social work, and work in children's camps. Pocket money is not paid on these camps. Work on farms for two to three months is available in Switzerland and Norway, for which pocket money is paid. At most camps English is used as the language of communication. A reasonable working knowledge of a foreign language is required at some camps, such as Tunisia.

Volunteers must pay their own travel expenses and make their own travel arrangements. Once at camp, board and lodging and insurance are provided free of charge. In some countries, sightseeing trips, cultural activities and excursions are organized for the volunteers. A registration fee and a small administration charge must be paid. Volunteers for international work camps abroad must be aged between 18 and 30 and British passport holders.

For more details write to the European Recruitment Secretary at the address above, enclosing a stamped addressed envelope or international reply coupon.

Council on International Educational Exchange (CIEE)

205 East 42nd Street, New York, NY 10017, USA (tel 212-661 1414).

The Council on International Educational Exchange is a non-profit making organization that, in affiliation with co-operating organizations throughout Europe, sponsors voluntary service projects for young people in the USA and abroad. Participants have the chance to explore, in a cross-cultural setting, international perspectives on global issues such as environmental protection, cultural preservation and development while working closely with 15 to 20 other volunteers from many countries.

The work, generally lasting for three weeks, involves manual labour or social service and is of great value to the communities in need. There is a wide range of project possibilities in the summer, including forest conservation in

Czechoslovakia, archaeological digs in Kentucky and Spain, care for the elderly in Germany, and construction of a water trench in Turkey. Participants' costs are minimal, being around $135 application fee plus transportation. Room and board are provided by the workcamp sponsor.

For further information please contact the International Workcamps Co-ordinator, at the above address. (Please note: the CIEE is involved with placing American citizens only. Other nationalities should contact a voluntary service organization in their home country).

Crusaders
2 Romeland Hill, St Albans, Herts, AL3 4ET (tel 0727-55422).

Crusaders runs Christian young people's groups and adventure holidays where the emphasis is on evangelism and Bible Teaching. Volunteers are needed to help with young people's holidays and expeditions in Britain and abroad.

Around 300 holiday helpers are needed during the summer vacation to help with young people's holidays and houseparties at over 50 sites in Britain. Camps may be for a week or a weekend. The children are aged from eight to 16 years old and the group size varies between 15 to 70 children. Helpers supervise and organize all of the group's activities, which include sports, crafts, Bible studies, etc.

The number of expeditions undertaken changes from year to year. In 1992 there were expeditions to India, Latvia, Romania and South Africa. Only two to four leaders are needed on each trip as the group size is usually just 10 to 20 young people, aged 16 to 21 years old. Expeditions last for one to two weeks.

All leaders must be aged 18 or over, speak English, have a Christian commitment and leadership qualities. Skills in specialist sports and outdoor activities are desirable but not necessary. Applicants must pay for all their own expenses.

Applications should be made to the Director at the above address.

Earthwatch
Belsyre Court, 57 Woodstock Road, Oxford, OX2 6HN (tel 0865-311600; fax 0865-311383).

Earthwatch recruits paying volunteers to help research scientists in fields from archaeology to zoology on short term research projects in over 40 countries and 27 states of America, around the year. The scholars who request Earthwatch volunteers are based at universities and museums worldwide. Around 3,400 volunteers each year take part in the projects which last for two or three weeks. Team volunteers may learn to excavate, map, photograph, observe animal behaviour, survey flora and fauna, gather ethnographic data, make collections, conduct oral history interviews, measure astronomical alignments, assist in diving operations, lend mechanical or electrical expertise, record natural sounds, and share all other field chores associated with professional expedition research.

All English speaking volunteers aged 17 and over are welcome although some projects may require special skills such as languages and sporting or practical skills. Some projects may also have health restrictions as they take place in remote areas or at high altitudes, etc. Volunteers pay a share of the project costs, ranging from £500 to £2,000 which includes accommodation costs but not travel.

Those interested should apply to the above address. US applicants should contact: Earthwatch, 680 Mount Auburn Street, Box 403N, Watertown, MA 02272, USA (tel 800-776 0188).

Education for Development
Woodmans, Westwood Row, Tilehurst, Reading R63 6LT (tel 0734-426772; fax 0734-352080).

This organization provides training visits to adult education, non-formal education, and extension in development programmes in countries including India, China, Namibia, Bangladesh, Sri Lanka etc. Volunteers, who must be qualified and experienced in adult education, are needed all the year round to help with all the above areas. Placements vary in duration , but usually last between 2-3 months. No expenses (including travel) are paid and volunteers must also pay for their accommodation.

Applications to Professor Alan Rogers at the above address.

Emmaus International
183 bis, rue Vaillant-Couturier, 94140 Alfortville, France (tel 1-48 93 29 50).

The Emmaus movement started in Paris in 1949 and there are now some 340 Emmaus communities in 35 countries, mainly in Europe but also in Africa, Asia and North and South America. These communities try to provide a meaning in life for those without one — that meaning being to help others in need. Each community is autonomous and independent of race, sex, religion, politics, age etc. Living conditions are usually simple and the work hard.

Two communities which accept long term volunteers are: Stichting Emmaus, Nederland, Julianalaan 25, PO Box 175, 3720, GD Bilthoven, Nederland and Emmaus Westervik, SF-10600, Ekenes, Finland. Other Emmaus communities in Europe organize workcamps for volunteers during the summer. Volunteers must usually speak English or the language of the country being visited, be over 16 years old and able to work at least two weeks. Accommodation and food are provided but volunteers pay all other costs.

Those interested in long term or summer voluntary positions should apply to the Secretary at the above address for more information on individual communities.

The Experiment in International Living
Otesaga, West Malvern Road, Malvern, Worcs WR14 4EN (tel 0684-562577; fax 0684-562212).

The Experiment in International Living (EIL) started in 1932 with the belief that the best way to learn about a foreign culture is to become for a short time a member of a family of that culture. For many people such an experience can be a life-changing one. Homestays are available in many parts of the world; Europe, North and South America, Africa, Australia and Asia.

Volunteer homestay families come from all walks of life. They may live in cities, towns, villages or in isolated rural areas. They may have children of all ages or none at all; they be a working couple, a single parent family or a single person in their own flat. The one thing they all have in common is that they look forward to welcoming visitors into their homes. The minimum age for most homestays is between 16-18. The average cost is £350, but this varies. A homestay 'guest' will gain a more complete picture of a country than one might on a package holiday, and EIL's worldwide network of 40 offices will help all guests settle in.

As well as enjoying an EIL homestay, there are opportunities to learn a language on one of EIL's many courses, with the advantage of practising on a long-suffering homestay family afterwards!

For more information and a brochure giving details of homestays etc. please contact the Outbound Department at the above address.

Foundation for Field Research

PO Box 2010, Alpine, CA 91903, USA (tel 619-445 9264; fax 619-445 1893).

The Foundation supports researchers in the field by recruiting volunteers willing to donate a share-of-cost and their labour to the projects. Projects all over the world involving research in archaeology, botany, wildlife research, paleontology, folk medicine, primitology, entomology, marine biology, marine archaeology, ornithology and ecology are supported. Around 500 volunteers are required annually on projects lasting from five to 28 days, all year round. Volunteers undertake whatever tasks the researcher feels are necessary to fulfill the goals of the project; on archaeological projects volunteers help with excavations, on wildlife project volunteers make observations and take notes, etc.

Some expeditions require the volunteers to have special skills such as scuba qualifications or the ability to hike distances. Volunteers may be of any nationality. Accommodation is provided but the volunteers pay a share-of-cost to support the project.

Those interested should send three International Reply Coupons to the above address in order to obtain a 40 page newspaper with details of current projects.

Gap Activity Projects (GAP) Limited

GAP House, 44 Queen's Road, Reading, Berkshire RG1 4BB (tel 0734 594-914; fax 0734 576-634).

GAP arranges work opportunities overseas for students working in their 'gap' year between school and higher education. GAP currently operates projects in 27 different countries all over the world. GAP is only available to school leavers aged 18-19 during their 'gap' year. GAP has approximately 750 volunteers working overseas and about 300 reciprocals working in the UK. It must be emphasised that GAP only sends British passport holders to work overseas due to pressure of places which are always oversubscribed. However, reciprocal schemes operate in Australia, Bulgaria, Canada, China, Germany, Hungary, New Zealand, Poland and Russia to enable those nationals to work in the UK.

Opportunities for UK volunteers vary from country to country but they include TEFL teaching in Bulgaria, China, Chile, Czechoslovakia, Ecuador, Hungary, India, Indonesia, Poland, Pakistan, Nepal, Russia, South Africa, Namibia; social work in Ecuador, France, India, Israel, Japan, Malaysia, Mexico, Poland, Singapore, USA, Hong Kong; teaching assistants in Australia, Canada and New Zealand; conservation in Australia, Chile and Namibia; farm work in Australia and the Falkland Islands and, finally, business in Canada, France and Germany. The relevant languages, preferably to A Level standard are required for the following projects; Germany (German), France (French), Russia (Russian), Chile, Ecuador, Mexico (Spanish). All those undertaking TEFL teaching are required to complete a basic TEFL course.

Most GAP placements last for 6 months, leaving time for travel in-country. Some last 3 months, others 9. Volunteers are required all year round; this is dependent on host and country requirements. Applicants, on selection, pay GAP a fee which varies from country to country — i.e. £150 for Israel and £350 for Australia and New Zealand. Applicants must also pay their own air fare and insurance costs. Once in a placement, volunteers are provided with free accommodation and food, and in most cases a small amount of pocket money.

The GAP brochure is published in September each year and is available free to all those interested in applying. The brochure contains detailed information on all projects and an application form. Applications must be made between the September and January of the last year of the Sixth form i.e. almost a year before intended departure. Early application is strongly recommended.

For more information, or a brochure, please write to the Registrar at the above address.

Global Outreach UK

108 Sweetbriar Lane, Exeter, Devon EX1 3AR (tel 0392-59673).

Global Outreach UK is a Christian evangelical missionary society with representatives in 26 countries. Christian camps, Bible courses, radio broadcasting and in particular establishing churches are all methods used to propagate the Gospel. Opportunities exist for volunteers as career and short term missionaries, members of summer outreach teams and itinerant evangelists. A whole-hearted agreement with Outreach's Statement of Faith is required and volunteers must be over 18 years old. Volunteers must supply a doctor's certificate of good health and are responsible for raising their own funds.

Around 40 volunteers are needed for the six week summer programme in which volunteers are attached to churches and share in special outreach and local programmes.

A short term missionary programme is designed for young graduates of Bible school, single or married couples, who require 'in service' training. The volunteers are attached to a local church for periods of 12 to 24 months and work with the pastor in all aspects of the church's programme.

Career missionaries are placed in churches financially unable to support a full time pastor, but able to provide accomodation and if possible, part salary, with the balance coming from interested churches and individuals.

For further details on volunteer requirements, financial information and other facts, contact the General Secretary at the above address.

Global Volunteers

375e Little Canada Road, St. Paul, MN 55117, USA (tel 612 482-1074; fax 612 482-0915).

Global Volunteers is a non-profit making US Corporation founded in 1984 with the goal of establishing a foundation for peace through mutual international understanding. The program centres around one, two, or three week volunteer work experience placements in rural communities in Africa, Asia, the Caribbean, Central America, Eastern Europe, North America or the South Pacific. 500 volunteers are engaged per year in these projects. At the request of local leaders and indigenous host organizations, Global Volunteers' teams live with and work alongside local people on human and economic development projects identified by the community as important to their long-term development. In this way, the volunteers' energy, creativity and labour are put to use amd at the same time they gain a genuine, first-hand understanding of how the vast majority of the world's people live day-to-day.

Projects vary from site to site, and from one season to the next. Most volunteers work in one of three areas. There are voluntary opportunities in the area of education such as teaching English, providing training in business, maths or basic sciences in the classroom, or tutoring small children. Volunteers are also needed in the area of community infrastructure to help with the construction of community centres and health clinics, the establishment of portable water systems, the repairing of classrooms and roads, and the building of houses. Finally, volunteers are also required to share their professional services such as dentistry, assisting rural health-care providers, identifying crop diseases and helping to establish small businesses. Sometimes volunteers are asked to simply assist with painting, planting or other beautification projects, for which specialized skills are not necessary. Everyone is welcome to apply, but minors must travel with a parent, guardian or adult group leader. Team members must be in good physical and mental health. Most teams' placements last for 1-3 weeks; about 60 teams are recruited each year. Volunteers must pay for their own trip. Costs range from $525 to $1,985 (1992 figures) excluding air fare. All trip-related costs are tax deductible to US tax payers. Volunteers are provided with accommodation in the community where they work.

Those interested should contact Michele Gran at the above address.

HCJB UK

131 Grattan Road, Bradford, West Yorkshire BD1 2HS (tel 0274-721 810).

HCJB undertakes media and medical ministries in Ecuador, South America, and the United Kingdom. Around 50 volunteers are needed each year to help with various projects. Audio and broadcasting engineers, announcers, scriptwriters and other volunteers with experience in communications are needed for media ministries; nurses and laboratory technicians are required for the medical ministries in Ecuador, and youth workers, printers, secretaries, office helpers, etc. are needed for each. Placements vary from one to three months or longer, all year round.

All volunteers are welcome but they must be committed Christians and in agreement with this organization's Statement of Faith. Only medical volunteers must speak Spanish but it is an advantage to speak Spanish or Italian if wishing to serve in Equador or Italy. Volunteers must raise their own financial support and accomodation on a rental basis is provided. No visas are required for periods of less than three months.

For more details contact the Personnel Secretary at the above address.

Health Volunteers Overseas

c/o Washington Station, PO Box 65157, Washington DC 20035-5157, USA (tel 202 296-0928; fax 202 296-8018).

HVO is a private non-profit organization committed to improving health care in developing countries through training and education. HVO currently recruits 150 trained medical volunteers per year to participate in programmes in the following specialities; anesthesia, dentistry, general surgery, oral and maxillofacial surgery and orthopaedics. Programme sites are in Africa, Asia, the Caribbean and Central America.

Although each programme is different in goals and content, the principal concept remains the same — that the volunteers should teach rather than just provide service. Applicants of any nationality are accepted; most programmes require Board Certified or Board Eligible physicians, dentists, oral surgeons or physical therapists, RNs and CRNAs. Restrictions on volunteers vary according to programme site. Usual length of placement is one month. A few sites provide housing for volunteers, but at other sites housing arrangements are made for the volunteers but the volunteers absorb the cost. No pocket money is provided; average expenses incurred for a one month assignment are $3,500 (transportation, housing etc.) and these must be paid for by the volunteer.

Those interested should contact Kate Skillman at the above address.

The Institute of Cultural Affairs

PO Box 505, London N19 34X.

The Institute of Cultural Affairs, a registered charity, runs a Volunteer Service Programme to select, train and place volunteers overseas. Opportunities for service are available in a wide variety of settings, in rural and urban areas in both developed and developing countries. About 200 volunteers have been trained and have served in 20 countries since the programme was set up in 1980. Interested enquirers are asked to attend an Orientation Weekend which sets out the issues and approaches of volunteering and local development. Prospective volunteers then spend a two week residential preparation period before final decisions about placement are made.

Volunteers spend a minimum of nine months overseas, and are responsible for raising money to cover all costs including travel, insurance, training, local accomodation and pocket money, usually totalling about £2,500. They may become involved in supporting local development activities, assisting in training courses, administration tasks, or research and development of new programmes.

The freshness and energy volunteers bring to their work overseas benefits them on their return due to their new and direct awareness of the cultural perspectives and socio-economic realities of other peoples. People with initiative, maturity and enthusiasm are encouraged to apply. Language ability and experience in health and teaching are advantages. School-leavers are considered if they have spent extended periods away from home. For further details contact the Co-ordinator at the above address.

International Christian Youth Exchange (ICYE)

International Office of ICYE, Goethe Strasse 85-87, 1000 Berlin 12, Germany.

ICYE is an international organization composed of autonomous national committees in over 30 countries which offers young people over 16 years old the chance to live overseas for six months or one year. The volunteers are hosted by a family or in an alternative living situation and attend high school and perform voluntary service work in the community in which they are living. Only volunteers aged over 18 years perform voluntary service work. This work may include work with children or the aged, involvement with rehabilitation, women's or disabled programmes, teaching, etc. ICYE is present in countries in Africa, Asia, Europe, Latin America, the Pacific and the United States of America. Departure to the host country takes place in July of each year.

Age limits vary for different countries but no special skills are required. Volunteers should supply a health certificate. There are scholarships available but usually a volunteer pays a participation fee to the sending committee, which covers administration, travel and insurance costs.

Volunteers should apply through the ICYE National Committee in their country. Where ICYE does not have such a committee the nearest committee suffices. Further information can be obtained from the Programme Executive at the above address, which can supply contact addresses for ICYE National Committees.

International Emergency Action

8 Bartletts Row, Somerton, Somerset TA11 6QW (information tel 0458-72863; secretariat tel/fax 0458-74747).

International Emergency Action is a Disaster Rescue, Relief, Reconstruction and Disaster preparedness Training charity. The agency responds to both humanitarian and environmental disasters and is actively involved in humanitarian and environmental projects in many countries throughout the world, including the UK and Europe, Russia, Ukraine, China, Bangladesh, Zimbabwe, Colombia, Chile. The agency has offices in UK, France, Chile and Morocco. Future plans include the opening of further offices in Southern Africa, the Far East and Maghreb countries. The agency also recruits for the Association of Pioneer Rescue Officers, 8 Waterpump Court, Thorplands, Northampton,.

During the last few years up to 50 volunteers per annum have been working for International Emergency Action. This figure is increasing as the environmental side of the charity increases its workload. A wide range of activities in the above countries is open to volunteers, including computer and satellite communications, basic rescue, secondary aid, water engineering, alternative energy sources, medical aid, women's projects, cultural projects, first aid training, children's welfare, mountain and flood plain erosion, tree planting, animal rescue, development education and preparing for disaster.

Volunteers may be of any nationality, and all volunteers are required to be fully inocculated before acceptance as operational personnel. All are required to have a valid passport of their country of citizenship to be accepted for overseas work. The agency requires many skills, some specialist and some general. The agency operates an equal opportunitites policy for all. Some projects require extensive experience, some require only basic skills; opportunities for handicapped and able-bodied persons of abilities great and small exist. Operational rescue personnel are required to have good health and be under 55 years of age. The agency tries to place volunteers in situations appropriate to their personal situations. Membership of the charity runs from year to year. Projects are negotiated individually, and may be from five days to two years, dependent on requirements and funding. Some expenses are paid; some projects provide pocket money or even a wage although this is not usual. Accommodation is only provided for volunteers if it is available.

Those interested should contact the Information Officer at the above address.

International Eye Foundation
7801 Norfolk Avenue, Bethesda, Maryland 20814, USA.

The International Eye Foundation send certified ophthalmological volunteers to developing countries. Opportunities also exist for short-term volunteer opthalmologists in the Caribbean and Eastern Europe. Opthalmologists for Eastern Europe must have a sub-speciality skill.

Applicants may be of any nationality provided they have the necessary qualifications and are in good health. Transportation is provided in most cases. Accommodation is either provided or covered, depending on the programme.

Those interested should contact either the Director of Programs, the Program Officer for the Caribbean, or the Executive Director at the above address for details.

Involvement Volunteers Association Inc.
PO Box 218, Port Melbourne, Victoria 3207, Australia (tel/fax 613 646-5504).

Involvement Volunteers exists to give people the opportunity to participate in volunteer activities related to environmental research, archaeology, history, or social welfare. Individual placements or Team Task placements run for 2-12 weeks, some with free accommodation and food, others costing up to £34 per week. Volunteers need to understand and speak some English. Individual and/or Team Task placements are available in Australia, California, Fiji, Germany, Hawaii, India, New Zealand and Thailand.

Involvement Volunteers is a non profit-making organization which charges a fee of approximately £130 to cover administration costs. For volunteers coming to Australia, this fee includes travel and visa advice, meeting the volunteer on arrival at Melbourne airport, initial accommodation, paid work introductions for volunteers with suitable work permits, advice on taxation and banking as well as a communication base for the visit. However, volunteers from overseas would have to pay for their own travel costs. Volunteers in Australia have access to discounted special coach travel passes and scuba diver training on the Great Barrier Reef.

For further information please contact Tim Cox at the above address.

The Lisle Fellowship, Inc
433 West Sterns Road, Temperence, MI 48182, USA (tel 313 847-7126).

The Lisle Fellowship is an educational organization which seeks to improve the quality of human life through human understanding among people of diverse cultures. The foundation of Lisle is aimed at creating an education for 'world mindedness'. Since the Fellowship's work began in 1936, over 11,000 persons have participated in its programme. Lisle offers programmes of up to six weeks in such places as Alaska,, Georgia, Columbia, India, Bali, Houston and the Middle East. Programmes emphasize personal development, inter-cultural group living experiences, small group field work assignments in the local community, and group times to integrate learning and usually take place in the spring and summer. Orientation takes place in a "home-centre" prior to field visits. Volunteers might find themselves working in an Indian rural village, an Eskimo community, or a Houston soup kitchen. Each programme is primarily designed as a personal learning experience.

Programmes are open to students, teachers and others over 18 years of age. Lisle looks for people from diverse cultural backgrounds who have an ability to get along with and work with others. Programme fees are offered at the lowest possible cost, in order to provide for people of all economic resources. Limited financial aid is available to participants who demonstrate a need for assistance. Participants in the Fellowship's programme may be eligible for college credits.

There is a programme fee, which covers board and lodging and travel related to the programme. Applications should be made to The Lisle Fellowship at the above address.

Mobility International USA (MIUSA)
PO Box 3551, Eugene, Oregon 97403, USA (tel 503 343 1284).

MIUSA is a non-profit making organization that exists to increase the opportunities for educational exchange and travel for people with disabilities. MIUSA's programmes include organizing international educational exchange programmes which include disabled and non-disabled people working together in the USA and overseas. MIUSA programmes have been in Italy, Mexico, England, Germany, Costa Rica, China, and the CIS. Themes of the exchanges vary but the goals are to increase international understanding through contact between people, and to improve the lives of disabled people around the world by sharing information and strategies for independent living. The exchange experiences last three to four weeks, and usually include a community service component and a stay with a family in the host country.

Persons with disabilities and able-bodied persons are encouraged to apply. Applicants must have an interest in independent living and an international understanding. Fees and specific requirements vary depending on the programme.

For further information regarding MIUSA contact the Director at the above address. Enclose an International Reply coupon and a self-addressed envelope.

Nothelfergemeinschaft der Freunde e.V
Auf der Kornerwiese 5, 6000 Frankfurt 1, Germany (tel 069-599557).

This organization recruits about 800 volunteers each year to work on workcamps in Germany, Israel, Ghana, Togo, Kenya, India and Tanzania. Activities include co-operation in non-profit institutions, construction work, path construction, painting etc, and domestic and social work. Food, accomodation and insurance are provided, but volunteers must be prepared to finance their own transportation and incidental expenses.

The camps, which are either for those aged 16-17 or for those 18 years and over, are of about a month's duration. But volunteers may attend two or three camps consecutively. The camps generally run fron the end of June to the end of October although occasionally there are camps in March/April. Applications for work outside Germany are open to Germans only.

Although applicants need have no special qualifications, manual skills are very useful. A knowledge of the English or French language is necessary.

Enquiries may be sent to the above address.

Operation Mobilisation
Quinta, Weston Rhyn, Oswestry, Shropshire, SY1 07L (tel 0691-773388; fax 0691-778378).

Operation Mobilisation is a global evangelist organization dedicated to training young people from Christian churches around the world to share their faith. It also organizes relief work in Kurdestan, South Africa, El Salvador, Nicaragua and India. About 700 volunteers per year are engaged by the organization doing almost anything they are skilled at or trainable for. Applicants of any nationality are accepted; currently volunteers of between 60 and 70 different nationalities are involved in the programmes. In the UK the minimum age limit is 16 years, while in Europe the minimum age limit is 17 years. There is no upper limit.

Long-term volunteers can work on a one-year training program, while during the summer volunteers can participate the various Love Europe Camps. These are mixture of Christian training, friendship groups, training and celebratrion, and they last for between one and two months. The cost ranges from about £249 to £390, depending on the length of the Camp; this covers food and accommodation. Volunteers can choose from a wide range of countries, and, naturally, the further a volunteer travels the higher the cost. Most participants are sponsored by their churches.

For further information please contact Mrs Sue Taylor, Personnel Manager, at the above address.

Project Concern International's OPTIONS Service
3550 Afton Road, San Diego, CA 92123, USA (tel 619 279-9690; fax 619 294-0294).

OPTIONS is the international health professional recruitment and referral service of Project Concern International. OPTIONS provides over 300 volunteer opportunities per year linking health and development specialists with programs, hospitals, and clinics worldwide. The voluntary positions are for professionals in the health field, including primary care physicians, nurses, physician assistants, therapists and other specialists to provide primary care, direct interventions and training for local country programmes.

Applicants of all nationalities are accepted, as long as they are certified in their field of expertise, but the organization only places volunteers in the US who have a US licence, and no students are accepted. Language requirements depend on the placement location. Volunteers are normally recruited for between one month and one year. The receiving agency provides expenses which usually includes room and board. If accommodation is not provided directly, assistance is given to find it locally.

Applications should be made to Susan West, OPTIONS Program Assistant, at the above address.

Project Hope
Health Sciences Education Centre, Millwood, VA 22646, USA (tel 1 800 544 4673).

Project Hope provides assistance in establishing or upgrading existing health personnel training programmes in developing countries. Around 300 volunteers are needed each year to act as educators in this project. Placements are for two months or more all year round as academic years differ from country to country.

Volunteers must be permanent residents of the USA with teaching experience within a health care profession, the ability to educate other trainers and a professional licence in the United States. Travel expenses, accomodation and meals are provided.

Those interested should apply to the Recruitment Assistant for further information.

Project Phoenix Trust
56 Burnaby Road, Southend-on-Sea, Essex 5S1 2TL (tel 0702-466412).

Project Phoenix Trust run group study-tour and interest holidays to Europe and North Africa for severely physically disabled adults. At present a minimum of two tours, lasting from seven to fourteen days, are organized each year — usually around Easter, September or December. Around 20 helpers are needed for each tour as the ratio of helpers to holiday makers is at least $1\frac{1}{2}$:1. Helpers are full members of the tour group and provide all the personal care needed by the holiday makers, from pushing wheelchairs to lifting and personal hygiene.

Volunteers must have a good command of English and should be fit, caring and between 19 and 50 years old. Applicants who are visually or hearing impaired or have obvious health problems will not be accepted. Nursing qualifications are needed for two of the helpers in each group and a knowledge of the language of the country being visited is useful. It is not essential to have experience of caring for disabled people as training will be given.

Volunteers are expected to contribute around one third of their own costs, with the Trust providing the balance. Accommodation, normally in a room with a disabled person, is provided but helpers must pay for incidentals. All excursions are included.

Inquiries should be made to the Secretary at the above address.

Quaker International Social Projects (QISP)
Friends House, Euston Road, London NW1 2BJ (tel 071-387 3601).

QISP recruits British applicants for its own community service projects in the UK and for those run by similar agencies overseas: mainly Eastern and Western

Europe, Scandinavia, Turkey, North America and North Africa. People sent abroad would be expected to have previous experience of voluntary work in Britain. The UK projects organized by QISP are one to three weeks in length, residential and composed of volunteer groups of seven to 20 people. Most take place in the summer although there are a few in the Spring. The projects aim to aid local communities and activities may be manually (decorating and construction,etc.) or socially (with children or people with a disability) based. All projects have a study element of some kind and there is usually at least one project each year studying a specific international issue: development, East-west relations or disarmament, for instance. Every year about 250 volunteers are involved, about half of whom come from countries other than the UK.

Essential qualities for applicants is that they speak good English and are able to work hard and get on with other people. A knowledge of foreign languages, first aid, craft skills or the ability to drive may also be useful on various projects. Volunteers should be over 18 years old. Volunteers with a disability are welcome to apply. Food and accomodation are free, but volunteers must pay their own travel expenses and provide their own pocket money. There is a registration fee that varies according to income.

UK applicants should write to the address above. Those from abroad should apply through an organization in their own country. A free newsletter is published three times a year.

Raleigh International
The Power House, Alpha Place, Flood Street, London SW3 5SZ (tel 071-351 7541; fax 071-351 9372).

Raleigh International is a youth development charity that carries out demanding environmental and community projects at home and abroad. During three months in remote areas volunteers, known as 'venturers', develop self-confidence and new skills which they are then encouraged to use on their return home. In 1992 Raleigh International ran expeditions in Zimbabwe, Chile, Malaysia, Brunei, Namibia, Mongolia, Guyana and Mauritius. About 1,000 venturers every year go abroad, but a further 1-2,000 ex-venturers work at home.

Venturers may find themselves helping with scientific research in tropical rain forests, building health centres and schools in remote villages, constructing bridges for the benefit of local communities or helping eye surgeons with cataract operations. All work is done with local venturers and volunteers. Applicants of all nationalities are welcome, but the ability to speak some English, as well as the ability to swim, is important. Voluntary staff are also needed to run projects, such as engineers, diving instructors, doctors and nurses. Venturers must be aged between 17 and 25, while skilled staff must be over 26. The length of placement is always three months, and there are about ten expeditions throughout the year. Venturers have to raise their own funds, but many national fundraising events are arranged and they also receive plenty of local support. Venturers don't have to carry tents although they often camp, or sleep in cabins etc. where possible.

Those interested should contact Tessa Kingsley at the above address.

Service Civil International /International Voluntary Service
Old Hall, East Bergholt, Colchester C07 6TQ.

International Voluntary Service (IVS) is the British branch of Service Civil International (SCI), an international voluntary movement which was begun in 1920 by Pierre Ceresole, a Swiss pacifist, with the aim of furthering reconciliation between participants in the Great War. Its objectives are to promote peace, international co-operation and friendship through the means of voluntary work. The 'Service Civil' in its name describes its role as an alternative to military service; for example during the Second World War International Voluntary Service, the British branch of the organization, was able to provide alternative service for conscientious objectors. There are now SCI branches in 25 countries and partner organizations in 20 more, which organize annually about 350 short term projects lasting for two or three weeks in Asia, Europe and the USA, involving up to 6,500 volunteers.

The national programme in each country is autonomous and develops its programme according to its special needs and possibilities. All volunteers accepted must appreciate the aims and objectives of SCI, and be prepared to work as a team in basic conditions.

An international workcamp consists of a group between 10 and 20 people from many different countries who live and work together for two to four weeks on a community project. Volunteers not only participate in the work, but also take part in discussions and the team life of the group. The projects undertaken vary from manual work with rural communities to helping with a playscheme for children in an inner-city area, or work and study on such subjects as ecology, conscientious objection, or solidarity with oppressed groups.

Service Civil International stress that a workcamp is not just a cheap holiday; volunteers are normally expected to work an unpaid 40 hours a week. Meals and basic accomodation are provided, but participants cover all other expenses themselves (including travel). Volunteers should be at least 18 years old. Applications are welcomed from people of all racial, cultural and social backgrounds and from people with physical disabilities.

For further information about Service Civil International projects applicants should contact the address in their own country listed below: where there is no address contact the International Secretariat at 73, 7th Main, 3rd Block, IV Stage, Basaveshara Nagor, Bangalore 560079, India.

Austria:	SCI, Schottengasse 3a/1/4/59, 1010 Vienna
Belgium:	SCI, Rue Van Elewyck 35, B 1050, Brussels
Belgium:	VIA Draakstraat 37, 2018 Antwerp
Finland:	KVT Rauhanasema, Veturitori, 00520 Helsinki 52
France:	SCI, 2 rue Eugene Fourniere, 75018 Paris
Germany:	SCI, Blucherstrasse 14, 5300 Bonn 1
Greece:	SCI 43 Arlonos Street, 10443 Athens
Rep. of Ireland:	VSI, 37 North Great Georges Street, Dublin
Italy:	SCI, Via dei Laterani 28, 00184 Rome
Netherlands:	VIA Pesthuislaan 25, 1054 Amsterdam
Northern Ireland:	IVS 122 Gt. Victoria Street, Belfast

Norway:	ID Langesgate 6, 0165, Oslo 1
Spain:	SCCT Rambla de Catalunya, 5 pral.2.a.08007 Barcelona
Sweden:	IAL Barnangsgatan 23, 11641 Stockholm
Switzerland:	SCI, Postfach 228, CH-300 Bern 9
USA:	SCI, Innisfree Village Rte 2, Box 506, Crozet Virginia 22932

Other organizations co-operating with Service Civil International

Czechoslovakia:	KMC Malostraske nabrezi 1, 111800 Prague
Denmark:	MS Bordergade 10-14, 1300 Copenhagen
Hungary:	SCI Olajliget utca 28, 1103 Budapest
Netherlands:	SIW Willemstaat 7, Utrecht
Poland:	SCI ul. Stefans-kiego 43, Poznan, Warsaw
Portugal:	Instituto da Juventude, Avenida da Liberdade, 1200 Lisbon
Turkey:	Genctur Cad 15-3 Sultenahmed Yerabatan Istanbul
Slovenia:	MOST Breg 12, PP279, Ljubljana
USA:	Volunteers for Peace, Tiffany Road, Belmont, Vermont 05370

Samaritans

5666 La Jolla Blvd.,La Jolla, CA 92037, USA (tel 619-456 2216).

Samaritans organize workcamps, study tours, and other mission programmes to enable youths and adults to serve others during vacation periods. As well as conducting programmes within the USA, Samaritans offer workcamps, usually on building projects, in over 20 other countries for periods of one or two weeks. Volunteers must be Christians and at least 16 years old.

   Those interested should contact the Executive Director at the above address.

Schools Partnership Worldwide

1 Catton Street, London SW1 R4AB (tel 071-831 1603; fax 071-831 1746).

Schools Partnership Worldwide organizes the secondment of 200 school leavers per year to a range of countries including India, Nepal, Zimbabwe, Gambia and Tanzania. Volunteers of all nationalities are mainly involved in teaching and social work. Voluntary teachers must have attained high grades in their A Levels. Only school leavers are accepted for this programme. The minimum length of placement is six months, while the maximum is ten. Placements start in September or January. No pocket money is provided, and volunteers must pay for all their expenses including air fares and travel costs. Accommodation is provided.

   For further information write to the Director at the above address.

Scottish Churches World Exchange

121 George Street, Edinburgh EH2 4YN, Scotland (tel 031-225 5722).

World Exchange is organized by a number of Scottish churches acting together. It offers volunteer opportunities ranging from six to 18 months for people with a wide variety of skills. In 1992 volunteers were placed in Asia, the Middle East, Africa and Central America. While teachers and medical staff are easiest to place,

World Exchange will also consider candidates who come straight from university or with other more practical skills.

Candidates can be of any age between 18 and 80. A small local allowance is paid and food and accommodation are provided. A travel pool operates on the basis that candidates are expected to do a considerable amount of fundraising before departure. Applicants should be Scottish and be a member of any Christian Church in Scotland. Scottish candidates resident elsewhere in the UK may also apply.

Those interested should write to the Director at the above address.

United Kingdom Jewish Aid and International Development

Drayton House, 30 Gordon Street, London WC1H 0AN (tel 071-387 3281; fax 071-383 4810).

UKJAID is a non-sectarian and humanitarian relief agency operating wherever demand leads and resources allow. It is currently operating on the Iraqi/Turkish border with Kurdish refugees, and in Zimbabwe. Ten volunteers are engaged per year. Volunteers of all nationalities are needed to work both in London and overseas on project research and negotiation and monitoring, database maintenance, recruitment and fundraising. Various skills are required although it is difficult to be specific as this need is demand-led.   The minimum length of time for which volunteers are required is three months; help is needed all the year round. Travel expenses are paid for UK volunteers; for volunteers involved in overseas work this is negotiable. Accommodation is usually provided.

For further information please contact Ansel Harris at the above address.

United Nations Association (Wales) International Youth Service

Welsh Centre for International Affairs, Temple of Peace, Cathays Park, Cardiff, CF1 3AP (tel 0222-223088).

The UNA (Wales) International Youth Service offers facilities for people from Great Britain to attend international volunteer projects within Wales and in most countries in Western and Eastern Europe, the United States, Canada, India as well as certain African countries. These projects usually last between two and four weeks during the summer and involve work on a variety of schemes including hospital and social work, playschemes, and environmental work. The aim of these projects is the encouragement of international understanding, and development of community projects. The projects normally consist of between 10 and 15 volunteers aged over 18.

Volunteers are required to meet their own travelling expenses to the projects, but once there they are provided with free board and accommodation. On acceptance, volunteers have to pay a registration fee, which is £45 for projects in Wales, and £50-80 for projects abroad.

Those interested should write to the IYS officer at the above address, enclosing an SAE, to receive membership details.

United Society for the Propagation of the Gospel (USPG)

Partnership House, 157 Waterloo Road, London SE1 8XA (tel 071-928 8681; fax 071-928 2371).

The Society organizes church-related projects in Britain, Africa, Asia, South America, the Middle East and the Caribbean. 50 volunteers per year are involved in a wide range of activities including root groups dedicated to parish work and community living in Britain, an experience exchange programme which organizes various overseas placements, overseas sabbaticals and overseas pastoral placements for theological students. Applicants of any nationality may apply, but most placements are only open to British citizens living in Britain. There exist some places in the root groups for 18-30 year olds from overseas, and these are recruited only through churches in partnership with the Society. Specialist skills are occasionally needed depending on placement.

Volunteers for the root groups are aged between 18 and 30, for all other placements the minimum age is 18 and there is no upper limit. Good health is essential. The length of time for which volunteers are normally recruited varies from three months to a year. The selection process takes place from November to May each year, with placements beginning in the autumn. Participants are expected to raise as much as possible towards costs and USPG can give grants in cases of need. Accommodation is usually available, depending on placement.

For further information please contact Nicki Donovan at the above address.

WEC International
Bulstrode, Gerrards Cross, Bucks SL9 8SZ (tel 0753-884631).

WEC International seeks to evangelize the remaining unevangelised areas of the world in the shortest possible time. As well as spreading the Gospel, WEC volunteers also give practical help with community development projects. Small numbers of volunteers are needed to help full-time WEC volunteers in over 50 countries of the world. Unskilled volunteers or students can give service during the summer to help with building work, looking after children and other practical work. For those with specific skills or training, (secretaries, teachers, mechanics, nurses, doctors, builders, etc), there are more opportunities and placements are for one or two years.

All volunteers must be evangelical Christians. Some knowledge of French and a driving licence are useful. Volunteers are responsible for their fares to and from the field, but while in the field, they receive a small monthly allowance.

Those interested should contact Francis Blackmore at the above address.

Working Weekends on Organic Farms (WWOOF)

WWOOF exists to give people the opportunity of gaining first hand experience of organic farming and gardening in return for spending a weekend or longer working on a farm. Since WWOOF began in England in 1971, similar schemes have developed in other countries around the world; in some countries WWOOF is taken to mean 'Willing Workers on Organic Farms'.

Each of the groups listed below is an independent group with its own aims, system, fees and rules. They are all similar in that they offer volunteers the chance to learn in a practical way the growing methods of their host. Each group will supply a worklist booklet to members from which volunteers can choose a farm. Send International Reply Coupons when writing to an overseas group.

WWOOF schemes:

Australia:	WWOOF (Aus), Lionel Pollard, Mt Murrindal Co-op, Buchan, Vic 3885.
Belgium:	WEEBIO, Dellissee Adolphe, Chaupreheld 64, 4081 Cherron.
Canada:	WWOOF (Canada), John Vanden Heuvel, RR2, Carlston Road, Blewett, Nelson, British Columbia VIL 5P5.
Denmark:	VHH, c/o Bent & Inga Nielsen, Asenjev 35, 9881 Bindslev.
Eire:	WWOOF (Eire), Annie Sampson, Crowhill, Newgrove, Tulla, Co. Clare.
Germany:	WWOOF (Germany), Stettiner Str 3, 6301 Pohlheim.
Hungary:	BIOKULTURA, c/o Mr Zsolt Meszaros, Biokultura Egyesulet, H-1023 Budapest, Torok u.7.em. 1.
Netherlands:	NVEL, Willemsvaart 1-304; 8019 AA Zwolle, The Netherlands.
New Zealand:	WWOOF (NZ), Jane Bryan-Strange, PO Box 10-037, Palmerston North
Norway:	ATLANTIS, Rolf Hofmogst, 18, N-0655 Oslo 6. UK:
UK:	WWOOF (UK), Don Pynches, 19 Bradford Road, Lewes, BN17 1RB, Sussex.
USA:	FRIENDS OF THE TREES, PO Box 1064, Tonasket, WA 98855, USA.
USA:	NATURAL FARMERS COOPERATIVE APPRENTICE-SHIP PROGRAM, c/o Doug Jones, Birdsfoot Farm, Star Rt, Box 138, Canton, NY 13617, USA.
USA:	NEWOOF, New England Small Farms Institute, PO Box 937 Belchertown, MA 01007, USA.

World Council of Churches — Youth Sub-Unit

150 Route de Ferney, PO Box 66, 1211 Geneva 20, Switzerland (tel 022-916 065).

The Youth Sub-Unit has a programme called Ecumenical Youth Action which sponsors workcamps in Africa, Asia, Latin America and the Middle East. Volunteers from all nationalities and faiths share in work and live in a local community. Theological discussions and manual work such as agricultural, construction and renovation projects form an important part of the programme. Workcamps are held between April and September with the length being from one to three weeks.

Volunteers should be aged 18 to 30 years. They must arrange and pay for their own travel and insurance. Around £3 per day is expected to be contributed towards the camp's expenses.

Those interested should write to the above address for a workcamp programme but should then apply directly to the individual camps.

World Horizons

Glanmor Road, Llanelli, Dyfed, Wales SA15 2LU (tel 0554-778035).

World Horizons is a modern missionary movement offering committed Christians the opportunity to be involved in expeditions and short-term placements, as well as long-term, with its full-time teams in Britain, Europe, the Middle East, Asia, Africa and South America.

No particular skills are required although administrative, secretarial, building or mechanical skills are always helpful. Most opportunities are between Easter and October; the minimum age for Europe is 17, and 18 for the rest of the world. Volunteers are responsible for raising their own finances; accommodation is provided but must be paid for by the volunteer.

Write to the Personnel Department at the above address for further details.

WORLDTEACH, Inc.

Harvard Institution for International Development, One Eliot Street, Cambridge, MA 02138-5705, USA (tel 617 495-5527; fax 617 495-1239).

WorldTeach is a small, private, non-profit-making organization whose purpose is to recruit about 200 volunteers per year and place them as teachers in countries that request assistance. It runs a two month summer English teaching program in China and a six month sports coaching program in South Africa. WorldTeach volunteers serve as full-time teachers at elementary and secondary schools, training colleges and universities. Most teach English, though volunteers in South Africa coach sports. A full-year teaching program in South Africa will probably be established in 1993.

Volunteers may be of any nationality but they must speak English with native fluency. Volunteers must have accquired at least 25 hours training or experience in Teaching English as a Foreign Language before they depart. For the summer program in Shanghai volunteers must be college or graduate students. For the coaching program in South Africa volunteers must have recent athletic or coaching experience. The full-year teaching program requires a university degree. There are no age limits and volunteers must be in good health and able to live and work under rigorous conditions. The summer program in China lasts for two months, while the sports program in South Africa lasts for six months.

Volunteers must pay a participation fee, which covers round-trip airfare (from the USA), health insurance, orientation, placement, field support and administrative costs. Current fees range from $3,300 to $4,360. While the volunteers are teaching, they receive either room and board or housing and a living allowance from the host school, community or government. Payments on student loans can be deferred during the term of service. WorldTeach offers fundraising advice and encourages volunteers to raise money for the participation fee in their own communities.

For further information write to Sydney Rosen at the above address.

United Kingdom

Archaeology

Council for British Archaeology
112 Kennington Road, London SE11 6RE (tel 071-582 0494).

The Council publishes *British Archaeological News* which carries advertisements for volunteer help on archaeological sites in Britain. This publication commences in January each year and comes out every two months thereafter. The annual subscription for 1992 was £10.50 for the UK, £11.50 for Europe, £12.00 for surface mail outside Europe and £20.00 for airmail outside Europe. US $ payments also acceptable (send an international reply coupon for details).

Dorset Natural History and Archaeological Society
Dorset County Museum, Dorchester, Dorset DT1 1XA (tel 03052-62735).

The Archaeological Society acts as a co-ordinating body for digs in the County of Dorset putting those interested in participating in excavations in touch with the Directors of particular projects. The number of volunteers needed each year depends on the number of excavations taking place, the needs being determined by the organizers of individual digs. The length of time for which volunteers are recruited will also be decided by the Directors.

Volunteers should be able-bodied and at least 18 years of age. No special qualifications are essential, but they are always useful. Applications may be of any nationality. Volunteers can obtain a list of excavations for a particular year from the Secretary of the Society at the above address in March, and they should apply to the Directors of individual projects.

North Yorkshire County Council, Archaeology Section
Planning Department, County Hall, Northallerton DL7 8AQ.

The Council's Archaeology Sections normally organizes one excavation per year. In 1993, the excavation at Wood Hall runs from June to the end of September. Volunteers are required to help with digging and other general archaeological tasks; they need possess no special skills and the minimum age is 16 years. Volunteers are usually recruited for a maximum of 12 weeks, and limited accommodation and camping facilities are provided. The current rate of pocket money is £5 per day worked, although experienced diggers or those on their second excavation with the Section receive £10 per day.

For the 1993 project enquiries should be sent to Ms V. Metcalfe, Wood Hall Moated Manor Project, Field Study Centre, Gale Common Cottage, Gale Common Ash Disposal Site, Cobcroft Lane, Criddling Stubbs, North Yorkshire WF11 0BB.

Upper Nene Archaeological Society
Toad Hall, Hackleton, Northampton NN7 2AD (tel 0604-870312).

The Society oversees the excavation of a Romano-British villa and underlying Iron

Age settlement. Volunteers are required to help with trowelling and a variety of excavation and post-excavation procedures. Volunteers may be of any nationality but they must be able to speak English. The lower age limit is normally 16; there is no upper limit. Applicants should consider themselves physically capable of carrying buckets of soil, pushing wheelbarrows and kneeling to work.

Volunteers are normally required for two weeks in August but anyone within daily travelling distance is welcome to come and help on Sundays throughout the year. Pocket money is not provided, but volunteers must pay a specified contribution towards the everyday expenses of running the excavation. Accommodation is available in the form of a basic campsite, or bed and breakfast accommodation at reasonable rates can be arranged locally. This must be paid for by the volunteer.

Those interested should contact Mrs D E Friendship-Taylor at the above address.

Child Care

Association for All Speech Impaired Children
347 Central Markets, Smithfield, London EC1 (tel 071-236 3632).

Each summer AFASIC organizes outdoor Activity Weeks at various outdoor pursuit centres, hostels and guest houses in Britain. Each child is attached to a 'Young person helper' (Link), a volunteer who acts as a friend and support for the week.

Volunteers should be over 18 years and in good health. No experience is required and a briefing is given. Board and lodging is provided. Volunteers must provide their own travel expenses though every effort is made to cut this cost by linking helpers to share transport or to use Association vehicles which are being taken for use on Activity Weeks.

Those interested should apply to the above address.

Basecamp
Marthrown of Mabie, Mabie Forest, Dumfries DG2 8HB (tel 0387-68493 or 0387-85493).

Basecamp organizes residential programmes for young people aged 15 to 19 years who are experiencing behavioural and emotional difficulties. Referred by Juvenile Courts, Children's Panels, Social Services and Social Work Departments, groups of five to ten children attend Basecamp, a remote residential centre, for short courses or programmes of adventure-based activities and group work.

During the summer around 16 volunteers are needed to assist in conservation work and site work at the residential centre. Workcamp volunteers should be over 16 years old, in good health and interested in the countryside and practical physical work. Board and lodging for the one to three week long camps are provided.

Around five volunteers are needed for a minimum of 12 months to act as Project Assistants on these programmes. Volunteers should be in good health, over 23 years old, licensed drivers and have experience in outdoor activities, expeditions, or youth social work. Board, lodging or food allowance are provided. Applications to the Director at the above address.

Birmingham Phab Camps

52 Green Lanes, Sutton Coldfield, Birmingham B73 5JW.

This organization runs holiday camps each summer in England for equal numbers of physically handicapped and able-bodied children, enabling the handicapped children to integrate with their able bodied contemporaries. There are five camps a year, three of which cater for different age groups; Junior (7-10), Senior (11-13), Teenage (14-16), and 16 plus. The first two camps take 40 children, the third 20 and the fourth 12 — 15. The fourth camp is run for severely multiple-handicapped children of various ages. This is a particularly demanding holiday and preference will be given to volunteers who have had experience of this type of work before. 20 volunteers are needed for this holiday.

Many children who are physically handicapped have little opportunity to mix and form friendships with their peer groups, and the camps are designed to remedy this isolation and overcome prejudice. There is a wide range of activities from swimming and discos to seaside and camping trips, in which all the children take part. The camps are run entirely by unpaid volunteers, of whom 80 are needed each year. The volunteer will work at a camp for up to 10 days with a team including an experienced leader, two cooks, and a qualified nurse. The Junior Camp is normally held in a boarding school, while the Army provides the Senior Camp with a site.

Volunteers should be aged between 17 and 30, and speak recognizable English which children will understand. Obviously the ability to communicate with children is important. Special skills in sports, crafts, and art plus previous initiative, resilience and a capacity for hard work are of much more importance. There are a limited number of places for disabled volunteers. Training days are held before each camp, where medical staff from special schools give advice on special problems, and the team plans the camp programme. Accommodation is provided, but expenses and pocked money are not. Transport from Birmingham to the camp and back is paid.

Volunteers should apply to the Volunteer Recruitment Officer at the above address.

Birmingham Young Volunteers

BYV Association, 4th Floor, Smithfield House, Digbeth, Birmingham B5 6BS.

This organization needs volunteers to help on its activity holidays for underprivileged children during the school summer holidays. Each volunteer would help for one week only. Four Adventure Camps are run in Pembroke, South Wales during July and August for children aged 10 to 15. Four residential holidays for children aged 5 to 10 are run in the Midlands during August.

Volunteers look after children on trips, take part in group activities, swimming, games, craft sessions, etc. It is hard work being with children 24 hours a day but, despite the stamina and patience required it is very rewarding. BYV also need mini-bus drivers with clean licences, and people prepared to cook for groups of up to 60.

Travel expenses to and from Birmingham may be paid, but personal expenses on the holiday are not. Accommodation and food are provided. Training weekends and introductory days are arranged for volunteers.

Applications are accepted from young people aged 17 and over and resident in the UK. They should be sent to the Co-ordinator at the above address.

Break
20 Hooks Hill Road, Sheringham, Norfolk N26 8NL (tel 0263-823170)

Around 40 volunteers a year are needed to help provide holiday, emergency, and short term care for handicapped and deprived children and mentally handicapped adults in three residential centres in Norfolk. Applicants are accepted for anything between one and 12 months. The work itself involves a certain amount of routine housekeeping, but most of it is with guests, with games, outings, and so on. It can be very demanding, and so good health is essential.

Anyone over 17 with a good command of English can apply, but expenses are only paid for travel within the British Isles. Food, accommodation, and pocket money of around £21 per week are provided.

Those interested should contact the Director at the above addres.

Caldecott Community
Mersham-le-Hatch, Ashford, Kent (tel 0233-23941).

The community is a residential treatment centre and special school for about 80 children between the ages of 5 and 18. The children are taken into care, which is provided around the year, after suffering complete breakdowns due to stresses at home. Contact is maintained with home as much as possible especially during the holidays. There is a primary school within the community which prepares the younger children for entry into secondary schools in the area. A few volunteers are taken on to assist the 70 adults in the community, living with family-type groups of 10 children.   There are no special skills required, but the volunteers should enjoy being with children and some ability in sports, music, arts and crafts or possession of a driving licence would be an asset. Volunteers are usually taken on for between three months and a year. Board, lodging, travelling expenses and £44 per week are provided.

Those interested should apply to Liz Fisher at the above address.

Camphill Rudolf Steiner School
Murtle Estate, Bieldside, Aberdeen AB1 9EP (tel 0224-867 935).

This is a residential school for children and adolescents in need of special care. Volunteers are needed to live-in and help care for the young people in a home and teach in the school setting. A full time commitment is required with volunteers expected to join in the community life as fully as possible, and emphasis is placed on Christian ideals, social responsibility and the development of the individual. Duties include caring for the young people both physically and emotionally in houses, teaching in classrooms, general domestic tasks, arranging sports and craft activities and working on the land. Around 80 volunteers of any nationality are needed all year round. Placements are usually for at least a year, but in some cases may only be for six months.

Applicants must be willing to live with and fully involve themselves in the community activities with the young people, physically fit, mentally stable, aged over 19 years and have respect for Christian ideals. Exceptions are made for people with certain medical conditions but otherwise no-one with drug habits is accepted. Board, lodging and weekly pocket money are provided. Volunteers who stay for the entire agreed period have their return fare home paid.

Apply to the Staff Committee at the above address.

Children's Community Holidays Ltd.
34 Mount Charles, Belfast BT 1NZ. (tel 0232-245650)

Children's Community Holidays is a non-profit making organization involved primarily with cross community work in Northern Ireland. The winter programme consists of running youth clubs and playgroups in various cities and organizing some residential weekend camps for children. During July and August about 800 children aged 8 — 16 are taken on seven-day residential holidays. The children are divided into two or three year aged groups but are mixed on terms of religious, geographic and economic backgrounds. Around 300 volunteers are needed for the 16 — 24 holidays run per summer. Positions offered include minibus drivers, caterers, domestics, matrons, clerical staff, supervisors and directors of holidays. Recruitment is for seven-day periods but volunteers may work for three consecutive periods. While the majority of positions are available during summer, some volunteers are needed in the winter.

All applicants are required to agree to the DHSS pre-employment vetting scheme which includes a scrutiny of police and statutory agency disciplinary records. Volunteers must have a basic understanding of English and applicants for supervisors positions must bave experience with working with children and take part in a seven-day training course in early July. Those wishing to work as domestics must be older than $16\frac{1}{2}$ years, while supervisory staff must be older than $17\frac{1}{2}$ years, on July 1st. Pocket money paid depends on the position held but is between £25 and £86 per seven-day period.

Apply to the Deputy Director at the above address

Children's Country Holidays Fund
First Floor (Rear), 42-43 Lower Marsh, London SE1 7RG (tel 071-928 6522).

Every year the Fund provides holidays in the country, at the seaside, in private homes or established camps, for almost 3,500 disadvantaged London children. The arrangements for the children's holidays are undertaken by voluntary workers, under the umbrella of a small administrative staff in Head Office. Volunteers are also needed to act as train marshals supervising the children's travel to and from London.

There are no special requirements for camp supervisors, beyond a minimum age of 18, good health, and the ability to supervise children aged between nine and thirteen. The holiday periods vary between ten to fourteen days, and holidays always take place during the six weeks of the school summer holidays. The Fund very much regrets that it can no longer accept applications from outside the UK.

Those interested should write to the Director at the above address to find out how they can help.

CLAN
40 Warren Road, Stirchley, Birmingham B30 2NY (tel 021-459 3723).

This organization provides short holiday breaks for children aged from 7 to 13 who would not normally be able to visit the countryside. The camps may be up to a week long and are held during the summer vacation at attractive sites in the West Midlands.

Around 10 volunteers a year are need to help look after the children and organize leisure activities. No special requirements are expected of volunteers other than that they be mobile and aged over 16. Board, lodging and reasonable travelling expenses within the UK are provided.

Applicants should contact the above address, enclosing a stamped addressed envelope or an international replly coupon.

Community Action Projects (C.A.P.)
Students' Union, Goodricke College, University of York, Heslington, York. YO1 5DD (tel 0904-412328).

CAP runs three types of holiday for a total of 200 children who would not normally get a holiday; most have special needs because they come from low income, broken or unsettled family backgrounds. Easter and summer camps for 6 to 13 year olds consist of site-based drama, craft, sport activities and day trips. Venture Weeks in August for 14 and 15 year olds are more adventurous outdoor pursuit bolidays, including hill walking and abseiling.

Around 100 volunteers are needed to help with the general running of the camps as well as participating in and initiating activities. Anyone over 18 years with enthusiasm would be welcomed, but people with specific skills including first-aid, driving and walking experience are also required. Accommodation is provided.

For further information contact the Community Action Officer at the above address.

The Cotswold Community
Ashton Keynes, Nr. Swindon, Wiltshire SN6 6QU (tel 0285-861239).

This community provides care, treatment and education for 40 severely emotionally deprived boys aged from nine to 18. The community consists of four separate households, a school and a farm. Around four volunteers are needed each year to teach and care for the boys. Placements are for a minimum of three months and may be up to a year long. Volunteers may be of any nationality provided that they are at least 20 years old, speak English well and are in good health. Full board and lodging and about £20 pocket money per week are provided.

For further information contact the Principal at the above address.

Flysheet Camps Scotland
Children's Wilderness Centre, Lockerbie, Finniegill, Dumfriesshire.

Since 1980 Finniegill has been developed as a wilderness centre by Flysheet Camps Scotland, a registered charity. It aims to provide a place for children to stay and gain some experience of living at close quarters with nature for any period from a day to a week. Most of the children come from vulnerable family situations, and only a limited number of really dedicated and hard-working volunteers are needed.

The camp is run by both long and medium term volunteers. The living conditions are very primitive; the farm has no electricity, and is very isolated. A contribution of under £2 a day towards the cost of food is normally expected. No particular skills or qualifications are expected of volunteers, but it is prefered that volunteers stay for a few days to get the feel of the place before they commit themselves to staying for a longer period.

Those interested should send a stamped addressed envelope to the Resident Organizer at the above address fur further details.

Glen River YMCA National Centre
143 Central Promenade, Newcastle, Co. Down BT33 0HN, Northern Ireland (tel 03967-24488).

The Centre is an outdoor education centre which needs volunteers to act as domestic staff and cooks, instructors in outdoor pursuits such as canoeing, hill walking, archery, etc, and tutors in personal development. Around 14 volunteers are required for eight or nine weeks during summer and in winter two or three volunteers are needed. An interest in community relations would be an advantage.

Volunteers should be physically and mentally fit, aged 18 years or older and fluent in English. Volunteers for instructor positions should be skilled in the relevant activity and for volunteers older than 25, a driving licence is useful. Board, lodging and pocket money of £18 per week are provided.

Applications should be made to the Programme Manager at the above address.

Leicester Childrens Holiday Home
Quebec Road, Mablethorpe, Lincs. LN12 1QX (tel 0521-72444).

This Home provides summer holidays for groups of 40 girls and 40 boys from socially deprived backgrounds in the Leicester area. The two week-long camps are held from May through to the end of August each year. Around 15 volunteers are needed for the entire season to help care for the children, to cook and undertake other duties including taking sports or musical activities.

Volunteers may be of any nationality provided they are 18 — 30 years old, fit, energetic and enjoy outdoor activities. Volunteers with musical or sporting skills are preferred. Board, accommodation and £43 per week are provided.

Applicants should contact the Matron at the above address

Liverpool Children's Holiday Organisation (LCHO)
Wellington Road School, Wellington Road, Dingle, Liverpool L8 4TX (tel 051-727 7330).

LCHO provides residential holidays for Merseyside children who would not normally get a holiday away from home. Volunteers are needed to act as supervisors and will be responsible for a small group of children 24 hours a day. Applicants must be over 18 and fit. Prior to working on the holidays, volunteers must be interviewed and complete a week-long residential training course run by LCHO.

Qualified first-aiders and mini-bus drivers are also needed.

Recruitment usually takes place between January and March for that year's summer holiday period. Accommodation is provided and expenses paid. Due to the interviews and training course the voluntary work is only really suitable for UK residents.

Applicants should contact the above address.

London Children's Camp
105 Bevan Street, Lowestoft, Suffolk NR32 2AF.

This organization needs some 75 volunteers to help run three 11 day camps on a site at Lowestoft in Suffolk each summer during the school holidays. The camps are for boys and girls from London, who would not otherwise get a holiday away from home. The age-group catered for is nine to fourteen year olds, and about 90 children attend each camp. An Organizer and three Team Leaders with a small catering staff and about 25 volunteer leaders run the camps. The children, in groups of six or eight, sleep in tents and a leader is assigned to each group to see that the most is made of the holiday. He or she is involved in running the widest possible variety of activities.

Outings and competitions are organized for larger groups and each leader takes a turn at the various duties: dining room, preparing supper, issuing sports equipment, etc. A converted farmhouse incorporates the cooking and dining facilities. The leaders sleep in tents but there are locker-rooms for storing possessions, and a wood cabin on the main field for relaxing and coffee. The site of the camp is 35 acres of grass and trees stretching to cliffs, foreshore and beach. Outbuildings house washing and toilet facilities, hot showers and drying rooms. There is usually some time during a hectic but rewarding stay for a quiet drink off site with new friends during moments of calm!

Applicants must be at least 18 years of age and in good health. An ability to get on with children (sometimes difficult ones) is essential. All nationalities are welcome, but spoken English must be excellent. The normal length of stay is two weeks. Free board and lodging are provided, and pocket money of £25 a week is paid.

More detailed information sheets will be supplied on application to the above address.

The National Autistic Society
276 Willesden Lane, London NW2 5RB (tel 081-451 1114).

There are limited opportunities for volunteers to work with children with autism on special projects lasting a week or a fortnight during the school vacations or on a longer term basis. Most of this work is in special schools.

Applicants who send their enquiries to the National Society office in London will be sent a list of the special schools and units around the country.

Phoenix YCP Ltd
16 Alexander Square, Lurgan, Craigavon, Northern Ireland (tel 0762 325927).

Phoenix YCP organizes youth work with children aged between seven and 13 years such as games, drama and art and crafts through a summer scheme programme in Northern Ireland. It also recruits volunteers for Fellowship of Reconciliation in Belfast and Pacem-in-Terris in Delaware, USA.

40 volunteers are needed for the summer scheme to act as Volunteer Leaders with the seven to thirteen year olds. Applicants of any nationality may apply, though all applicants must have previously worked with children, and have a fair knowledge of English. The minimum age limit is 17 years. Volunteers are required for one month between July and August. They must pay for their own travel expenses, as well as £30 for accommodation, food and a social programme.

Enquiries should be made to Donna McConville at the above address.

Tadworth Court Children's Hospital Holiday Project
Tadworth Court, Tadworth, Surrey, KT20 5RU (tel 0737-357171).

Between July and September every year the Project provides a programme of extra social activities for mentally and physically handicapped children coming to Tadworth Court for respite care. At any one time there are up to 20 children on the unit aged up to 19 years. Help is needed from eight to ten volunteers a year to provide care feeding, bathing and changing the children, organizing play and activities and generally befriending them. Volunteers also act as escorts for children on outings on a one to one basis. Trained staff are available to assist at all times.

Participants must be at least 18 years old and should preferably have some experience with children: they are required for periods of at least one month. Accommodation and a meal allowance of £5 per day are provided, as are travelling expenses within the mainland UK.

For further details contact Rachel Turner, Volunteers Organizer, at the above address.

Conservation and the Environment

British Trust for Conservation Volunteers
36 St Mary's Street, Wallingford, Oxfordshire OX10 0EU (tel 0491-39766).

BTCV is the country's leading charity protecting the environment through practical action. A network of over 80 field offices allows some 60,000 volunteers of all ages and from all sections of the community to train and take part in a wide range of environmental projects. These include planting trees and hedges, repairing footpaths and drystone walls, improving access to the countryside and creating urban wildlife sanctuaries.

BTCV's Natural Break programme of conservation working holidays enables nearly 6,000 volunteers between the ages of 16 and 75 to spend a week in a spectacular setting, learning new and challenging conservation skills from the repair of drystone walls to the construction of steps and stiles. Around 600 holidays take place throughout the country all year round offering the perfect opportunity for individuals to make a practical contribution to the protection of the environment. Volunteers from overseas must be over 18 and speak good English. Prices start at around £29 a week including food, simple accommodation and all training.

A free brochure is available from the above address (48p stamp appreciated).

Cathedral Camps

Manor House, High Birstwith, Harrogate, North Yorkshire HG3 2LG (tel 0423-770385).

Cathedral Camps undertake the conservation and restoration of Cathedrals and their environments, including tasks that have hitherto been postponed because of a lack of resources.

Volunteers are needed to work in groups of 15-25 people undertaking the above types of conservation work on Cathedrals and their surroundings throughout the country. Hours of work are normally 08.30-17.30 four and a half days per week. The Camps take place from July to September and each one lasts for a week. A contribution of approximately £30 is asked to go towards the cost of the Camp and board and lodging. The minimum age is 16 and most volunteers are aged between 17 and 25. Foreign applicants are accepted.

For further details and an application form contact Mrs Shelley Bent, 16 Glebe Avenue, Flitwick, Bedfordshire MK45 1HS (tel 0525-721697).

The Centre for Alternative Technology

Machynlleth, Powys SY20 9AZ (tel 0654-702400; fax 0654-702872).

Established in 1974, the Centre for Alternative Technology is an internationally renowned display and education centre promoting practical ideas and information on technologies which sustain rather than damage the environment.

The Centre runs a short-term volunteer programme, from March to September inclusive, for stays of one or two weeks. There is also a long-term volunteer programme for individuals to help in specific work departments for up to 6 months. Short term volunteers help with gardening, landscaping, site maintenance and preparation for courses. Long term jobs for volunteers include engineering, gardening, information and site maintenance.

Applicants for the long-term programme should have relevant experience. Applicants for either programme can be of any nationality; long-term volunteers must be eligible for British state benefit payments, or be able to fund themselves. Accommodation is basic in Youth Hostel-style, shared with other volunteers; food, drinks, soap, shampoo, toothpaste, tampons etc. are all provided.

Applicants for the 90 places available annually, whether short or long term, should contact Rick Dance at the above address.

Conservation Volunteers — Northern Ireland

The Pavilion, Cherryvale Playing Fields, Ravenhill Road, Belfast BT6 0BZ (tel 0232-645169).

Conservation Volunteers involve people in all types of practical conservation work throughout Northern Ireland. Tasks include dry-stone walling, erosion control, tree planting, creating nature areas, etc. Projects continue all year round and volunteers are needed on a day-to-day or project basis, but working holidays lasting for one week are offered only during the summer months.

Volunteers must have reasonable English skills and, for the working holidays, be aged at least 16 years old. On-site training is given for those with no experience. Food and accommodation is provided for volunteers on the working holidays but travel and lunch expenses are paid for local volunteers only.

Enquiries should be sent to the Publicity Officer.

Countryside Resources
Ashcroft, Rectory Lane, Scrivelsby, Horncastle, Lincs. LN9 6JB.

Countryside Resources publish the *Organic Holiday Directory* for Working Guests which provides full details of organic farms, vineyards and gardens etc. requiring voluntary help in the UK. Type of work, length of stay, accommodation and food provided varies between hosts. All arrangements for placements are made between host and visitor, not with Countryside Resources. A wide variety of agricultural and horticultural work is open to volunteers, ranging from standard crop production to working with heavy horses. Hosts give more skilled work at their discretion depending on ability of volunteer.

Placements are available all year round with obvious seasonal fluctuations and their lengths vary from one day to six months. Individual hosts may provide expenses or pocket money, depending on circumstances, but this is not a general rule. All hosts provide accommodation and food and many will collect volunteers from nearest bus or rail station. Applicants must be over 16 years. Enthusiasm and a genuine interest in rural skills and organic methods are essential. To obtain a copy of the Directory please send £8.00 and two stamped addressed envelopes, plus two first and one second class stamps to the above address. Those in the EC should add £1.00 to the cost, those in Australasia, the Far East and Pacific should add £2.60 while those in all other countries should add £2.20.

Enquiries should be sent to Christopher Mager at the above address.

Dyfed Wildlife Trust
7 Market Street, Haverfordwest, Dyfed SA61 1NF (tel 0437-76542; fax 0437-767163).

The Trust runs working holidays on Skomer island between Easter and late October every year. The island is internationally famous for its seabird colonies, especially the estimated 160,000 pairs of Manx Shearwaters — the largest colony in the world. Volunteers may stay on the island at any point during the above period for a maximum stay of two weeks. Volunteers help with a wide variety of tasks, including the repair and maintenance of buildings, hides and footpaths, and at appropriate times may help with scientific work, bird surveys and generally contribute to the island's records. Help will also be needed to meet the boats bringing visitors to the island, collect landing fees and patrolling the Reserve.

No previous experience is necessary, but volunteers should be physically fit and able and willing to work for long hours, if necessary. The Trust provides a free boat passage to Skomer and simple but adequate accommodation. Volunteers may well have to share rooms and the kitchen is communal. Participants must bring sheets or sleeping bag, pillow case, towels, soap, matches, a good torch and a plentiful supply of food. Warm and waterproof clothes, plus stout footwear and wellingtons are essential. Unfortunately, conditions on the island are not suitable for the disabled. Applicants of all nationalities are welcome to apply; the minimum age limit is 16 years.

Those interested should contact Mrs June Glennerster at the above address.

Festiniog Railway Company
Porthmadog, Gwynedd, North Wales (tel 0766-512340).

Hundreds of volunteers are needed throughout the year to help in the operation and maintenance of the narrow gauge railway between Porthmadog and Blaenau Ffestiniog. Railway enthusiasts and non-enthusiasts of any nationality may apply provided they speak good English. The minimum age is 16 years.

Further information may be obtained from the Volunteer Officer, Festiniog Railway Company.

Forest School Conservation Camps
19 Acorn Road, Hemel Hempstead, Herts HP3 8DP.

Forest School Conservation Camps, a national organization for young people, aims to encourage the idea that socially necessary work should be undertaken by volunteers on behalf of the general community. It carries out small practical conservation jobs throughout Great Britain, in particular assisting the John Simonds Trust at Bradfield in Berkshire to establish a children's Country Centre on an old manor farm complex where there is a wide variety of work to be done. Similar camps can be found in Dorset, Essex and Cambridgeshire, providing plenty of scope for the conservationist.

There are no special requirements to be met, beyond a minimum age of 17 years (18 for those from abroad). Each camp lasts for one or two weeks, but weekend activities are also included. Volunteers are asked to bring their own (lightweight) tents if possible but they can be borrowed when necessary. No travel expenses or wages can be paid, and contributions towards food and expenses depend on the arrangements made with the sponsors of the work to be done. Efforts are made to keep expenses down.

Those interested should contact the Work Camps Secretary at the above address for further details.

Garry Gualach Outdoor Centre
Invergarry, Invernesshire, Scotland (tel 08092-230).

Garry Gualach is an estate in the Western Highlands on which there is a large guest lodge providing residential holidays with activities such as riding, sailing, windsurfing, lake canoeing, etc. There are three semi-voluntary positions each summer for people with experience of the above activities (either horses or watersports). They should also be willing to do cleaning, babysitting, agricultural work and general guest entertainment. Interested parties should apply with cv and references. Accommodation, keep and renumeration of £35 per week are all provided.

Several volunteers are also required for path-building and mountain hut-building in the summer.

For further details contact Jane and Peter Isaacson at the above address.

HT Scotland
4 Drum Street, Gilmerton, Edinburgh EH17 8QG (tel 031 658-1096)
HT Scotland is a voluntary organization which provides advice, information and support to projects using horticulture in their work with people with disabilities. The organization also recruits volunteers to establish the use of horticulture in a variety of settings such as hospitals, rural communities, residential care facilities, working directly with people who have disabilities — physical or mental. After a placement volunteers usually go on to become horticultural therapists, with the same or another agency.

Whilst on placement the volunteer works a maximum of 40 hours per week and gets a week's 'paid' leave for every four months worked. They usually get fully involved in the life of whatever community they are placed in. Volunteers of any nationality are accepted as long as they have experience in gardening or horticulture and are able to speak English. Placements vary between 6 months to one year, and volunteers are required all the year round. The project where the volunteer is placed provides board and accommodation plus pocket money of £20 per week.

Those interested should contact Anne Jepson at the above address.

Ironbridge Gorge Museum
The Wharfage, Ironbridge, Telford, Shropshire TF8 7AN (tel 0952-583003; fax 0952-432204).

The Ironbridge Gorge Museum is widely regarded as one of Britain's premier museums. Set amongst the beautiful Shropshire countryside, it is an independent educational charity enjoying hundreds of thousands of visitors each year. The Museum was founded in 1967 with the aims of conserving, restoring and interpreting the unique heritage of the Gorge.

Approximately 30 local volunteers help at the Museum complex every year, while a further 50 volunteers staying in accommodation provided by the Museum also participate. Volunteers are required to help with a huge variety of activities in all the different sections of the Museum. Most opportunities for volunteers are with the Blists Hill Open Air Museum. Demonstrators, clad in Victorian style costume, are required to work in exhibits, explaining the site and its shops, works and houses, to visitors, including school parties. The opportunity also exists for volunteers to learn and use traditional skills within the exhibits. Good communication skills and an ability to speak English are essential. There is also the opportunity to research and present street activity of the period. Good communication skills and the ability to work partly unsupervised are needed.

Volunteers are also required to assist with general site maintenance and with the making, repairing and maintenance of the period style clothes worn at the Open Air Museum. Volunteers are required to help with research and documentation. Such volunteers must be graduates or undergraduates with an interest in social and industrial history, possessing neatness, patience and accuracy.

At the Coalport China Museum volunteer demonstrators are needed to work in a ceramic workshop making and painting porcelain flowers. The possibility also exists for work with historic printing and manufacturing equipment. In the pottery workshop, volunteers can have the opportunity to make, decorate and fire earthenware items, or help with school parties. Good communication skills and an ability to speak English are essential. Voluntary researchers are needed at the Long Warehouse, Coalbrookdale where a variety of research, cataloguing and interesting projects are always waiting to be undertaken. A knowledge of library and archive procedures would be a distinct advantage, as well as an interest in history. Volunteers are also required to assist with documentation; the ability to type and to do a repetitive job is essential. Computer skills and a good command of the English language would also be useful.

At the Jackfield Tile Museum demonstrators are required in the Tile Works, explaining and practising the art of decoration and glazing. There would be opportunities to work as a guide or with school parties.

Local volunteers assist at the Museum for an indefinite period, while volunteers needing accommodation are requested to stay a minimum of two weeks between March and October. The basic self-catering volunteer accommodation on the Blists Hill site provides carpeted dormitories fitted with bunk beds, a kitchen/dining area, washing facilities and toilets, at a cost of £1.15 per night. As space is limited, please book in advance. No expenses are paid but a main course meal is provided at lunch-time, and hot drinks are provided at any time of day. Applicants may be of any nationality, but the ability to speak good English and to work well with the general public are essential. Training, costume, equipment and supervision are all provided as appropriate.

For an application form please contact Jan Jennings at the above address.

The Monkey Sanctuary
Murrayton, Nr. Looe, Cornwall PL13 1NZ (tel 0503-262532).

The Monkey Sanctuary was established in 1964 near Looe in Cornwall. As the first place where the Woolly Monkey has survived and bred outside of its natural habitat in the South American rain forests, it serves as a conservation centre and is open to the public at Easter and during the summer months.

Most of the several dozen volunteers taken on every year are needed during these periods to help with various duties including preparing food for the monkeys, maintaining and cleaning the monkey enclosures, performing domestic tasks and attending to the public. During the winter volunteers are still needed mainly for maintenance work. Volunteers can choose to stay for periods of from two to several weeks but only volunteers staying for long periods or making repeated visits would be asked to take on more responsible tasks with the monkeys.

Applicants must be fluent in English, in good health and over 18 years old. Board and lodging are provided and depending on the individual's need, pocket money or expenses may be paid.

For further information contact the Volunteer Co-ordinator at the above address.

The National Trust Volunteer Unit: Acorn Projects
PO Box 12, Westbury, Wiltshire BA13 4NA.

The National Trust organizes Acorn Projects for outdoor conservation work tasks throughout England and Wales from January to late October. Projects vary in size from 12 to 20 volunteers, and last for from a weekend to a week. The volunteer may join two or more projects.

The minimum age for participants is 17 years or for overseas visitors 18 years. Volunteers pay £34 minimum a week to help cover cost of board and lodging, and must pay their own travel expenses. Accommodation is provided but volunteers must bring their own bedding or sleeping bags.

Application forms and further details can be obtained from Beryl Sims at the above address. All requests should be accompanied by postage (or an international reply coupon, if applicable). Early application is advisable.

The National Trust (Northern Ireland)

Northern Ireland Regional Office, Rowallane, Saintfield, Ballynahinlh, Co. Down, Northern Ireland BT24 7LH (tel 0238-510721; fax 0238-511242).

The National Trust in Northern Ireland offers approximately 500 volunteers per year many opportunities for voluntary work, mainly of a practical nature, at National Trust properties (houses, gardens and countryside) in the area. Short-term volunteers can participate in week-long residential camps in which activities for volunteers are centred around practical conservation including tasks such as path,pond or scrub clearance, general garden work and fencing. There is a limited range of other activities such as event management/stewarding and office work.

Volunteers must be over 16 years of age and in good health; the minimum age limit for those from overseas is 18 years. Most volunteers join the one week Acorn Camps in the summer; accommodation is provided. Those resident in the area work on a more regular basis. Travel expenses that occur on the job will be reimbursed, but volunteers must pay their own travel costs to the Camps.

General enquiries should be sent to Diane Forbes at the above address, while those interested in the Acorn Camps should contact Beryl Sims, The National Trust, PO Box 12, Westbury, Wilts BA13 4NA.

National Trust for Scotland (Thistle Camps)

5 Charlotte Square, Edinburgh EH2 4DU (tel 031-226 5922; fax 031-243 9302).

The National Trust for Scotland runs over 80 properties and more than 80,000 acres of land in Scotland which are open to the public. Approximately 250 volunteers are needed for one or two weeks on a seasonal basis to carry out practical conservation work on NTS properties such as fencing, footpath repair and tree planting.

There are no restrictions as to age or nationality, although applicants must speak reasonable English. Volunteers must pay an administrative charge of £20 per week. Accommodation is provided but pocket money is not.

Those interested should write to the Conservation Volunteer Co-ordinator at the above address for further details.

Royal Society for the Protection of Birds (RSPB)

The Lodge, Sandy, Bedfordshire SG19 2DL (tel 0767-680551).

Volunteers are needed to take part in the RSPB's Voluntary Wardening Scheme which operates on 25 of their nature reserves throughout England, Scotland and Wales. Duties vary but may include basic management such as building paths, digging ditches, or dealing with visitors, as well as bird monitoring.

The scheme operates throughout the year, and volunteers aged 16 years or over and in good general health are welcome to take part. There are some openings for slightly handicapped volunteers. An interest in natural history is desirable. Accommodation is provided free but volunteers are responsible for their own travelling expenses and food during their stay. The minimum stay is one week, though many volunteers work for a fortnight or more.

Further information and application forms may be obtained from the Reserves Management Department at the above address.

The Scottish Conservation Projects Trust
Balallan House, 24 Allan Park, Stirling, FK8 2QG (tel 0786-79697).

The Scottish Conservation Projects Trust was founded specifically to support and promote practical outdoor conservation in Scotland. Conservation tasks include the management of nature reserves and other places of wildlife interest, the improvement of public amenities and access to the countryside, the environmental renewal of Scottish towns and cities and educating the public to appreciate Scotland's natural heritage.

Around 5,500 volunteers are needed annually to help with all aspects of practical outdoor conservation work on residential and non-residential projects, fund-raising and publicity. Training in tree-planting, dry-stone dyking, fencing and habitat management is given. Long term volunteers are recruited for several months while residential projects normally run for 10 days. Most volunteers are needed between March and October but some projects are undertaken during winter.

A working knowledge of English is desirable. The minimum age of volunteers accepted is 18 years and volunteers must be aware that some tasks are physically demanding. Accommodation and food are provided at a cost of £3.00 per night.

Those interested should apply to the Programmes Administrator at the above address.

West Wales Trust for Nature Conservation
7 Market Street, Haverfordwest, Dyfed SA61 1NF (tel 0437-765462).

The Trust is responsible for two island reserves (Skomer and Skokholm) and various other woodland, river and marshland nature reserves within Dyfed. Between 75 and 100 volunteers are needed to help with scientific research, patrolling reserves, advising visitors and repairing and maintaining buildings, hides and footpaths. Most volunteers are recruited from April to September but on some sites volunteers are needed all year round.

Volunteers may be of any nationality provided they are at least 17 years old. Accommodation and free transport are provided on the island reserves but volunteers must supply their own food. Contact the Administrative Officer at the above address for further information.

Religious Projects

Careforce
c/o Scripture Union, 130 City Road, London EC1V 2NJ (tel 071-782 0013).

Careforce is a scheme set up by four Evangelical Christian bodies in which young Christians are placed in inner-city churches and organizations caring for the needy throughout the UK and the Irish Republic. Around 100 volunteers are needed to undertake practical work such as cooking, cleaning, administration, visiting, youth and community work, etc., and when suitable assume varying degrees of responsibility and leadership in spiritual work. Placements begin in September and last for ten to twelve months.

Volunteers must be committed Christians with an above average degree of maturity, aged 18 to 23 years old and in good health. For practical reasons Careforce cannot accept applications from abroad. Board, lodging and an allowance of £20 per week are provided.

Those interested should apply to the Organising Secretary at the above address.

The Corrymeela Community
Ballycastle, Co. Antrim, BT54 6QU, Northern Ireland (tel 02657-62626).

Corrymeela is an ecumenical Christian community working for reconciliation in Northern Ireland and the world at large. It runs an administrative centre in Belfast and a residential centre at Ballycastle on the North Antrim coast where people from all backgrounds can come together and meet in an easy relaxed atmosphere.

Opportunities exist at the Ballycastle centre for volunteer helpers on both a long and short term basis. The commitment of the long term volunteers is generally for 12 months commencing in September of each year, and the volunteers receive their room and board plus a small weekly allowance. During the months of July and August, a number of additional volunteers are welcomed for periods of one to three weeks, to assist with family groups and projects or as summer staff helpers, assisting with recreation, arts and crafts, cooking, laundry etc. The lower age limit for all volunteers is 18 years.

Those interested in long term volunteer work should contact the Volunteer Co-ordinator at the above address. A leaflet, *Summer Opportunities*, which details all possible involvement during July and August is published in March of each year and those interested should apply to the above address. In England, further information about Corrymeela is available from the Corrymeela Link, P.O.Box 118, Reading.

The Grail
125 Waxwell Lane, Pinner, Middlesex HA5 3ER (tel 081-866 2195/0505).

The Grail Centre in North London is a centre for courses, conferences and workshops. The subjects range from prayer, spirituality, art and psychology to complementary medicine and ecological issues. Grail Volunteers help the resident Christian community of women with domestic work, household management, conservation, maintenance, cooking, gardening and reception and office tasks. No special qualifications are required, but skilled people are particularly welcome.

Applicants must be 19 or over and in good health. A knowledge of basic spoken English is required and it is important to be able to withstand the pressure of non-stop visitors.

Volunteers are asked to stay for a minimum of three months, though an occasional concession is made in the summer where academic vacations do not allow for that. Board and lodging are provided plus £15 pocket money per week. Applicants should apply four to six months ahead of the time they wish to come. Religious observance is not a requirement.

Apply by letter and include a CV and photo. UK applicants are asked to enclose a stamped addressed envelope and overseas applicants a postal reply coupon. They should also note that the Grail is not a vast organization and can accommodate only 15 volunteers a year.

Hothorpe Hall
Theddingworth, Lutterworth, Leicestershire LE17 6QX (tel 0858-880 257).

Hothorpe Hall is a Christian conference and retreat centre which needs volunteers throughout the year to look after its guests as well as maintain its facilities. The wide range of jobs includes kitchen work, housekeeping, maintenance, and gardening.

Volunteers should have a firmly rooted commitment to the Christian faith, although participants are accepted from many different denominational backgrounds. Participation in community worship, devotions and discussions will be expected. Applicants must be over 18 years and in good health. The centre endeavours to create an international mixture among its staff, although all must conform to British immigration regulations.

Applications and information may be obtained by writing to the Secretary at the above address.

London City Mission
175 Tower Bridge Road, London, SE1 2AH (tel 071-407 7585).

The London City Mission has a varied programme of voluntary work within the Greater London and inner city areas which includes Christian community work, open air meetings, door-to-door visits, working with homeless people, running youth camps and children's clubs and providing a support system for the 35 Mission centres in London. One year voluntary evangelism schemes run from September to August, summer projects are held in July and August (two weeks minimum) and a one-week scheme operates all year round. Approximately 200 volunteers are taken on each year.

All volunteers must be committed Christians with membership of a church which is in sympathy with the evangelical tradition and speak English. Volunteers should also be 18 to 30 years old, in good health and willing to undertake a variety of projects requiring hard work and commitment. All the schemes are free but volunteers are asked to contribute, if possible, towards the board and accommodation that they receive and the one-year volunteers are also allocated a small amount of pocket money.

Those interested should apply to the Youth Secretary at the above address.

Time for God
2 Chester House, Pages Lane, London. W10 1PR (tel 081-883 1504).

This is a scheme which provides an opportunity for the applicant to serve for between six months and one year in a church-based placement. The scheme is sponsored by the Methodist, Anglican, Baptist, Congregational, and United Reformed Churches, the National Council of YMCA's and the Church Army.

Every year some 60 volunteers are needed to care for children, the elderly, the homeless or the handicapped in caring organizations such as the National Children's Home, YMCA, or to help with work of all kinds in local churches or community centres. Full board and lodging is provided by the placement. Volunteers receive £22.00 (1992 figure) per week pocket money, and travel expenses are paid for the journey to the placement for an exploratory visit and on start of service. Volunteers are entitled to a week's holiday, with pocket money and fares home, for each three months of service (volunteers from overseas should be given fares for a reasonable journey in Britain). Christian applicants of any nationality or denomination are welcomed, provided that they speak fluent English and are between 17 and 25 (or between 18 and 25 for overseas applicants).

Those interested should write to the above address for more information about the scheme.

Social and Community Schemes

Ashram Community Service Project
23-25 Crantham Road, Sparkbrook, Birmingham B11 1LU (tel 021 773-7061; fax 766-7503).

There are four projects based at the above address in the multi-racial and inner city area of Sparkbrook which seek to respond to poverty, unemployment and racism in the district. The Community Service Project is an employment project, developing small business and self-employment initiatives. Ashram Acres is a land reclamation project, using the farming skills of local people. Ashram Volunteers Project is specifically for integrating volunteers from other sections of the projects and also developing other activities. Volunteers have the chance to live as members of a radical Christian community and so share in the social life and household tasks. Ashram Community House is deeply involved in the life of the neighbourhood, and gives volunteers a fantastic opportunity to meet and learn from people of different cultures. The local population is predominantly Muslim/Pakistani in origin.

About 100 volunteers are involved in the Project, participating mainly in back-up work; cleaning, gardening, building, animal husbandry, cooking and decorating. The range of activities grows according to the length of the volunteer's stay. A volunteer might eventually take responsibility for one particular area, organize social events and become involved in publicity. Applicants of all nationalities are welcome but some degree of commitment and a basic level of maturity are essential. No particular skill is essential, but the following are particularly welcomed; horticulture, animal care, driving, office skills, Asian languages. The minimum age limit is 20 years. Disabled people are welcome, but the building is not suitable for wheelchairs.

The minimum length of time for which volunteers are recruited is two weeks but volunteers come for varying lengths of time — from one month to over a year. Volunteers are expected to contribute what they can towards expenses and the amount due is worked out according to the financial situation of each volunteer. Accommodation is provided in either Ashram Community House or connected accommodation in Sparkbrook. Volunteers are required throughout the year.

Those interested can obtain further information from the above address.

Bondway Night Shelter
35-40 Bondway, PO Box 374, London SW8 1SJ.

Bondway provides emergency accommodation for 120 homeless people and operates a soup run for these forced to sleep out. 14 full-time volunteers assist a salaried staff group with practical work, administration and supervision of the shelter. Volunteers work throughout the week with shifts covering the full 24 hours. They must be prepared to stay for 6 months. In exchange they receive accommodation, travel expenses to the project and an allowance of £53.50 per week (1992 figure). Applicants need to be available for interview and aged over 19. For more information contact the volunteer co-ordinator at the above address.

The Carr-Gomm Society Ltd.
38 Gomm Road, Rotherhithe, London SE16 2TX (tel 071-277 5050; fax 071-277 6750).

The Carr-Gomm Society is a charitable housing association which provides small permanent homes for single people with a range of special needs. The resident group consists of both men and women of all ages and from a wide variety of backgrounds. In each Carr-Gomm house, residents have their own room and share meals and communal areas; in most houses there is a residential Support Worker who looks after the day-to-day needs of the residents. Founded in 1965, the Society currently manages 70 houses in 14 London boroughs.

The Society needs full-time volunteers in London, the average length of stay being six months. Volunteers are normally based at the Society's Head Offices; besides helping there, volunteers assist with the day-to-day running of the houses.

Volunteers should apply directly to the Head Office of the Society at the above address.

Cecil Houses (Inc)
2 Priory Road, Kew, Richmond, Surrey, TW9 3DG (tel 081-940 9828).

Cecil Houses was founded in 1926 and consists of two hostels for homeless women, two residential homes and sheltered accommodation for the elderly of both sexes. Volunteers are required to assist either in the care of the elderly or the homeless women, or with domestic work, etc.

The minimum age is 18 years, the period of engagement four to 12 months. Volunteers work a 39 hour week over a seven day shift, with two days off a week. They receive £21 (1992 figure) per week in payment, and free board and shared accommodation is provided. All nationalities are welcome although they must be able to read, speak and understand English.

Applications should be made in English to Mrs M Richmond at the above address.

Community Service Volunteers
237 Pentonville Road, London N1 9NJ (tel 071-278 6601).

Community Service Volunteers is an agency that offers all young people aged 16-35 the opportunity to experience the challenge, excitement and reward of helping people in need.

Every year 2,500 volunteers work throughout England, Scotland and Wales with elderly or homeless people, adults or children with disabilities, learning difficulties or mental illness and young people who are in care or in trouble. Volunteers work hard, have fun and gain valuable experience. They are needed to work away from home, full-time from four to twelve months. They receive full board, lodging and a weekly allowance.

Applications are welcome throughout the year.

Edinburgh Cyrenian Trust
20 Broughton Place, Edinburgh EH1 3RX (tel 031-538 4871).

The Edinburgh Cyrenian Trust runs two communities for single, homeless men and women aged 18 to 30 years old; one in Edinburgh and another on a smallholding outside Edinburgh. Around 22 volunteers are needed each year to live with the residents and befriend them. Other tasks include performing various housekeeping and book-keeping tasks. Placements are for 6 months at a time.

Volunteers must be fluent in English, 18 to 30 years old, energetic and have initiative. Applicants with a full driving licence are preferred. Travel expenses to attend an interview are paid. Successful applicants receive one-way travel to the project, accommodation, pocket money and holiday and termination grants.

Applicants should apply to Gordon Annand at the above address.

Great Georges Community Cultural Project
Great George Street, Liverpool L1 5EW (tel 051-709 5109).

The Project is a centre for experimental work in the arts, sports, games and education housed in the centre of Liverpool. At any one time there are both full time and short term volunteers on the staff who spend up to 12 months on the project. Ideally one month is seen as the minimum period, although there are exceptions, e.g. some volunteers join the Project specifically to work on a playscheme which lasts for two weeks. The general work of the scheme is shared as equally as possible, with everyone being prepared to do some administration, cook, sweep the floor, play with kids, talk to visitors as well as supervise the activities.   The centre, or the 'Blackie' as it has become known, has gained an important position in the life of the city, as it provides opportunities for local people which would otherwise simply not exist. Among these are work shops for photography, cooking, dance, music, film, pool, reading, writing, drawing and typing. In addition entertainments are arranged there, which have recently included original poetry, performance art, contemporary music, modern dance and the showing of films.   A bed and food are provided for £17.50 per week, unless some arrangement is made in advance. The minimum period of voluntary work is four weeks. Although skills in arts and crafts are useful, more important are stamina and a sense of humour. Volunteers must also bring their own sleeping bag.

Requests for further information should be made to the Duty Officer at the above address, enclosing a stamped addressed envelope. Overseas applicants are welcome as long as they are fluent in English.

Homes for Homeless People
90-92 Bromham Road, Bedford MK40 2QH (tel 0234-350853).

Homes for Homeless People, (formerly National Cyrenians) is a national federation of local housing groups running projects for single homeless people throughout the UK. Most projects are long or short-term houses but there are some emergency accommodation centres and day centres as well. The aim of the organization is to treat the homeless as individuals with individual problems.

The local groups are legally and financially autonomous. They run over 70 projects staffed by approximately 65 temporary project workers (volunteers) and 40 permanent salaried workers.

These groups are constantly needing new workers to help in the running and day-to-day life of their projects. No experience or qualifications are needed. The work is demanding (both physically and emotionally), and involves the ability to get on with people in residential situations and often take responsibility. It is particularly relevant and rewarding to those who wish to gain experience for socal or community work courses or future work. Workers receive board and lodging, plus pocket money. There is usually a minimum 6 months commitment but shorter periods can sometimes be arranged.

If interested contact TPW Recruitment at the above address.

Iona Community
Iona Abbey, Iona, Argyll, Scotland (tel 068-17 404).

The Iona Community receives groups of people, mainly from areas of social deprivation, during a season from March to October. Approximately 70 volunteers aged 18 years upwards, are required each year to assist with catering, housekeeping, driving, guiding, gardening, crafts, programme leadership, music, coffee house staffing and maintenance.

Volunteers stay for between six and eight weeks. The only requirements are a driving licence and a minimum age of 23 years for the person doing the driving job and some kind of practical experience for those doing the maintenance, craft, music and programme work.Travel expenses within Britain are paid plus a weekly allowance. Board and lodging are provided.

Those interested should apply to the Administrator at the above address.

The Ockenden Venture
'Ockenden', Guildford Road, Woking, Surrey GU22 7UU (tel 04862-772012).

Volunteers are needed to assist in the care of refugees in the UK. Mainly

Vietnamese, many of these are family groups and housed in one of three reception centres. Unaccompanied refugee minors are cared for at a Children's Home in Haslemere, whilst a small group of young handicapped refugees stay in a home in Camberley, Surrey. At present Ockenden recruits around 12 volunteers each year. They are required to stay for approximately 12 months each year although shorter term vacancies do occasionally arise during the holiday periods. The minimum age of acceptance is 18 years. Volunteers receive £22 or £25 per week, plus free board and accommodation.

The work involved is partly domestic but can include driving, property maintenance and gardening. It involves a full involvement with the refugees, assisting the older ones to become adjusted to life in the UK and the younger ones to develop by encouraging and helping them in their studies, etc.

Further details are available from the Personnel Officer at the above address.

Petrus Community Trust
82 Holt Road, Liverpool L7 2PR (tel 051-263 4543).

Petrus provides a variety of accommodation and support for homeless single people in Liverpool. Currently operated are three residential projects, two long stay hostels and a group home. Around 24 volunteers are needed year round to undertake a mixture of domestic, welfare and administrative tasks. Placements are for three, six or nine months.

Volunteers need no special skills but should be fluent in English and 18 to 25 years old. Travel expenses to attend an interview are not paid. Successful applicants receive travel expenses on arrival, board, accommodation, weekly pocket money of £30 and holiday and termination payments.

Those interested should contact the Assistant Director at the above address.

Sidmouth International Festival of Folk Arts
The Festival Office, 6 East Street, Sidmouth, Devon EX10 8BL (tel 0395-515134).

This Festival encourages international friendship and understanding via the promotion of folk music, dance and song. The Festival is usually held in late July and lasts from seven to ten days. Around 200 volunteers are needed for the duration of the festival to act as stewards at events, guides and interpreters for overseas performers, etc. It must be stressed that there is absolutely no paid work whatsoever available at the Festival.

Volunteers of all nationalities are accepted provided they speak English. Interpreters must have workiong knowledge of a foreign language, but otherwise volunteers need no special skills.

The dates for the '93-'96 Festivals are as follows:

1993 — 30th July-6th August	1995 — 4th July-11th August
1994 — 29th July-5th August	1996 — 2nd July-9th August

For further details contact the Festival Director at the above address.

The Simon Community
PO Box 1187, London NW5 4HS (tel 071-485 6639).

The Community offers residential care for the homeless and rootless in London in four houses. Both full and part-time volunteers are needed to help with the running of the houses as well as helping with the Community's commitment to outreach work.

Full-time workers live in the projects and must commit themselves to living in the Community for 24 hours per day (although they do get 40 hours off per week). The work is demanding and varied and workers are given a great deal of responsibility, so they need to have maturity, patience and self-confidence; a sense of humour is an advantage. Volunteers should be prepared to experience situations which will test their initiative and stamina. Community life is not recommended for those who require large amounts of personal space and time.

Volunteers should be over 18 and able to speak fluent English. £12 pocket money is given each week, and volunteers must be able to work for a minimum of three months.

Applicants should contact the Community Leader at the above address.

Work With the Sick and Disabled

Association Of Camphill Communities
Camphill Rudolf Steiner Schools, Murtle House, Bieldside, Aberdeen AB1 9EP.

This Association was set up in 1978 to bring together the many different interests and concerns of the 30 or so Camphill communities in the British Isles. These communities for handicapped children and adults or those with special needs are all based on anthroposophy as founded by Rudolf Steiner. Opportunities for living and working as volunteers within a Camphill community exist for longer and shorter periods. In general, one able bodied volunteer is needed for every two community members.

The Association can supply more information on individual member communities but applications to work as volunteers should be sent to the individual centres. The addresses of current member communities are given below.
Bolton Village, Danby, Whitby, North Yorks YO12 2NJ (tel 0287-60871).
Cherry Orchards Camphill Community, Canford Lane, Westbury-on-Trym, Bristol BS9 3PF (tel 0272-503 183).
The Croft, Highfield Road, Old Malton, North Yorks YO17 0EY (tel 0425-474 291).
Camphill Devon Community, Hapstead Village, Buckfastleigh, South Devon TQ11 0JN (tel 0364-42631).
Delrow College and Rehabilitation Centre, Hillfield Lane, Aldenham, Watford, Herts. WD2 8DJ (tel 0923-856006).
Grange-Oaklands, Newnham-on-Severn, Gloucs. GL14 1HJ (tel 0594-516246).
Larchfield Community, Hemlington, Middlesborough, Cleveland TS8 9DY (tel 0642-593688).
Camphill Milton Keynes Community, 7 Sterling Close, Pennyland, Milton Keynes MK15 8AN (tel 0908-674856).
Mount School Community, Wadhurst, East Sussex TN5 6PT (tel 089-288 2025).
Penine Camphill Community, Boyne Hill House, Chapelthorpe, Wakefield WF4 3JF (tel 0924-255281).
Shelling Community, Horton Road, Ashley, Ringwood, Hants. BH24 2EB (tel

0425-477488).
Camphill Houses, Heathfield Cottage, 32 Heath Street, Stourbridge, W Midlands DY8 1SB (tel 0384-372575).
William Morris Camphill Community, William Morris House, Eastington, Stonehouse, Gloucestershire GL10 3SH (tel 045382-4025).
Coleg Elidyr, Nangwyn, Rhandirmwyn, Llandovery, Dyfed SA20 0NL (tel 05506-272).
Clanabogan Camphill Community, Omagh, Co. Tyrone, BT78 1TL (tel Omagh 41627).
Glencraig Community, Newry Road, Kilkeel, Co. Down BT34 4EX (tel 06937 -62229).
Ballytobin Community, Callan, Co. Kilkenny (tel 056-25114).
Dunshane House, Brannickstown, Co. Kildare (tel 045-83628.
Duffcarrig House, Gorey, Co. Wexford (tel 055-25116).
Beannachar, Banchory-Devenick, Aberdeen AB1 5YL (tel 0224-868605).
Camphill Blair, Drummond, Blair Drummond House, By Stirling FK9 4UT (tel 0876-841341).
Corbenic College, Drumour Lodge, Torchry, Nr. Dunkeld, Perthshire PH8 0BY (tel 03505-206).
Loch Arthur Village Community, Beeswing, Dumfries DG2 9JQ (tel 038776-224).
Newton De Village, Bielside, Aberdeen AB1 9DX (tel 0224-868701).
Ochil Tower, Auchterade, Perthshire PH3 1AD (tel 07646-2363).
Camphill Rudolf Steiner Schools, Murtle, Bieldside, Aberdeen AB1 9EP (tel 0224-867935).
Simeon Care Communities, Cairnlee Estate, Bieldside, Aberdeen AB1 9BN.
Templehill Community, Glenfarquhar Lodge, Auchilblae, Kincardine AB3 1UJ (tel 05612-230).

Association for Spina Bifida and Hydrocephalus
42 Park Road, Peterborough PE1 2UQ (tel 0733-555988).

The Association needs volunteers each year to help run independence training courses for young people with spina bifida and hydrocephalus. The courses are designed to help the young people, who are physically handicapped, to look after themselves, learn basic skills such as shopping, cooking, etc., and gain social independence. Each volunteer is matched with a young person to work on a programme with advice from ASBAH's professional staff. The courses last for one week and are held at the Association's residential centre in Ilkley, West Yorkshire.

All nationalities are accepted but volunteers must have sufficient knowledge of English to communicate with the young people. The minimum age is 18. Accommodation and meals are provided.

Applications should be made to Sarah Peat, Five Oaks Centre, Ben Rhydding Drive, Ilkley, West Yorkshire LS29 8BD.

Beannachar
Beannachar, Banchory-Devenick, Aberdeen AB1 5YL (tel 0224-861825).

Every year the Beannachar Community takes on between 6 and 10 volunteers to live and work with young adults with special needs. Work is to be done in the kitchen, laundry, garden and on the farm; tasks also include making herbal medicines and candles and weaving. Volunteers are also expected to participate in evening and weekend leisure activities. Volunteers need not be British, but they must speak fluent English and make a minimum commitment of six months. Board and lodging will be provided, plus pocket money of £18 if applicants stay for a full year and one paid holiday and journey home (within reason!).

Applications may be sent to Elisabeth Phebhean, Housemother, at the above address.

CARE for Mentally Handicapped People
9 Weir Road, Kibworth, Leicester LE8 0LQ (tel 053-753 3225).

CARE establishes communities with residential and workshop facilities for adults with a mental handicap. Residents undertake a variety of activities in workshops including printing, market gardening and horticulture, woodwork and making soft toys.

20 to 30 volunteers aged 19 years and over are needed at any time of year to help with caring and social activities for residents in communities in Devon, Kent, Lancashire, Leicestershire, Northumberland, Shropshire and West Sussex. Placements may be from one to six months. Board, lodging and £25 pocket money per week are provided.

Those interested should apply to the Community Director at the above address.

Churchtown Farm Field Studies Centre
Churchtown Farm, Lanlivery, Bodmin, Cornwall PL30 5BT (tel 0208-872148).

Churchtown Farm provides outdoor, environmental and adventurous training courses accessible to everyone, regardless of degree of special need. As well as the more traditional courses, in ecology and outdoor pursuits, a new development is the provision of personal development programmes which concentrate on personal growth, encouraging a positive image of self and promoting self-confidence. In-service courses for teachers and carers can be organized and opportunities exist for tean building and development courses, suitable for all staff groups. The Centre is attractively converted and well equipped with an indoor swimming pool, farm, nature reserve and attractive grounds. Sailing and canoeing takes place on the nearby River Fowey and the Centre is only five miles from the coast. Help is available with care requirements and a qualified nurse is on call on site throughout the night.

Ten volunteers are needed at a time to support the professional staff. Accommodation is in a shared house adjacent to the main Centre. Applications are invited from anyone who feels they have an empathy with people with special needs. Whilst a background in environmental, outdoor or medical areas would be an advantage, volunteers are welcome regardless of academic qualifications. Currently an allowance of £20 per week is payable and providing volunteers stay for longer than three weeks a return train fare is payable within mainland UK.

Those interested should apply to the Head of Care at the above address.

The CRYPT Foundation

Forum, Stirling Road, Chichester, West Sussex PO19 2EN (tel 0243-786064).

CRYPT (Creative Young People Together) provides small group homes in the UK for young people with disabilities who wish to study any of the creative arts. A CRYPT Community Volunteer is responsible, with other CCVs, for the safety and the care of students within the project. Applicants of all nationalities are accepted, but they must be able to speak English.

Volunteers must be aged between 18 and 30. The students are often profoundly disabled and need to be lifted etc. A timetable is arranged and will generally involve twenty-four hours on duty, followed by 24 hours off duty, with alternative weekends free. Pocket money, accommodation and living allowances are all provided. Volunteers stay for 4-6 months, and are required all the year round except August.

Applications from inside Britain should be sent to Community Service Volunteers or Gap (see the index); others should contact the above address.

The Disaway Trust

2 Charles Road, Merton Park, London SW19 3BD (tel 081 543-3431).

The Disaway Trust is a charity which provides group holidays for physically disabled people. The organization is run by a Committee of volunteers and is entirely supported by voluntary help and contributions. Disaway relies on voluntary help to achieve its objective of providing disabled people with holidays. Each helper is asked to look after the needs of one holidaymaker during the holiday. This will include helping with, amongst other things, needs like washing, feeding, dressing and helping in the lavatory. Most holidays last for about a week. Inexperienced helpers will be allocated a holidaymaker needing minimal care and every effort is made to match helpers and holidaymakers with similar interests. Helpers have to be reasonably fit and strong, and every applicant is required to complete a medical form; acceptance is at the discretion of the Medical Officer. Minimum age limit for volunteers is 18 years. Children accompanying their parents will be at the discretion of the Committee.

Helpers are asked to make a financial contribution towards the cost of the holiday including a deposit of £25-£50 to be submitted with the application form. Costs are given with holiday details. Many people enjoy this type of holiday and previous helpers will vouch for their enjoyment of a fulfilling vacation in a friendly atmosphere. There is no limit to the number of helpers needed.

For an application form, please write to Miss N. Green, 24 Curtis House, Morecambe Street, London SE17 1EB.

Discovery '80' Share Limited

Share Centre, Smith's Strand, Lisnaskea, Co. Fermanagh, Northern Ireland BT92 0EQ (tel 03657-22122; fax 03657-21893).

This organization operates a residential outdoor activity centre on the shores of Upper Lough Erne in County Fermanagh for the integration of able-bodied and disabled people. The centre offers a wide range of outdoor sports holidays and courses, enabling breaks for people of all ages, backgrounds and disabilities. 12 volunteers are needed for a one-year placement while 50 short-term volunteers are needed per year for periods of 14-90 days. Volunteers are needed to act as companions to disabled guests, on the outdoor activity programme which involves sailing, archery, windsurfing or hillwalking, or to with the catering, domestic or maintenance teams.

Applicants may be of any nationality, but should be qualified and experienced in their chosen area of work. Accommodation is provided, as is an allowance of £10 per week. The minimum age limit for long-term volunteers is 18 years, while for short-term volunteers it is 16 years.

Apply to R. Johnston, Volunteer Co-ordinator, at the above address.

Help the Handicapped Holiday Fund
147a Camden Road, Tunbridge Wells, Kent TN1 2RA.

This Fund arranges for about five group holidays for handicapped people each year. Recent holidays have been to the Costa Brava, Blackpool, Cornwall, Clifton and Chichester. All holidays last for one week and last between May and September. Each year around 100 volunteers are required to care for the disabled participants on these trips. Volunteers may apply to assist with one or more holidays.

Volunteers may be of any nationality provided they are strong and healthy and are between 18 and 60 years old. Experience in helping disabled people is an advantage. Full board, accommodation and travel from Tunbridge Wells are provided but no other expenses are paid.

Those interested should apply to the Holiday Organiser at the above address.

Horticultural Therapy: Land Use Volunteers
Goulds Ground, Vallis Way, Frome, Somerset Ball 3DW (tel 0373-64782).

Horticultural Therapy is a charity that helps people with handicaps or disabilities to enjoy and benefit from gardening, horticulture and agriculture. Its volunteer service, Land Use Volunteers, posts people who have training or experience in horticulture or agriculture at hospitals, residential homes and daycentres to set up projects based on these two fields of activity. They thus provide training, work and recreation for people who are physically and mentally handicapped. Volunteers must be over 18 years old and must have experience or training in horticulture or agriculture. The minimum length of a placement is usually six months. Free accommodation and meals are provided together with a minimum allowance of £20 per week.

Land Use Volunteers can only consider people for interview if they are already resident in or visiting the UK. No registration fee is charged. Costs of travelling to the UK cannot be paid.

For an application form, contact the Co-ordinator, Land Use Volunteers at the above address. Enclose a stamped addressed envelope or international reply coupon.

Independent Living Alternatives
Fulton House, Fulton Road, Wembley, Middlesex HA9 0TF (tel 081 902-8998 ext. 270; fax 081 903-1465).

Independent Living Alternatives is an initiative which has been established to promote independence and freedom for people with supportive disabilities. The

Company quite simply aims to enable people who need to use physical support to be able to live independently in the community, taking full control of their lives and thereby having individuality and spontaneity. This is achieved by recruiting and placing full-time support on a voluntary basis. The Company brings two or three people together to live on a semi-communal basis in an atmosphere of mutual inter-dependence. About 30 volunteers in all work as full-time carers each year, providing physical support to disabled people within the London area.

Volunteers help people to go to the toilet, get dressed, washed etc., and give practical support in terms of housework, shopping, cleaning, cooking, etc. Applicants may be of any nationality, but they must speak English to a very high standard. Overseas volunteers require visas; ILA does not finance visas. A driving licence would be useful, as would the ability to lift heavy loads. Volunteers are needed all the year round and the minimum length of placement is 4 months. Voluntary carers receive £20 per week as pocket money, as well as £20 per week for food and £10 to cover travel. Accommodation is provided as mentioned above.

For further information and an application form contact Tracey Jannaway, Volunteer Co-ordinator, at the above address.

Independent Living Schemes
Lewisham Social Services, Laurence House, 1 Catford Road, Catford, London SE6 4SW (tel 081 695-6000 ext. 8639; fax 081 690-9924).

Special projects known as Independent Living Schemes have been set up in Lewisham with the aim of enabling people with disabilities to lead the lifestyle

of their choice. About 50 Volunteer helpers are wanted to assist with these schemes; applicants should be aged between 18 and 50. Volunteers provide care for a severely disabled person; tasks include toiletting, bathing and administering suppositories. The volunteer helper would be expected to accompany that person on social, business and cultural activities. The helper also helps with the cooking, cleaning and shopping under the direction of the disabled person. Applicants may be of any nationality, although basic English and reading skills are essential. Applicants must be willing to enable severely disabled people to regain their civic rights.

Volunteer helpers are asked to spend six months on a scheme. There is a one month trial period, which means that a helper is not bound to stay. However, most volunteers do settle and stay with the scheme; some like it so much they sign on for a further six months. Rent-free accommodation is provided for helpers in a fully furnished two or three bedroomed flat to be shared with other helpers situated near the scheme. Heating and lighting bills as well as local telephone charges are met, and everyday household items like cleaning materials, light bulbs, bed linen etc., are supplied. A weekly allowance of £45-£25 for food and £20 for pocket money is paid, and is payable for up to a fortnight's sickness. There are also monthly allowances for recreation (£5) and clothing (£7). A week's paid leave is given after a helper has been with the scheme for four months. Helpers get a Saver Return Rail Travel Warrant to any mainland UK destination, if required, or a Travel Card if they decide to stay in London. Helpers' return fares to and from their home are covered at the beginning and end of their involvement with the scheme. A scheme supervisor is available to offer guidance and advice to helpers.

Apply to Kenneth Smith at the above address.

Leonard Cheshire Foundation
236-29 Maunsel Street, London SW1P 2QN (tel 071-828 1822).

The Leonard Cheshire Foundation is a registered charitable trust running homes throughout the UK for people with severe disabilities, mainly physically disabled adults. Voluntary workers are needed in many homes to assist with the general care of residents who require help with washing, dressing and feeding as well as with hobbies and other recreational activities.

Volunteers cannot be aged under 18. Preference is generally given to people under 35 planning to take up medical or social work as a career. Volunteers work up to a 39 hour, five day week, with one week's paid holiday for every four month's service. The minimum period is one month, but most jobs are for between three and 12 months.

Full board, lodging and pocket money of £25 per week is provided, this rate being reviewed each April. Volunteers must pay their own travel costs to the home. Overseas applicants must be able to speak good English. Applications should be sent to the Secretary to the Personnel Advisor at the above address.

MENCAP — The Royal Society for Mentally Handicapped Children and Adults
MENCAP Holiday Services Office, 119 Drake Street, Rochdale OL16 1PZ (tel 0706-54111).

Each year the MENCAP Holiday Services Office arranges a programme of holidays for mentally handicapped people of all ages, based in premises of many kinds — schools, farmhouses, adventure centres and guest houses — and covers the country from the Lake District to Cornwall. Some children are severely and multiply handicapped and will need almost constant care. Others who are less handicapped may enjoy adventure or guest house holidays where the accent is placed upon enjoying outdoor activities or the 'traditional' type of seaside holiday. The success of these holidays depends upon volunteers who spend a week or two helping each year, receiving assistance towards their travelling costs with MENCAP providing for their board and lodging.

Prospective volunteers should be over 18 years old, enjoy using their initiative and have a sense of fun. Flexibility is essential due to the wide range of jobs to be done.

Those interested should contact the Holidays Officer at the above address.

Otto Schiff Housing Association

Central Office, The Bishop's Avenue, London N2 0BG (tel 081-209 0022; fax 081-201 8089).

The Association provides sheltered accommodation and both residential and nursing care in London for elderly, mainly Jewish, refugees from Nazi persecution. It runs five residential care homes and sheltered accommodation for a total of 290 elderly people, and aims to enable residents to maintain their personality and dignity by providing an ambience that makes them feel part of the community and allows them to regard their environment with affection.

Six full-time residential volunteers are engaged by the Association at any one time. There are also approximately 50 non-residential volunteers who visit homes, help with care/domestic work, give clerical asistance, help with gardening and maintenance and befriend residents. Applicants of any nationality are welcome, and any skills a volunteer can offer will be considered. The full-time live-in volunteers must stay for a minimum of six months; they receive board and lodging, as well as £15.25 pocket money per week.

Those interested should contact Mary Copsey at the above address.

Queen Elizabeth's Foundation for the Disabled

Leatherhead, Surrey, KT22 OBN (tel 037 284-2204).

Approximately 300 helpers a year are needed in the Foundation's four units for the disabled in the South of England. The different units have different functions: Queen Elizabeth's Training College in Leatherhead provides vocational training and hostels for 192 disabled people; Dorincourt, off Oaklawn Road, Leatherhead, is a hostel and workshop for 55 severely disabled employees; Banstead Place, off Park Road, Banstead, Surrey is a residential centre for the assessment and further education of severely handicapped school leavers; and Lulworth Court on Chalkwell Esplanade, Westcliff-On-Sea, Essex, is a holiday and convalescent home for severely paralysed men and women. The voluntary work undertaken can vary from assisting with all kinds of fund-raising to helping the staff to look after and entertain those on holiday at Lulworth Court. Some 150 resident volunteers give their services in this way every summer.

Anyone over 18 is welcome to help: every possible qualification and skill are needed, but the only necessities are cheerfulness and a will to help. Travel expenses are refunded in part for those who have to travel long distances, and in full for those who live locally. Bed, board, and out of pocket expenses are paid to residential volunteers. Applicants should contact the Director at the above address.

Richard Cave Multiple Sclerosis Home
Servite Convent, Leuchie, North Berwick, East Lothian EH39 5NT (tel 0620-2864).

The Home is run by the Order of Servite Sisters as a holiday home for sufferers of multiple sclerosis of all ages. Around 25 volunteers a year are taken on to assist with health care, take patients for walks, write postcards for them and accompany them on special outings. Placements are for a minimum of two months from March until December or January and although it is possible to stay for as long as 12 months, most stays are for around eight weeks.

Driving licences, nursing qualifications and any other skills are useful but not essential. Applicants should be between 17 and 25 years old and English speaking. Board, lodging and £25 pocket money per week are provided.

Apply to the Matron at the above address.

Ritchie Russell House Young Disabled Unit
The Churchill Hospital, Headington, Oxford OX3 7LJ (tel 0865 225482).

The Unit cares for disabled people aged between 16 and 65. Volunteers are required as carers on the Unit holidays for the disabled on a day-to-day basis. They are also needed to help on the Unit in Oxford. The number of volunteers engaged depends entirely on the nature of the work; for the holidays, as many as 30 carers may be required. The Unit organizers aim to take four or five holidays away per year for which carers over the age of 19 are needed. Help is also needed in the Unit with creative activities, gardening, table games, story groups, computers and the cooking group, as well as with outings and publicity.

Applicants of all nationalities are welcome. although perfect English is essential as the Unit's clients have hearing and communication problems. Applicants must be fit and healthy, patient and willing to work hard. They must be aged between 19 and 60. The holidays last for between one week and ten days, but helpers on the Unit will be required on occasional days for an indefinite period.

Holiday carers must pay a contribution of £25 for food, but accommodation and travel are paid for by the Unit. Carers must be prepared to work a 24-hour day. No accommodation is provided for regular Unit volunteers.

Enquiries should be sent to Mrs Barbara Martin at the above address.

The Royal Association for Disability and Rehabilitation (RADAR)
25 Mortimer Street, London W1N 8AB (tel 071-637 5400).

Every year RADAR publishes a list of holiday centres for the disabled which require help from volunteers for a few weeks. These centres are run by several agencies and organizations including Social Services Departments, MENCAP, BREAK,

The Shaftesbury Society, The Winged Fellowship Trust, and PHAB. The list published by RADAR specifies the type of help needed. In some cases the volunteer must be fit or have medical training while in others the job may be suitable for an active pensioner. The list also mentions whether food, travel expenses and accommodation are provided.

Those interested should write to the Holidays Office at the above address.

SHAD Haringey

Winkfield Resource Centre, 33 Winkfield Road, London N22 5RP (tel 081-365 8528).

The Centre runs a scheme in which more than 30 volunteers per year work with physically disabled people in their own homes assisting with all aspects of independent living including personal care, housework, cooking and helping with leisure, work and educational activities. Applicants of any nationality are welcome, although usually only those from EC countries are accepted, as applicants must come to London for an interview. An interview does not guarantee a placement. Good English and a driving licence are essential. Volunteers must be in good health and able to lift people, although training will be given. They must be aged between 18 and 30.

The usual minimum length of placement is three months and volunteers are required all the year round. Volunteers are accommodated in a shared flat with all bills paid by SHAD, and a pocket money and food allowance of £48 per week is provided. Travel expenses up to £40 will be reimbursed as will all out-of-pocket expenses.

Applications should be made to Sue Denney at the above address.

SHAD Wandsworth

c/o The Nightingale Centre, 8 Balham Hill, London SW12 9EA (tel 081-675 6095; fax 081-675 3542).

SHAD Wandsworth is an independent living scheme which works with people with severe disabilities to enable them to live independently in their own homes. This is achieved by recruiting teams of two or three full-time volunteers who act as physical facilitators. The organization is user-managed. SHAD also informally recruits volunteers for other independent living schemes and independent individuals. Between 70 and 80 volunteers are recruited every year to work for SHAD. They work with people with severe physical disabilities to enable them to live a full and independent life in their own homes, or at work, or at college, or at play. The work involves personal care, taking people out, driving them around, cooking for them and doing their housework.

Applicants of all nationalities are welcome, but all applicants must be able to attend an informal interview — usually in London, but SHAD Wandsworth sometimes interviews groups of people in Europe. Good English is essential and a driving licence is an advantage, but otherwise no particular skills are needed. Volunteers must be people with a strong but flexible character. The minimum age limit is 17 years. There is no upper limit in principal but most volunteers are within the age range 18-30. Volunteers must be fit and healthy, with no back problems.

The minimum length of time for which volunteers are recruited is four months; there is no upper limit. Interview expenses are paid (for overseas volunteers SHAD can only pay for travel from British coast or airport). Accommodation is provided free, either in a flat shared with other volunteers or in a single room in the disabled person's home. In 1992 an allowance of £47 was paid which included £21 for pocket money and £26 food allowance, as well as one zone travel card monthly and all household costs — cleaning, rent, heating and light etc.

Those interested should contact Eamon Durkan, Co-ordinator, at the above address.

The Shaftesbury Society

2A Amity Grove, Raynes Park, London SW20 OLH (tel 081-946 6635).

The Society runs a holiday centre for the physically handicapped and elderly in Essex, which operates between April and October. 200 volunteers are needed each year, for a maximum of two weeks, to help guests with their personal needs, to get about, dress, etc.

At any one time the Society likes to have someone who can drive, and someone with nursing experience at the centre. However volunteers with no special qualifications are welcome to apply. The minimum age for helpers is 16 years and the maximum age for new helpers is 70 years. Applicants should be sympathetic to the Christian aims and principles of the Society. Assistance will be given with travel expenses (UK mainland only) and food and lodging provided.

Applications should be sent to: Pat Ford, Volunteers Secretary, Shaftesbury Holiday Centre, Low Road, Dovercourt, Essex CO12 3TS.

Stallcombe House

Sanctuary Lane, Woodbury, Nr. Exeter EX5 1EX (tel 0395-32373).

Stallcombe House is a residential farm community in East Devon for mentally disabled adults. Residents of the three households are involved in all aspects of the community, 55 acre farm and small organic horticultural area. Two volunteers are needed annually to help care for the residents: cooking, cleaning and assisting the residents with their daily activities including personal hygiene, hobbies and outings. Placements are for 6-12 months. Other volunteers are needed seasonally to help with farm and garden work, and local volunteers who can work daily or less frequently on an on-going basis will be welcomed.

Residential care volunteers must want to work with people in a caring environment. All volunteers need a working knowledge of English and should be in good mental and physical health. Residential care workers receive accommodation and pocket money of £20 per week but assistance with travel expenses depends on the individual volunteer's circumstances.

Applicants should apply to the Principal at the above address.

Sue Ryder Foundation

Sue Ryder Home, Cavendish, Sudbury, Suffolk (tel 0787-280252).

This international foundation runs more than 20 homes for the sick, disabled and physically handicapped, as well as cancer patients and those suffering from Huntingdon's Disease.

Volunteers are needed throughout the year to do essential duties at Headquarters or in the Sue Ryder Homes which may include helping with the patients, and any domestic, office or any other work that arises. Minimum period of service is normally eight weeks. Free simple accommodation, meals and pocket money are provided. Minimum age is 16.

Please apply to the above address. A stamped addressed envelope or international reply coupon with applications is appreciated.

Winged Fellowship Trust
Angel House, 20-32 Pentonville Road, London N1 9XD (tel 071-833 2594).

Every year some 4,000 helpers are needed in five holiday centres for physically disabled people located in Surrey, Essex, Lancashire, Hampshire and Nottinghamshire. The purpose of the Trust is not only to provide holidays for severely physically disabled people, but also to enable the families who normally care for them at home to take perhaps their first worry-free holiday in years. Volunteers live in the centres and are given free board and lodging, during which time they not only take care of the physical needs of the guests and help with the domestic chores, but also provide companionship for them.

All that is required of volunteers is that they be over 17 years. Those with nursing qualifications would be particularly welcome. The centres are in operation for 11 months of the year, so although travel expenses are not normally paid, there are certain times of the year when help is in short supply, and requests for assistance will be considered, especially if those who are volunteering are unemployed.

Those interested should apply to the above address.

Woodlarks Camp Site Trust
Woodlarks Camp Site, Tilford Road, Farnham, Surrey, GU10 3RN (tel 0252-716279).

Over the summer the camp site offers the opportunity for physically handicapped children and adults to have a camping holiday on a wooded camp site. Facilities include a heated outdoor swimming pool, a trampoline, and archery. The camp site is run entirely by voluntary help; every summer around 500 volunteers assist some 500 handicapped people.

Volunteers are normally taken on for the duration of one camp, lasting one week, but some stay for more than one camp. Accommodation is provided in tents, a small fee is usually paid by helpers to cover the cost of food.

Those interested should contact the Honorary Secretary at the above address, enclosing an SAE or an International Reply Coupon.

Young Disabled on Holiday
33 Longfield Avenue, Heald Green, Cheadle, Cheshire SK8 3NH.

Some 80 — 100 volunteers are recruited annually to help with holidays for the young disabled. Young Disabled on Holiday began in 1970 with a group of young helpers who were involved in the parent organization — holidays for the Disabled

— which provides a large scale annual holiday for all ages of physically handicapped people. Noticing that the needs of the young were not adequately catered for on this type of holiday, they decided to organise a holiday purely for the young with an age limit for both disabled and helpers, of between 18 and 35. The organization runs a wide range of interesting holidays in the UK and abroad. In addition to holidays at fixed locations ere are boating and camping trips. Activities on the holidays include discotheques, swimming, horse riding, wheelchair sports, barbecues and banquets.

No special qualifications are needed and all nationalities are recruited. The age range is 18 — 35 years, and the length of time for which helpers are needed is usually one week. Helpers are asked to pay a contribution towards 40% of the total cost of holidays abroad and 25% on holidays in the Uk.

Those interested should apply to the organization at the above address.

Youth Activities

Brathay Exploration Group
Brathay Hall, Ambleside, Cumbria, LA22 OHP (tel 05394-33942).

The Group organizes expeditions and leader training courses in the British Isles and overseas. Expedition members are aged from 15 — 26 years old. A variety of expeditions are organized by voluntary leaders each year, combining adventure with field study work, and volunteers are needed to participate. In some circumstances assistant leaders may be required and would have experience in the outdoors or scientific skills.

Around 100 physically fit volunteers are needed each year. To be considered for a place in an expedition leader team, applicants must be 20 to 60 years old and have expedition experience, or specific scientific or medical knowledge.

Applications should be sent to the above address.

Fellowship of Reconciliation in Ireland
224 Lisburn Road, Belfast BT9 6GA, Northern Irelend (tel 0232-660194).

The Fellowship helps recruit volunteers for playschemes in Northern Ireland for Catholic and Protestant children aged between 5 and 16. The sites chosen are usually deprived and segregated areas as the long term aims of the playschemes are understanding and reconciliation. Volunteers act as play leaders and should be older than 18 years and able to cope with tense situations.

About 30 volunteers are needed for three weeks during the summer. Volunteers receive board and lodging but must pay their own travel expenses.

Apply to Anne Wilson at the above address.

Pax Christi
9 Henry Road, London N4 2LH (tel 081-800 4612).

Pax Christi is the international peace movement of the Catholic Church. In July and August it recruits a total of 130 volunteers to help run four childrens playschemes in Northern Ireland and temporary youth hostels in school buildings in London.

Playscheme volunteers work for a minimum of three weeks while those in youth hostels work for either two or four weeks. They are given free board and lodging. No special skills or experience are expected of volunteers but they must be aged over 18. One of the main objectives of these schemes is to further the cause of international understanding, and volunteers taking part may be of different religions and nationalities.

Those interested should contact the Workcamps Organiser at the above address for further details.

Quaker Youth Theatre
Leaveners Arts Base, 8 Lennox Road, London N4 3NW (tel 071-272 5630).

The Youth Theatre runs summer and Christmas residential theatre projects for young people aged between 16 and 23 in Britain. In addition, it runs community arts projects involving volunteers devising and running a children's performance and co-operative playscheme in Northern Ireland and central London. Each year, the Theatre recruits between 24 and 36 volunteers to work with 50-100 young people.

For the residential projects volunteers are needed to work as directors, musical directors, pastoral care/youth workers and technical assistants on the production team, as well as helping with scenery construction. For the community arts project voluntary devisor/performers are needed for the children's production. The Youth Theatre runs an equal opportunities policy and all posts are open to all nationalities or religions. Applicants, however, must speak and read English; some previous experience in the theatre or possession of music, dance or circus skills is desirable. They must also be in good health generally, although effort will be made to accommodate people with some disabilities. The minimum age limit for the community arts project is 18 years, and 23 years and over for the residential projects. The residential projects last for between 10 and 15 days, while the community arts projects last for between three and four days. Volunteers are required on a seasonal basis; at Christmas time, in the last week of July or all of August. There is no pocket money, but accommodation is provided.

Those interested should contact Tina Helfrich at the above address.

Tent City Ltd and Hackney Camping
PO Box 1197, Shepherd's Bush, London W12 (tel 081-743 5708).

Tent City is a place where tourists can stay in London cheaply, and is open from June to September, 24 hours a day. It has 450 beds in 14 large tents, men's, women's and mixed. It is run by an international team and supported entirely by volunteers.

Over 60 volunteers of all nationalities are needed over the summer months to help with cleaning, reception, tent maintenance, the snack-bar and cooking. The only requirement is that volunteers should command a good level of spoken English, and that they should stay for four to six weeks. Food, accommodation and pocket money of £30 per week are all provided.

The same team runs a normal campsite called Hackney Camping and volunteers are also required there. Conditions and benefits as above.

Those interested should contact Paul Callery at the above address.

Other Short Term Residential Opportunities

The following organizations have been included in the *Non Residential* chapter, but under certain circumstances or on specialized projects some residential volunteers are also needed.

British Wheelchair Sports Society
Endeavour Training
International Flat
Meldreth Manor School

New Consumer
Saturday Venture Association
St. Mark's Church Kennington
Tools for Self Reliance.

Europe

Multi-National

The ACROSS Trust

Bridge House, 70-72 Bridge Road, East Molesey, Surrey KT8 9HF (tel 081-783 1355; fax 081-941 2730).

The Trust is a registered charity that arranges weekly pilgrimages and holidays for the sick and disabled (the unable) from March to November each year. These last 10 days. Places visited on pilgrimages include Lourdes, Rome, the Holy Land and Poland. Places visited on holidays include Belgium, France, Spain, Switzerland, Austria, Ireland and Holland. Transport is by Jumbulance, a purpose-built jumbo ambulance, which carries all the necessary facilities for the unable.

Each group consists of two to three nurses, a doctor (if necessary), a chaplain and male and female helpers, all of whom volunteer their time and pay their own expenses to care for the ten unable in the group. ACROSS gives priority to those with terminal illness, with progressive diseases, those confined to bed or wheelchair, and people with illnesses that make other forms of travel impossible or unsuitable. The group, with a maximum of 24 or 44 persons, live together as a family throughout their holiday, with everyone devoting themselves to the needs of the group 24 hours a day. The work of caring for the unable, i.e. feeding, dressing, toileting, etc. is shared among all the group.

Volunteers need to be in good health and dedicated. Nurses and helpers pay the same as the rest of the group. Accommodation is provided in Lourdes at the Trust's purpose-built homes. Once volunteers apply, they will be offered the available dates. Enquiries for the appropriate application form (eg doctor, nurse, chaplain, lay helper) should be sent to the Group Organizers at the above address.

APARE

41 cours Jean Jaures, 8400 Avignon, France (tel 90 85 51 15).

APARE organize voluntary workcamps dedicated to the restoration of historic buildings and sites particularly in Provence but also throughout the rest of Europe.

600 volunteers are needed in the summer to work on the sites; applicants must be aged over 16-18 years old and be fit. No particular skills are required as each work-camp composed of about 15 people is supervised by a technical group leader. Placements last for 3 or 4 weeks. Accommodation is provided, although pocket money is not and participants have to pay a fee of 600 francs.

For more details write to Marie-Auge Lemaire at the above address.

APENA

Hameau de la Pinede, Traverse Valette, 13009 Marseille, France (tel 91 25 05 30).

APENA runs two children's holiday camps, one in Marseille and the other in Switzerland. Between 20 and 25 volunteers are needed for one month in the summer to act as instructors. Each instructor will be responsible for looking after a group of eight children aged between 6 and 15.

Applicants of all nationalities are welcome, but fluent French and previous experience with children are both essential. Applicants must also be at least 18 years of age. Accommodation is provided, and instructors have one day off per week. Volunteers must pay for their own travel costs.

Those interested should apply to Jean Luc Recordon at the above address.

BTCV International Working Holidays
36 St Mary's Street, Wallingford, Oxon OX10 0EU (tel 0491-39766; fax 0491-39646).

BTCV has grown to become the UK's leading charity for improving and protecting the environment. The Trust aims to harness people's energies and talents to protect the environment by practical action. To this end the Trust organizes international working holidays for 500 volunteers a year lasting from one to three weeks throughout Europe. The holidays offer an exotic blend of sun, companionship and challenging experiences.

The variety of sometimes unusual assignments range from building a tortoise village in Corsica to creating a bird reserve in the grounds of a Belgian chateau. The working day is 9am to 5.30pm and the evenings are free. The average cost is about £50 a week inclusive of basic accommodation and food. Whilst undertaking traditional conservation projects, it is hoped that volunteers will adapt to local life-styles as well as participate in community affairs.

Those interested should write to the International Development Unit at the above address for further details enclosing a stamped addressed envelope.

Bouworde
Tiensesteenweg 145, 3010 Leuven, Belgium (tel 016/25 91 44; fax 016/25 91 60).

Bouworde needs around 800 volunteers every year to do manual work helping to improve unhealthy and unmodernized housing. These projects take place around the year in Flanders and also in France, Germany, Austria, Italy, Spain, Hungary,Croatia, Slovenia, Lithuania, Russia, Poland, Romania and Czechoslovakia in the summer (July, August and September).

The minimum period of work is three weeks. Free board, accommodation and insurance are provided, but volunteers must pay for their own travel costs. Participants must be aged at least 18.

Applications should be sent to the above address.

Box-Aid
11 Hill Top Lane, Saffron Walden, Essex CB11 4AS (tel 0799-523321).

Box-Aid makes, demonstrates and cooks with solar cooking and 'Wonderboxes' at Green Fairs in the UK, and also at Sunseed's desert technology centre in Spain. Box-Aid also works in co-operation with Compassion and other similar organizations in southern Africa, and recruits volunteers for the Sunseed Trust.

Volunteers, of any nationality, would begin by experimenting with the cookers. If keen, they could then demonstrate them in the UK or spend anything from one week to 6 months at the Spanish centre cooking food in them for other volunteers. After that they might be able to go to other VSO countries where this fuel-saving type of cooking is needed. Board and lodging is provided in Spain, but not in the UK. There is free transport to Spain and an optional allowance of £10 per week once there. No special qualifications are necessary; a driving licence is an advantage in Spain for those aged over 27 . A knowledge of any extra languages is useful but not essential.

Applications can be sent, all the year round to Anna Pearce at the above address.

Centre Mediterraneen de l'Environnement
41 Cours Jacques Jaures, 8400 Avignon, France (tel 90 27 08 61; fax 90 86 82 19).

The Centre organizes and recruits volunteers for the European Group of Campuses for the Environment. This extensive network of university workshops is intended for all young people interested in the environment. As training projects, but also tools of action for the benefit of local initiatives for the environment, the campuses allow the participants to become part of multidisciplinary teams working voluntarily on research/action programmes in such varied fields as the Gdansk local environment plan in Poland and the programme for eco-tourism in the Zagorie Natural Park in Greece. These truly practical university workshops last from between 3 weeks to a month. In 1992 the Centre offered 15 of these Campuses. To volunteer, applicants must have a university degree, with additional experience in environmental disciplines. Applicants must also speak several European languages. The groups of 15 are led by university tutors.

The Campuses are free and provide board and lodging though not the return fare. The determining factor in the choice of candidates will be their commitment to a multi-disciplinary, practical experience.

For more information on the Campuses please write to Christine Dantaux at the above address.

Ecumenical Youth Council in Europe
Youth Unit, British Council of Churces, Inter-Church House, 35-41 Lower Marsh, London SE1 7RL (tel 071-620 4444).

EYCE organizes work camps for study, manual labour and social development in most countries in Europe. The camps last two to three weeks throughout the summer and provide places for about 30 volunteers each. Both the activities and the studies have topical objectives, and aim to promote Christian understanding and faith. Participants must contribute towards their expenses and food costs, but accommodation is provided. Volunteers must be over 18 years of age and able to adapt to communal life in a Christian environment.

Applications may be sent to EYCE, Youth Matters, at the above address if from British citizens; the international headquarters of EYCE is PO Box 464, Belfast BT4 2DE (tel 0232-651134). Please enclose a stamped addressed envelope or an international reply coupon with your enquiries.

HF Holidays Ltd
Imperial House, Edgware Road, London NW9 5AL (tel 081-905 9556).

HF Holidays was established in 1913 as a non profit-making society intended to further the open air leisure movement. In addition to its head office in London it has 22 regional centres around the United Kingdom from which walking excursions, lasting five days each, are organized. It also organizes walking holidays abroad from hotels in Austria, France, Italy, Norway, Spain and Switzerland.

Around 500 volunteers a year are needed to assist as walking and social leaders on these excursions. Volunteers are needed around the year for periods of up to 6 weeks. Accommodation, food and expense, in the form of a clothing allowance, are provided, and travel is paid for.

Those interested should contact the Chief Executive at the above address.

Internationale Begegnung in Gemeinschaftsdiensten (IBG)
Schlosserstrasse 28, D-7000 Stuttgart-1, Germany

IBG was founded in 1965 by the Boy Scouts' Association. International workcamps lasting three weeks are organized in Germany and Switzerland in close conjunction with local villages. Chosen projects are designed to benefit the whole community, such as the construction of children's playgrounds, hiking paths, public gardens, afforestation, etc. In exchange for 30 hours of work per week, volunteers receive food and lodging, insurance and some spare-time excursions.

Applicants between 18 and 30 from all over the world are welcome. Volunteers are advised to bring a sleeping bag and heavy footwear, as well as musical instruments, games and records from their own countries. The registration fee is 120DM (about £40) which should be submitted with anapplication form. Enquirers to the above address will be sent a brochure containing dates and locations of the various workcamps.

International Bouworde-IBO
St Annastraat 172 6524 GT Nijmegen, The Netherlands (tel 080-226 074).

Internationale Bouworde (or International Building Companions) gives volunteers the opportunity to assist in socially useful building projects in about 35 countries throughout the world. British participants will be integrated in international groups, especially in Belgium, Holland, Germany, France, Switzerland, Austria, Italy, Poland*, Hungary, Czechoslovakia*, and Romania*.

The workcamps last for three weeks. The actual construction work provides the most important element of the camps, and volunteers are expected to treat it as such. It acts as a focus for the other aspects such as encounters with fellow participants and with the local population.

Volunteers should be at least 18 years old and able to meet the physical demands of the camp which are eight hours per day of labouring work. They must also be willing to adapt to foreign attitudes and life-styles. Volunteers have to pay their owntravel costs to and from the project. IBO pays the insurance and provides board and lodging. Candidates should apply to the relevant address below. Applications for countries marked with * should be made to the above address.
IBO-Osterreichischer Bauorden, Hornesgasse 4, A-1031 Wien, Austria
IBO-Bouworde, Tiensesteenweg 145, B-3200 Kessel-Lo, Belgium
IBO- Compagnons Batisseurs, 6 Av Charles de Gaulle, F-81100 CastresFrance.

IBO-Les Compagnons Batisseurs, Rue Notre-Dame de Graces 63, B-5400 March-en-Famenne, Belgium.
IBO-Internationaler Bauorden, PO Box 1438, D-6420 Worms,Germany
IBO-Internationale Bouworde, St Annastraat 172, NL-6524 GT Nijmegen, Holland.
IBO-Soci Costruttori, Via CBattisti 3, 1-20 071 Casalpusterlengo (MI) Italy.
IBO-Internationaler Bauorden, Kirchweg 7, CH-9438 Luchingen SG, Switzerland.
IBO-Epito Baratok, Blathy Otto u. 10, H-1089 Budapest, Hungary.

Ocean Youth Club
The Bus Station, South Street, Gosport, Hants. PO12 1EP (tel 0705-52841/2).

The Ocean Youth Club needs volunteers to act as First and Second Mates on its expeditions and cruises from March to October. There are expeditions to Norway and the Outer Hebrides and cruises to Spain, Northern Europe, the Baltic and the Shetland Islands. The aim of the club is to provide young people aged 12-24 with the opportunity to take part in adventurous offshore sailing, and so to develop their sense of awareness and responsibility and their ability to work in a team. It has bases throughout the UK. Volunteers work for weekends, weeks and occasionally, on the cruises, from two to three weeks.

All First Mates must have a Yachtmaster Certificate or Professional Sea Qualification, and must have been assessed as suitable by the Club. They should ideally be under 55. Second Mates must have been on an assessment cruise. All volunteers must be fit and able to swim. Accommodation is provided, as are safety and foul weather equipment. First Mates are asked to make a contribution towards their upkeep, and second mates pay £8 a day towards the cost of food.

Applications should be made to the Director at the above address.

RIGPA
330 Caledonian Road, London N1 1BB (tel 071-700 815; fax 071-609 6068).

RIGPA is a Buddhist Centre providing a focus for both those who follow Buddhism, and for those who may not be Buddhist but may want to explore meditation or a Buddhist perspective on areas such as death, dying and compassion. There are also RIGPA Centres in the USA, France, Ireland and Germany. The number of volunteers engaged annually varies; for a big event 30-40 volunteers may be needed but on a daily basis between two and five volunteers are sufficient.

There is a wide range of activities open to volunteers. In London help is needed with office work, tape copying, cleaning, building work, and for those with the suitable skills, computer work. In France and Ireland, volunteers are needed to help with general outdoor work, particularly building retreat centres. Volunteers may be of all nationalities, but they should be interested in and sympathetic to Buddhism. They should also be able to speak English and be in good health. Volunteers are required all the year round in London, Ireland and France. Expenses are not usually paid; accommodation is provided in Ireland and France but volunteers are recruited in London on a non-residential basis.

Those interested should contact Rosamond Oliver at the above address.

La Sabranenque
Saint Victor la Coste, 30290 Laudun, France (tel 33-66 50 05 05).

La Sabranenque is a non-profit making organization working for the preservation of the rural habitat by restoring abandoned rural sites for present day use. Saint Victor la Coste serves as the headquarters for the organization as the work projects are mainly in southern France, although there are three sites in Italy. Around 150 volunteers are needed for work which includes restoration of roofs, terraces, walls and paths, planting local tree species and the reconstruction of small houses. Techniques are learned on-the-job. Workcamps last a minimum of two or three weeks during the summer, and occasionally stays of two months or more are possible.

Volunteers must be at least 18 years old and in good health. No language skills or previous experience are required for summer workcamps, but non EEC volunteers must obtain a French visa for their period of stay. Board and lodging are provided at a cost of about £200 per two-week project.

Applications to the Programme Co-ordinator at the above address.

Sunseed Trust
PO Box 3000, Timworth 10, Bury St. Edmunds, Suffolk 1P3 1HY (tel 0284-728031; fax 0284-728240)

Sunseed Trust is a registered charity which develops new ways to reclaim deserts such as arid-land tree trials growing in affordable low-irrigation enclosures, purifying water with low-cost solar stills, solar cooking, new composts for organic vegetables, etc. Volunteers are required to assist with projects in Spain, France and England. In Spain volunteers are required for research and appropriate technology; in France they are needed to help with forestry; and in England they are needed to help with office work. Help is needed with building and organic gardening everywhere. Some qualifications are required depending on the job. About 500 short-term volunteers are engaged annually, as well as about 20 long-term volunteers, preferably qualified for the positions open.

Skilled and/or qualified applicants are needed to head various projects in tree trials, hydrophonics, appropriate technology, crop research or building. Unskilled volunteers are needed to assist in the above projects, or to help with the infrastructure of meals, lodging and communication, etc. Individuals of all nationalities are welcome to apply. A driving licence is needed; applicants should note that they must be aged over 27 to qualify for a driving licence in Spain. Linguistic ability is always in great demand. The minimum age limit is 12 years old, but all under the age of 16 must be accompanied by a parent. There is no upper age limit but applicants should be aware that the work is hard. Volunteers are recruited for six months or one year, and are required all year round. Travel, pocket money (up to £10 per week) and board and lodging are provided. Some volunteers may be given accommodation in dormitories.

Applicants should apply to Mrs N Pepin at the above address.

TOC H
1 Forest Close, Wendover, Aylesbury, Bucks, HP22 6BT (tel 0296-623911; fax 0296-696137).

Toc H runs short-term residential projects throughout the year in Britain and Germany, usually of from a weekend to up to three weeks in duration. Projects undertaken can include work with people with different disabilities or children in need; playschemes and camps; conservation and manual work; study and/or discussion sessions.

These projects provide those who take part with opportunities to learn more about themselves and the world. Whilst foreign applicants are welcome, a preference is held for those living in the EC. The Toc H programme is published twice yearly on the first Mondays in March and September. Whilst there is a minimum age limit of 16 years, there is no upper age limit. There is no closing date for applications but you are advised to apply early. Over 500 volunteers a year are recruited. Toc H does not offer any long-term paid employment opportunities or supervised placements.

Enquiries should be sent to the Publicity Officer at the above address enclosing a stamped self-addressed envelope.

Tutmonda Esperantista Junulara Organizo — TEJO (World Organisation of Young Esperantists)

Nieuwe Binnenweg 176, NL-3015 BJ Rotterdam, Netherlands (tel +31 10 4361044; fax +31 10 4361751).

In addition to arranging Esperanto courses for workcamps organized by other organizations, TEJO also co-ordinates the recruitment of volunteers for Esperanto workcamps in the several European countries.These camps include work on building sites and enhancing the environment. There is also a system of half-work, half-learning Esperanto 'camps'. Volunteers are usually recruited for one or two months, and accommodation is provided.

No prior experience is needed; although a few camps are limited to Esperanto speakers, some camps include Esperanto lessons for beginners. The camps are usually composed of people aged 18-30.

Enquiries should be sent to the Commission of External Relations at the above address.

Universities and Colleges Christian Fellowship (UCCF)

38 De Montfort Street, Leicester LE1 7GP (tel 0533-551700).

All of the fellowship's activities have Christian teachings and evangelical aims as their basis. Around 300 volunteers are needed to take part in evangelical teams, help with camps, community activities and church-based work in Britain, Ireland and Europe. These activities may last from one week to one month during the summer vacation.

Volunteers may be of any nationality but must be committed Christians. Languages may be required for some evangelical teams in Europe. Most activities require a contribution for board and food although some may pay expenses. The volunteer meets all travel expenses.

UCCF also publish *Vac Acts*, a directory of summer volunteer activities for Christian students. It is available each February at no cost.

Those interested in UCCF's activities or *Vac Acts* should apply to the Assistant to Head of Student Ministries at the above address.

Belgium and Holland

Annee Diaconale Belge
Service Protestant de la Jeunesse, Rue de Champ de Mars, 5, 1050 Bruxelles, Belgium (tel 02-513 24 01).

Part of the Service Protestant de la Jeunesse, or Protestant Youth Office, arranges for volunteers to spend between ten and 12 months in Christian or other institutions in Belgium. Around 10 volunteers a year are placed in childrens homes, old peoples homes, etc. Volunteers receive free food, accommodation and laundry, their travelling expenses and pocket money of around £65 per month. Placements begin in September.

Participants should be aged between 18 and 26 and have a basic knowledge of French. Whatever their background all candidates' applications will be welcome. Possession of a driving licence and/or a teaching certificate would be advantageous.

Contact the Secretary at the above address for further details.

Archeolo-J
Avenue Paul Terlinden 23, 1330 Rixensart, Belgium (tel 02-653 8268).

Archeolo-J organizes international workcamps at archaeological excavations in Belgium. Volunteers assist with all aspects of the excavations, digging, drawing finds and surveying the sites. Around 100 volunteers aged 12 years and older are needed to work for periods of 3 weeks in July. Accommodation in tents is provided.

Write to the President at the above address for more information.

Belgian Evangelical Mission
20 Vicarage Farm Road, Hounslow TW3 4NW.

The Belgian Evangelical Mission conducts summer evangelical campaigns in a number of towns and villages in both French and Dutch speaking Belgium. Around 60 volunteers from Britain are needed to join the international campaign teams which last from two to six weeks. Another three to six volunteers are needed to join church-planting teams, also in Belgium. These teams start each September and last until the following July.

Volunteers may be of any nationality provided they are Christians and can provide a home church recommendation. Applicants for the church-planting teams must speak either French or Dutch and pay around £250 per month. Summer evangelical team members pay £50 per week and a £5 deposit. All volunteers must pay for their own travel but accommodation is provided.

Those interested should apply to Richard Martin at the above address.

NATUUR 2000: The Flemish Youth Federation for the Study of Nature and for Environmental Conservation
Bervoestraat 33, B-2000 Antwerpen, Belgium (tel 3 231 26 04; fax 3 233 64 99).

NATUUR 2000 organizes nature study and nature conservation activities for young people aged between eight and 25 including birdwatching camps, management of nature reserves, etc. It also runs an environmental information centre for young people. About 10 volunteers per year, preferably with experience in field biology, are required to help prepare and lead the study and working camps. Help is also needed in the Antwerp and Ostend based offices; those with computer experience will be preferred. Applicants of any nationality will be considered, as long as they are interested and motivated. They must also have experience in field biology and computer/clerical work. An international driving licence could be helpful. The maximum age limit is 25.

Volunteers are required for from two weeks to one month, or longer. The camps take place between mid-June until Mid-September, and volunteers are also needed in the offices all the year round. Accommodation, food and insurance are all provided.

Those interested should contact Julius Smeyers at the above address.

Universale Esperanto-Asocio
Nieuwe Binneweg 176, 3015 BJ Rotterdam, Netherlands (tel 010-4361539).

Esperanto is the international language invented by Zamenhof, a Polish oculist, in 1887. It now has more than a million speakers throughout the world. The Universala Esperanto-Asocio is the world organization for the advancement of Esperanto. Its Head Office is situated in Rotterdam, where a staff of ten to twelve workers from various parts of the world, both paid and voluntary, are involved in day-to-day administration, accounts, mail order services, congress organization, editing and production of books and magazines, and maintaining a library. The Association has another office in New York to deal with contacts with the UN. Thus the Association needs one or two volunteers from time to time to help with its work. The minimum period of service for volunteers is nine months, the maximum one year.

Volunteers must speak Esperanto fluently as this is the working language of the organization. Other qualifications may be necessary depending on the specific vacancy. Applicants must be between 18 and 29 years of age. Free accommodation is provided, and insurance and a small living allowance is paid. Residents of EC countries do not need a visa or work permit. Volunteers from other countries will need both. A period of six to twelve months should be allowed for the acquisition of these permits.

Applications should be made to the Director at the above address

Eastern Europe

The Body Shop Eastern Europe Relief Drive
Watersmead, Littlehampton, West Sussex BN17 6LS (tel 0903-731010; fax 726250).

At present, the Relief Drive operates in Romania and Albania but will eventually be extended to include the rest of Eastern Europe. The organization is involved in the refurbishment of orphanages and hospitals, and the running of healthcare programmes, playschemes and community work. Qualified nurses, doctors, child carers, builders, electricians, plumbers, HGV drivers and artists are needed to volunteer their skills for up to a year.   There are also two to four week opportunities for unskilled volunteers to work on the playschemes for children, or to work on refurbishment trips, or to paint institutions. Applicants, either skilled or unskilled, are invited to apply all the year round. Accommodation is provided; volunteers should raise funds for their airfares and a little more, though long-term volunteers who are skilled in a trade or in healthcare are sponsored. Applicants of all nationalities may apply, and the minimum age limit is 18.

To apply, or to obtain an information pack, please contact Rachel Bentley, Project Co-ordinator, at the above address.

International Committee of Youth Organisations (ICVO)

7/8 Maroseika, Moscow 101846, Russia (tel 095-206 85 42; fax 206 81 73)., Russia.

ICVO (formerly the Committee of Youth Organizations of the USSR) organizes international voluntary workcamps in the Confederation of Independent States and also sends volunteers from there to other countries. Around 350 volunteers are needed to help with agricultural, construction and conservation work. Workcamps are only held during the summer and last for two weeks. No special skills are required but volunteers must be at least 18 years old and physically able.

Volunteers must pay a registration fee but accommodation is provided, and the host organization pays local costs. An invitation to attend a workcamp is sufficient to obtain a visa.

Applications should be addressed to the Co-ordinating Committee for International Voluntary Service, 1 Rue Miollis, 75015 Paris, France.

International Ecological Camp

665718 Bratski-18, Irkutsk Region, PO Box 52, Russia.

The International Ecological Camp has organized voluntary service workcamps in Siberia since 1989. It gives volunteers the opportunity to go to the heart of Russia and learn the legends, ideas and priorities of the Russians; the reality behind the news stories.

Each year about 80 volunteers live, play and work with people from many continents on these workcamps. Each camp lasts for two to three weeks. Free time is spent swimming in nearby lakes, enjoying the campfire and the forest, sightseeing and experiencing local culture. Accommodation is basic but comfortable, and food is either cooked by the group or enjoyed at a local cafe.

Volunteers are also needed to lead the work camps for 2-3 months; they must be fluent in Russian, as well as being both independent and flexible. There also exist opportunities for teaching English for a period of 5 months in Siberia. Teachers must be qualified and experienced TEFL teachers. Volunteers must be over 16; interest in or experience of the Russian language and culture is important. The camp is not currently accessible to wheelchairs. Volunteers are needed all year, with the greatest demand in the summer. The Camp cannot, unfortunately, pay any expenses but accommodation is provided and it may be able to assist with visas.

Applicants, of any nationality, should contact Sergei Malinin at the above address.

International Exchange Center

2, Republic Square, 226168 Riga, Latvia (tel/fax 0132-327476/323400).

The Center recruits volunteers of any nationality to work on summer farm camps in Latvia and Russia, in addition to arranging placements for westerners as au pairs and camp counsellors. Placements usually last for between four and twelve weeks. A basic knowledge of Russian or Latvian is necessary, and applicants should be aged between 18 and 35.

For further details contact the above address.

Jacob's Well Appeal
2 Ladygate, Beverley HU17 8BH (tel 0482-881162; fax 0482-865452).

The Appeal is a Christian Charity that organizes medical aid to Eastern Europe and Asia. The Appeal sends volunteers to work in a mentally handicapped children's hospitel in Siret, Romania. The minimum length of placement here is two weeks, and the maximum placement can be as long as two years. Doctors, nurses, volunteer nurses, teachers, physiotherapists, pharmacists, administrators and students over 18 years are all desperately needed both in Romania and in Afghanistan. Volunteers are also needed to work with understimulated and unloved children in a Romanian Neuropsychiatric hospital, and in an orthopaedic workshop for caliper and splint production. There is a great need for qualified physiotherapists here as well.

In addition there are opportunities for voluntary work in the Appeal's warehouse in the UK; sorting of medicines and equipment, packing containers and collecting supplies by van or lorry. Volunteers are also required to help with the Appeal's administration, and to act as couriers. About 80 volunteers per year work for the Appeal, both abroad and in the UK. Applicants may be of any nationality, but they must be qualified in their chosen area of work, and fluent in English. A certificate of health is needed for all work in Romania and Afghanistan, and volunteers must accept the principles of the Appeal's constitution. The average length of placement in Romania is 2-3 months, at all times of the year. Local volunteers working in the UK headquarters stay for a year. Accommodation is provided for volunteers working abroad, and expenses (apart from travel costs) are paid for all volunteers except for short-term workers in Romania.

For further information please contact Dr. Beryl Beynon at the above address.

MOST
Breg 12 — PP 279, 61000 Ljubljana, Slovenia (tel 3861-153244-ext.43).

MOST organizes voluntary work in Slovenia, particularly in areas not adequately covered by the government such as ecology, care of the handicapped and refugees. MOST also organizes workcamps mainly in summer, and an exchange scheme for local volunteers with organizations abroad. 200 Slovenian volunteers and 400 foreign volunteers are engaged per year.

There are opportunities for volunteers to participate in manual work such as building, painting or decorating. Ecologically minded volunteers are needed to help with gardening and research work and also to find data and run campaigns. There are volunteer opportunities in the area of social work including work with mentally or physically handicapped children, elderly people and refugees, and also to organize study sessions among marginalized groups. Applicants of all nationalities are welcome; there is no need for a visa or work permit. Volunteers must, however, be able to speak English and preferably have previous experience of voluntary work. The minimum age is 18.

Foreign volunteers usually join the summer workcamps, which last from two to five weeks, but there are also medium-term placements of six months and long-term placements of one year. Workcamp volunteers get food and accommodation free, while for the medium and long-term volunteers accommodation and pocket money are provided. On workcamps the accommodation is usually basic and communal.

Those interested should contact Dominique Cochard, Long-Term Volunteer Exchange Officer, at the above address, who will then forward applications to the relevant organization.

OHP: Voluntary Work Corps
International Workcamps, Grzybowska 79 00-844, Warsaw, Poland (tel/fax 32 43 99).

OHP organizes international workcamps and brigades to undertake social, preservation and conservation projects within Poland. Over 350 volunteers help each year by undertaking unskilled manual work, study and social projects. The workcamps are held during the summer and last from two to four weeks.

Volunteers must be English speaking, 18 — 35 years old, in general good health and have obtained a Polish visa. Board and lodging are provided.

Those interested should apply through a Service Civil International member organization in their home country as no individual applicationscan be accepted by this organization.

Orphan Aid — Romania
2 Wycliffe Street, Leicester LE1 5LP (tel 0533-510051; fax 0533-511636).

This is a registered charity founded in October 1990 with the sole objective of relieving the suffering of sick and handicapped children in Romania; improving their living standards, bringing love and purpose into their lives and helping to educate the Romanians with Western ways of health, hygiene, care and stimulation.

It operates in two orphanages and a hospital in Foscani, 130 miles north of Bucharest; the orphanages have over 190 babies from birth to the age of five. Around 75% are HIV positive; some have Hepatitis B, others have Aids. Even with Orphan Aid's help there are still some rooms with 14 or so babies who spend all day in their cots with no stimulation whatsoever. The hospital has antiquated machines, some of which do not work, and very little in the way of drugs and surgical equipment.

There is, therefore, an urgent need for a qualified paediatrician, qualified nurses and qualified nursery nurses to offer their services on a voluntary basis. Other volunteers are also required to work as child carers, and to assist with cooking, washing and general housekeeping duties. The minimum age limit is 20 years and the minimum length of contract is three months. Volunteers must pay their own airfare to Romania (currently £250), but living expenses, accommodation and travelling expenses will be met by the organization.

For further information please contact Anthony J. N. Holt at the above address.

Republic Belarus; Students and Youth Employment Service
40 Tikotski Street, PO Box 641, Minsk, Belorus.

This service organizes and co-ordinates workcamps in Belorus in different fields including ecology and many other social issues. It acts as an advisory service for overseas volunteers coming to Belorus. It also places 150 volunteers from Belorus in workcamps throughout Europe. About 150 volunteers come to these workcamps every year to take part in activities and study programmes, or to help with office work, or to lead the camps and help with the co-ordination of the summer exchgange. Applicants of any nationality are welcome; some exchanges have only participants from one country. Volunteers from abroad are assisted with visas, etc.

No special skills are needed, apart from Russian language skills for some of the programmes. The minimum age limit is 18 years and there is no upper limit. Disabled applicants are welcome, but they must contact the organization prior to application. The usual length of placement is three or four weeks between June and September, although some volunteers can be placed for two to four months. Volunteers must pay an application fee, but during the workcamp they are provided with free food, accommodation and health insurance. Accommodation is provided in student hostels.

For further information contact the above address.

Romania Information Centre
The University, Southampton, Hampshire 5O9 5NH (tel 0703-593406; fax 0703 593939).

The Information Centre provides a volunteer list for any organization that works for Romania and requires volunteers; there are currently over 500 such organizations in the British Isles, though not all use volunteers. The volunteer list is compiled from a volunteer database which is updated every two to three months. The Centre places over 100 volunteers per year.

Volunteers are usually involved in caring roles in Romanian institutions for the elderly and disabled, or in orphanages. They can also assist with painting, decorating and building work on refurbishment projects. The Centre can also offer short-term professional roles for medical volunteers including doctors, dentists, nurses, physiotherapists and occupational therapists. Drivers of heavy goods vehicles are also needed. Volunteers may be of any nationality, but the minimum age limit is usually 18 years of age and they should enjoy good health.

Volunteers can work for as little as two weeks, or as long as one year. The Centre does not pay any expenses as it merely facilitates recruitment. Volunteers are normally expected to find their own travelling and living expenses, but this does vary between one organization and another. Accommodation of some kind is normally provided. The Centre publishes a newsletter called *Information Romania* which contains articles and adverts concerning the current situation in Romania, as well as a useful *Romanian Phrasebook*. The newsletter costs £2.50 for six issues, while the phrasebook costs £4.50; both can be obtained from the above address.

For a volunteer form and a list of national and local groups concerned with aid to Romania, send a large stamped addressed envelope to the above address.

The Training Trust
145 Great Charles Street, Birmingham B3 (tel 021-200 1140; fax 021-233 0573).

The Trust organizes a training project for the staff of orphanages for severely handicapped children in Romania. The Trust trains in specialist skills such as speech therapy, occupational therapy, physiotherapy, special education, management and general caring. The Trust is planning to expand its operations into Albania and Bulgaria.

Between five and ten volunteers with specialist health/therapy skills are needed to train, or to give direct skill input to, Romanian staff. Applicants may be of any nationality, but they must be qualified in one or more of the above skills. Lengths of placements vary from three weeks to 12 months, but the length of placement depends on the demand and the volunteer's situation. Accommodation is provided. Expenses may be provided by arrangement.

Those interested should contact Rachel Wilkinson at the above address.

Eire

An Taisce — The National Trust for Ireland
The Tailors' Hall, Back Lane, Dublin 8, Eire (tel 01-541786).

An Taisce is concerned with the conservation of all aspects of the physical environment, natural or man-made. It has over 5,000 members and works through local associations throughout the country.

Enquiries should be addressed to the Central Office Secretary at the above address.

Groundwork (Ireland)
132a East Wall Road, Dublin 3, Eire (tel 01-366821).

Groundwork organizes workcamps of varying duration in order to conserve areas of natural wealth currently under threat in Ireland. Projects include conserving the oakwoods of the west coast of Ireland and the raised bogs of the midlands.

Volunteers are needed for various tasks including removing raised bogs. The work is usually quite strenuous. Workcamps are usually conducted in summer and autumn; those on the oakwoods last for one week while one day or weekend camps are used to care for the bogs. Volunteers must be in good health and aged between 16 and 65 years. Accommodation is provided.

Those interested should contact the Secretary at the above address for a brochure and application form around March of each year.

Irish Wild Bird Conservancy
Ruttledge House, 8 Longford Place, Monkstown, Co. Dublin, Eire.

The Irish Wild Bird Conservancy undertakes reserve management, species protection and environmental surveys and research in the Republic of Ireland. Around 10 volunteers a year are needed to assist with this work as voluntary wardens for periods of one week to three months. Volunteers should be over 16 years old and in good health. Previous ornithological experience is an advantage. Accommodation in caravans or camp sites is usually provided.

Those interested should write to the Reserves Division at the above address for further information and an application form, enclosing a stamped addressed envelope or international reply coupon.

The Simon Community
P.O. Box 1022, Lower Sherriff Street, Dublin 1, Eire (tel 01-711606).

The Simon Community is a voluntary organization which provides accommodation, food and companionship for homeless and rootless people. Full and part-time volunteers run night shelters, community houses, soup runs and other services for the homeless in Cork, Dublin, Dundalk and Galway.

All nationalities are welcome and no formal or special qualifications are required. Personal qualities such as compassion, sensitivity, and adaptability are most important. Fluency in English and the ability to communicate are essential. Accommodation and a weekly pocket money allowance are provided. Volunteers are expected to stay for a minimum of three months; two weeks holiday, with an allowance, are given after every three months of a stay.

Further information can be obtained from the Recruitment Co-ordinator.

France

Amis de Pax Christi
58 Avenue de Breteuil, 75007 Paris, France.

The French branch of Pax Christi, the international peace movement of the Catholic Church, runs a temporary youth hostel over the summer in Lourdes. The hostel is run by an international team of about 10 volunteers. Volunteers should be aged over 18 and be prepared to live together as a close Christian Community sharing the work, leisure time, etc.

For further information contact the above address.

Association Alpes de Lumiere
Prieure de Salagon, Mane, 04300-Forcalquier, France (tel 92 75 19 13).

The Association organizes several camps around Provence lasting about three weeks between June and September dedicated to the restoration of historic buildings, and the development of historic sites. These sites become recreational and cultural centres. Food and basic accommodation, but not pocket money, are provided for the volunteers. The emphasis of the camps is also on enriching the participants' awareness of the culture and customs of the area. The working day begins at 07.30 and ends at 13.30; the afternoons are free. Participants work a thirty hour week under the direction of a specialist and a group leader.

Applicants of all nationalities will be accepted for the 100 places available each year. The minimum age limit is 18 years, and applicants must be fit and not subject to any allergies.

Enquiries should be sent to Vincent Bobillier at the above address.

Association Chantiers-Histoire et Architecture Medievales (CHAM)
5 et 7, rue Guilleminot, 75014 Paris, France (tel 43 35 15 51; fax 43 20 46 82)

The Association is dedicated to the conservation and restoration of medieval buildings around France. 600 volunteers per year are needed to work in July and August for a minimum of ten days on the restoration of monuments, chateaux, bridges and abbeys.

Applicants should be enthusiastic and have a very good knowledge of French; they must also be over 15 years of age. No pocket money is provided and applicants must pay, not only for their travel expenses, but also a contribution of 100 francs, plus 50 francs per day for their board and lodging.

Those interested should apply to Francoise Blusson at the above address.

Association de Recherches et Etudes d'Histoire Rurale
Maison du Patrimonie, 21190 Saint-Romain, France (tel 80 21 28 50).

This association is conducting a long term research project on the archaeological, ethnolological and historical development of the Saint-Romain area.

Approximately 40 volunteers per year are needed to work for the month of August. The work consists of digging and restoration. No qualifications or experience are needed, and volunteers may be of any nationality. The minimum age is 17. Pocket money is not provided, but accommodation is available either at the Association's Centre or on a nearby campsite.

Applicants should write to Serge Grappin, the Director, at the above address before May 30th.

Association le Mat
Le Viel Audon, 07120 Balazuc, France (tel 75 37 73 80).

This Association undertakes restoration, reconstruction, farm and agricultural activities at the village of Audon in the Ardeche region of France. Around 300 volunteers are needed each summer to assist with this work, although only groups of 80 people can be catered for at any one time. Volunteers can choose their daily task from those offered as long as they work at least five hours per day.

Volunteers should be 17 — 25 years old. Camping areas are provided and some beds are available but volunteers must pay for food (about £4 daily), £1 for insurance and a joining fee of around £5.

Those interested should contact the Co-ordinator at the above address for more information.

Association des Paralyses de France
17 Boulevard Blanqui, Paris 13, France (tel 1-40 78 69 00).

The Association needs some 1,500 volunteers each year to help in its work with people suffering from paralysis. Much of the work is a matter of helping the handicapped get around, i.e. pushing wheelchairs, etc. and assisting the handicapped when they go on holiday usually in specially organized groups.

Volunteers may be of any nationality, but must be at least 18 years old and enjoy good health. Boys who can speak at least a little French are especially needed. Expenses and pocket money are paid. The length of time volunteers work for is a month on the holidays. No special qualifications are needed.

Applications should be made to the Holiday Officer at the above address.

Centre Nationale de la Recherche Archeologiques

1 Place Artistide Briand, 92190 Meudon, France (tel 1 45 07 50 04; fax 1 45 07 58 99).

This organization is undertaking an archaeological excavation at Verberie in France. The aim of this project is to reconstruct the everyday life and economy of the reindeer hunters who inhabited the area by excavating an open air site consisting of structures and hearths. Around fourteen volunteers are needed in July and the first half of August to assist with the diggings and to be trained in fine excavation techniques. Volunteers are normally recruited for three week periods.

Volunteers with archaeological experience are preferred. They must be able to speak some French and the minimum age limit is 18 years. Board, lodging and insurance are provided, but special diets cannot be catered for.

Applications should be sent to Francoise Adouze at the above address.

Chantiers d'Etudes Medievales

4 Rue Du Tonnelet Rouge, 67000 Strasbourg, France (tel 8837 17 20).

These workcamps lasting between 10 and 15 days undertake to restore and maintain mediaeval buildings and sites. The projects include two fortified chateaux at Ottrott near Strasbourg and another castle Petit Koenigsburg near Selestat. These sites become cultural and recreational centres. Food and basic accommodation in tents or huts are provided for the volunteers on payment of fees which vary between £38 and £53 per session. Apart from preserving historically important buildings and converting them into places which will benefit the community the Chantiers d'Etudes Medievales also aims to provide the participants with cultural enrichment and physical exercise.

Applicants of all nationalities will be accepted for the 250 places available each year. The minimum age limit is 16 years although applicants under the age of 18 require parental permission.

Enquiries should be sent to the Secretary at the above address.

Chantiers de Jeunes: Provence/Cote d'Azur

La Ferme Giaume, 7 Ave. Pierre de Coubertin, 06150 Cannes, La Bocca, France (tel 93 47 89 69).

This organization provides voluntary activity holidays for teenagers between the ages of 14 and 18 on the island of St. Marguerite. 30 different holidays are held on the island each year, each one consisting of 15 teenagers. Volunteers work on the restoration of historic buildings for five hours in the mornings, while sport and a wide range of activities take place in the afternoons and evenings. Volunteers are expected to help with general domestic chores as well. Each holiday lasts for 15 days, and food and accommodation are provided. The cost is 1,900 francs.

Applicants of all nationalities are welcome. Please apply to Lavier Bouniol at the above address.

Club Du Vieux Manoir
10 Rue de la Cossonnerie, 75001 Paris, France (tel 1-45 08 80 40).

This non-profit making association is dedicated to the rescue and restoration of endangered monuments and historical sites. Each year 4,000 volunteers contribute to the preservation of France's heritage and at the same time accquire manual and technical skills as well as some knowledge of archaeology and history. Apart from working on a site, club members may take part in research, publication or committee work. There are three permanent sites: at Guise in the province of Aisne, at Argy in Indre and at Pontjoint in Oise.

Volunteers are invited to arrive at any time provided they come equipped with sleeping bag and camp cooking utensils. Special arrangements can be made for groups of scouts, factory employees and children from holiday camps. There are several summer vacation sites throughout the country at which the minimum length of stay is 15 days. Participants must pay 55-60 francs per day for their board and lodging, which may entail accommodation in the monument itself.

All volunteers must be very fit. Initial membership in the Club de Vieux Manoir costs 70 francs. The minimum age is normally 14; however, at the centre for specialized courses in restoration at the Chateau d'Argy, the minimum age is 17. All nationalities may participate.

Further details may be obtained by sending a stamped self-addressed envelope to Therese Beckelynck, Animatrice Permante, at the above address.

College Cevenol (International Workcamp)
Chambon-sur-Lignon 434000, Haute Loire, France (tel 71 59 72 52).

This workcamp takes place for three weeks in July each year at the College Cevenol International in the Massif Central. The surrounding country is wooded and mountainous and provides an invigorating setting for the camp activities.

The present school at Chambon-sur-Lignon has been partly built by workcamps held at the site, and in fact it is this construction work, landscaping and maintenance with forms the work done in the summer. The camps may also offer language classes for foreigners run by the campers themselves. In the evenings discussion groups meet or those who wish to can use the time for relaxation. Some outings are organized in the area. It will suit those who like a bracing experience, and mixing with young people of all nationalities. Volunteers should be aged between 16 and 30 years, and in good health. Accommodation is provided at the school itself, food is provided, and all other facilities. The participation fee is about 815 francs. Campers are expected to join in all group activities. All nationalities are welcome. The volunteers may go, at a very reduced price, on the Discovery trip of France organised by the College at the end of the Workcamp. Application forms can be obtained from Monsieur le Directeur du College Cevenol, Camp International de Travail, at the above address.

Les Compagnons du Cap
Pratcoustals, 30120 Arphy, France (tel 67 81 82 22).

Les Compagnons du Cap organize the rebuilding and restoration of a small village in France that was abandoned fifty years ago. Volunteers, from France and abroad, are needed to help with dry-stone walling, rejointing and re-roofing. There are also opportunities for voluntary work in a nearby forest, garden and on the fruit-trees. While adult volunteers are engaged entirely on the restoration, volunteers aged between 14 and 17 years can participate in a programme that combines the restoration work with other activities such as mountain biking.

It would be useful for participants to know some French. Participants can come for more than a fortnight at any time of the year; board and lodging are provided. However, pocket money is not provided and volunteers must pay for their own travel expenses.

Those interested should write to the above address or to Union REMPART, 1 rue des Guillemites, 75004 Paris, France.

CONFLUENCE — Enfants et Amis de Beauchastel
Rue de la Breche, 07800 Beauchastel, France (tel 78-84-70-30).

CONFLUENCE oversees the restoration of a medieval village; about 100 volunteers are needed every summer for two weeks to help with many jobs including masonry, carpentry, roof and floor tiling, paving and cooking. Applicants of any nationality may apply, and no experience is needed but some knowledge of French would be useful. Volunteers will be given accommodation in a village schoolroom; they must pay for their own travel costs and a participation fee to cover insurance, board and accommodation.

Apply to Christian Coulet at the above address.

The Department of Archaeology and Prehistory (The Auvergne Survey)
Sheffield University, Sheffield S10 2TN (tel 0742-78555).

The Department is conducting archaeological excavations and fieldwork mainly in the Auvergne in France around Clemont Ferrand. The objective is to learn more about the origin and development of urbanization in the area in the 2nd and 1st centuries BC and its impact on rural settlement, and the interaction between man, settlement and environment in post-glacial times.

30-40 volunteers are needed to help the Department's own students with excavation, processing of finds and surveying. The excavations normally take place from July to September, and participants should be prepared to stay for at least three to four weeks. Accommodation is provided on a camp site, and meals are taken at the camp base, a late medieval house, at a cost of 35 francs a day.

Those interested should write to Professor J. R. Collis at the above address.

Department d'Histoire Universite
Avenue O. Messiaen, 72 017 Le Mans, France (tel 43 83 31 63).

About 20 volunteers are required for three weeks in July or August to assist in the archaeological excavation of a 10th-12th century motte and bailey castle of the Counts of Champagne at Chavot-Epernay. Volunteers of all nationalities are welcome but they should be able to speak French or English, be in good health and at least 18 years old.

Accommodation is provided, and those who have archaeological experience receive free meals. Others must pay for the evening meal.

Applications should be sent to Annie Renoux at the above address.

Etudes et Chantiers (UNAREC)
33 rue Campagne Premiere, 75014 Paris, France (tel 331 453-89626; fax 331 432-28636).

UNAREC is involved in both short-term conservation projects during the school holidays and long-term projects for professional training throughout the year. UNAREC also organizes short-term volunteer exchanges with 30 countries.

About 800 volunteers every year are needed for both short and long term projects, to help with conservation and building work, to lead groups and to take part in international exchanges. Applicants can be of any nationality. Those applying for posts as group leaders need an international driving licence and knowledge of French. Those aged between 14 and 17 years can volunteer for teenage workcamps, for which camp fees have to be paid. Those over 17 years of age can apply to join youth workcamps, for which there are no camp fees. Projects last for 2-4 weeks. No pocket money is provided. Accommodation and insurance is provided; European volunteers must bring an E111 form. For workcamps in France there is an application fee of 500 francs; 700 francs for workcamps abroad.

For further information please contact Francois Ribauld at the above address.

France Mission Trust
The Old Chapel, Chapel Lane, Minchinhampton, Gloucester GL6 9DL (tel 0453-884454).

This Trust offers volunteer opportunities in France to evangelical Christians. Volunteers may join evangelistic teams during Easter and summer vacations, undertake building and decorating of church properties or perform bi-lingual secretarial work. Around 20 volunteers are recruited annually; team members usually serve a minimum of two weeks while other volunteers work for a maximum of two years.

Volunteers must be at least 18 years old and of normal health. Evangelistic team members must speak conversational French and pay for their travel, insurance and board, although accommodation is provided. Other volunteers need to be skilled and experienced in the appropriate field and must pay for their travel and insurance but receive free board and lodging.

British residents should apply to the British Director at the above address while other volunteers should apply to France Mission, 22 avenue Saint Monde, 75012 Paris, France.

Groupe Archaeologique du Mesmontois
Marie de Macain, 21410 Pont de Pany, France (tel 80 30 05 20).

The organization undertakes archaeological digs and restoration work near Dijon, France. About 40 volunteers are needed to help with tasks which include sketching and photographing the finds, model making and restoration. The digs last from one to eight weeks and are held during July and August.

Volunteers skilled in any of the above areas are especially welcome but no qualifications or skills are obligatory. The minimum age of volunteers accepted is 17 years. Volunteers pay about £10 per week towards the board and lodging provided.

Those interested should apply to M. Roussel at the above address.

Labo Anthropologie: UPR 403 du C.N.R.S.
Campus de Beaulieu, 35042 Rennes Cedex, France (tel 99 28 61 09).

This project is concerned with archaeological digs in Brittany, France. Around 60 volunteers are needed to take part in the digs held during the summer each year. Volunteers should be at least 18 years old, physically capable of undertaking outdoor work and interested in archaeology. Camping and board are provided.

Those interested should apply to Dr. J. L. Monnier at the above address.

Laboratoire d'Archeologie — Universite
Avenue O. Messiaen, 72017, le Mans, France (tel 43 83-3163; fax 43 83-3144).

The Laboratoire is undertaking the archaeological excavation of a chateau that belonged to the Counts of Champagne between the tenth and thirteenth centuries. The chateau is situated in Chavot, near Epernay and Reims in Champagne, France. Approximately 20 volunteers per year help with the excavation; the minimum length of stay is three weeks.

Volunteers help both with the digging and the recording of archaeological finds which includes their cleaning, numbering and eventually sketching. Applicants of all nationalities are welcome, but knowledge of English or French is essential. Volunteers must also be interested in history and archaeology, as well as being in good health. The minimum age is 18 years. Volunteers are needed throughout July until the beginning of August. Free board and accommodation are provided but volunteers from overseas must pay for their own travel to and from France.

Those interested should contact Annie Renoux at the above address.

Ministere de la Culture
Direction de l'Archeologie, 4 Rue d'Aboukir, 75002 Paris, France (tel 40 15 73 00).

The Ministry compiles an annual list of archaeological excavations requiring volunteers in France. The list is drawn up during spring for that summer season. Around 10,000 volunteers are needed in total, as assistants in all aspects of archaeological excavations for periods of two weeks to one month. The minimum age of volunteers accepted is usually 18 years. No special skills are needed for most teams but some leaders may require experienced volunteers. Accommodation in houses or at campsites is provided.

Write to the Information Scientist of Excavations to receive a list.

Ministere de la Culture et de la Communication
Direction Regionale des Affaires Culturelles, Service Regional de l'Archeologie, 6 Rue de Chapitre, 35044 Rennes Cedex, France (tel 99 84 59 00).

This Ministry organizes archaeological excavations in Brittany. About 200 volunteers are needed each year to assist with all aspects of the excavations. The excavations occur mainly from April to September for periods of two to four weeks and cover from prehistoric times to the Middle Ages.

Volunteers must be at least 18 years old, need a basic knowledge of French and those with practical archaeological or related experience are welcome. Good health and an anti-tetanus injection are essential. Accommodation is provided.

Write to the Director at the above address for detailed information on the sites, enclosing an International Reply Coupon.

Museum National d'Histoire Naturelle
Institut de Paleontologie Humaine, 1 Rue Rene Panhard, 75013 Paris, France.

The Professor at this museum organizes archaeological excavations in France each year from April to August. Volunteers are required to assist with these excavations and they should be prepared to stay for the duration of the camp which is between two weeks and one month. There is a camping site but volunteers must provide their own tents, etc. They must also pay their own travelling expenses although expenses will be paid while at the camp.

Further information can be obtained from Henry de Lumley at the above address.

La Riobe
c/o J. P. Burin, President, 4 Rue Jobbe Duval, 75015 Paris, France (tel 01-48 28 87 05).

In August La Riobe organizes an archaeological dig lasting for two weeks on a Gallo-Roman site 72 km to the east of Paris; for the rest of the year work is conducted over the weekends. The work to be done includes digging, cleaning and restoring the finds and organizing a collection of finds. Around 20 volunteers help in the summer workcamp, and between 60 and 70 in all take part in the weekend camps.

Participants should be aged 18 or over and speak enough French to make themselves understood. They should also possess proof that they have had an anti-tetanus injection. They must also pay around 15 francs for insurance and 35 francs a day towards their food.

For further details contact Mr J. P. Burin, President, at the above address.

SADRAH (Societè Alpine de Documentation et de Recherche en Archeologie Historique)
Centre d'Archeologie, Musee Dauphinois, Montee de Chalemont, 3800 — Grenoble, France (tel 76 86 72 87).

SADRAH organizes a wide range of voluntary archaeological and construction work camps dedicated to the preservation of the cultural heritage of the Grenoble area. Recent projects have included the excavation of a medieval chateau and an ancient episcopal palace.

Volunteers work full-time, usually with Sundays off. Food and accommodation is provided on all the work camps, though volunteers must pay a fee which ranges from £3-£8 , and the minimum length of placement ranges from 1 to 5 weeks depending on the camp. The camps run during summer months from July to the end of September, and the minimum age is 18 years. Volunteers must speak good French and have previous experience on archaeological excavations. Motivation and interest are essential.

For an up-to-date list of SADRAH's work camps please contact Chantal Mazard, Conservateur du Patrimoine, at the above address (preferably in French).

Service Archaeologique du Musee de la Chartreuse
191 Rue St-Aubin, 59500 Douai, France (tel 27 96 90 60; fax 27 96 90 75).

This organization conducts archaeological excavations in the medieval town of Douai. Volunteers are needed to assist with the excavations and drawing of maps. Workcamps generally consist of 150 volunteers for a minimum of 15 days during the months of July and August. All volunteers are welcome provided that they speak English or French and are at least 18 years old. No special skills are necessary but volunteers with experience may be able to obtain a staff position. Innoculation against tetanus is advisable.   Accommodation is provided and staff receive expenses and pocket money. A registration fee of £10 to cover insurance costs must be submitted with the application form.

Contact the Director at the above address for more details.

Service Archeologique d'Arras
80 rue Meaulens Prolongèe, 6200 Arras, France (tel 21 50 86 32).

This organization carries out archeological research on the sanctuary of Attis and the Byzantine barracks of the ancient town of Nemetacum. About 30 volunteers per year help with the excavations, and with the washing and cataloguing of the archaeological finds.

No special skills and/or qualifications are required. The minimum age limit is 18 years, the maximum is 30. The minimum period for which volunteers are normally recruited is 15 days between July and August. No expenses are paid, and pocket money is not provided. Volunteers will be provided with accommodation..

Those interested should apply to the above address.

Union REMP.ART (pour la Rehabilitation et L'Entretien des Monuments et du Patrimonie Artistique)
1 Rue des Guillemites, 75004 Paris, France (tel 1-42 71 96 55).

Over 150 workcamps are operated by REMP.ART in every part of France. About 4,000 volunteers are employed each year to restore and maintain chateaux, churches, villages and the old quarters of cities which are of unique historical or cultural value. REMP.ART strives to revivify rather than merely preserve ancient buildings and sites. Another of their aims is to remain sensitive to the temperament and requirements of the local community. Volunteers are accepted for weekend workcamps and for spring and summer vacation projects; the usual minimum length of stay is 15 days.

Participants must pay 30 or 40 francs per day for food and accommodation in cabins or tents. For people whose tastes, studies or professional aspirations have prompted an interest in archaeology, architecture or the history of art and ecology, the association organizes courses which provide an opportunity to learn the practical techniques of restoration.

Volunteers of all nationalities are welcome, although knowledge of some French would be an asset. The minimum age is generally 16, but is set at 18 for more difficult jobs.

Applications and enquiries should be sent to the above address.

Germany, Switzerland and Austria

Aktionsgmeinschafts Dienst fur den Frieden (AGDF) (Action Committee Service for Peace)
Blucherstrasse 14, 5300 Bonn, Germany (0228/2291 92; fax 0228/2193 29).

This is an umbrella committee for 24 Christian, peace development and social service organizatiòns within Germany, many of which recruit from around the world. The function of AGDF is primarily a co-ordinating one, acting as liaison between its member organizations, willing volunteers, the government and the Federation of Protestant Churches. Altogether approximately 5,000 persons per year participate in workcamps, work with conscientious objectors and other services supported by the members. The type of work and length of employment varies according to the country of service and the type of volunteer service. There are both short term projects of under three months and longer terms of up to two or three years in development services.

Applications which are sent to the above address will be forwarded to the most appropriate organization. These include Aktionsgemeinschaft Friedenswoche Minden: Aktion Suhnezeichen Friedendikcnste; Eirene, International Christian Service for Peace; Christlicher Friedensdienst (CFD); Versohnungsbund; Welfriendensdienst; and Oekumenisches Begegnungszentrum.

Arbeitskreis Freiwillige Soziale Dienste
Stafflenbergstr. 76, 7000 Stuttgart, Germany (tel 0711-2159 420 417).

This organization, which is somewhat similar to CSV in the UK, organizes volunteer work for one year in the Evangelical Church of Germany. Volunteers work mostly with people who are in difficulty and in need of a helping hand, for example, with ill, handicapped or old people, but work also to a certain extent in kindergartens or homes for children and young people. Throughout the one year's programme there are seminars and discussions led by trained group leaders. Keeping in contact with other people during the practical work and the seminars, gives a chance for each volunteer to increase his personal growth and learning through new experiences.

Volunteers must have a good knowledge of the German language and should be 18 to 25 years of age. Accommodation is provided and social security and pocket money is paid. Volunteers must pay their own travel expenses to and from Germany.

Applications should be sent to the above address, where they will be forwarded to a regional centre. The one year programmes start every summer. Those interested need to apply one year ahead.

Christlicher Friedensdienst Deutscher Zweig e.V.
Rendeler Strasse 9-11, 6000 Frankfurt-Bornheim 60, Germany (tel 069- 459072).

This organization conducts international work camps on ecological and peace projects in Germany for volunteers. Volunteers work in childrens' centres, on conservation projects, etc. which require light manual work and occasionally campaigning activities. Ample time is provided for the discussion of questions which arise from the work and for leisure activities. Workcamps are from two to three weeks long, and take place from June to September and cater for around 200 volunteers.

No special skills are required but a knowledge of English would be beneficial. Volunteers should be at least 18 years old. Board and lodging are provided but volunteers must pay their own travel expenses.

Interested volunteers should contact the above address, who will refer their application to an organization in their own country.

Friedensdorf International (Peace Village International)
Aktion Friedensdorf e.V., Pfeilstr. 35, 4200 Oberhausen 11, Germany (tel 0208 670051-53; fax 0208 675445).

Peace Village International takes up wounded children from wartorn and crisis areas including Afghanistan, Vietnam, Romania, Haiti, Sri Lanka, Lithuania and Jamaica. for medical treatment in German hospitals. After the appropriate treatment the children live in the Peace Village International in Oberhausen for rehabilitation until they return to their native countries and to their families. About 5 volunteers work in the Village every year.

Volunteers are required all the year round to take care of the children in the Peace Village. Duties include the preparation of meals and working in the Village's educational institution. Volunteers may also be needed to help with practical work under the janitor's guidance, which might include general repairs on or to the houses. Applicants of all nationalities are welcome; no special qualifications are needed, but experience as a social worker is desirable. Minimum placement is 3 months. Accommodation and board are provided, but the Peace Village is unable to pay any other costs or expenses. The minimum age limit is 18 years and volunteers must be free from infectious illnesses.

Applications to Ronald Gegenfurtner at the above address.

Gruppo Volontari Della Svizzera Italiana
CP 12, 6517 Arbedo, Switzerland (tel 072 27-4520).

The GVSI is a voluntary group consisting of adults and young people from the Italian part of Switzerland as well as foreign volunteers, that organizes relief programmes in crisis-struck areas and work camps and activities for the handicapped. In 1991-92 GVSI volunteers were engaged on reconstruction and maintenance work in the mountain areas of Fusio and Peccia in Switzerland. Volunteers were provided with accommodation in a house in one of the villages and were expected to help with normal tasks within the community such as helping the aged, cutting wood and working in the stables and orchards. Participants also share daily tasks such as cleaning and cooking. Most volunteers stay in workcamps run from the end of June until September; they must be at least 18 years of age, adaptable hardworking,and must pay their own travel costs.

For more information on GVSI write to Mari Federico at the above address.

Heimsonderschule Brachenreuthe
7770 Uberlingen, Germany (tel 07551-8007-0; fax 07551-8007-50).

This community for handicapped children needs about 15 volunteers, of any nationality, every year to work with children within the community's homes and to help with household chores. Applicants must have a good command of German and the minimum age limit is 19 years of·age. Volunteers can stay for 6 months or a year. Accommodation, board and insurance are all provided plus £100 pocket money per month.

For more information contact the Director at the above address.

IJGD (Internationale Jugendgemeinschaftsdienste Bundesverein eV — Gesellschaft fur Internationale und Politische Bildnung)
Kaiserstr. 43, 5300, Bonn 1, Germany (tel 0228-22 10 01).

IJGD organizes a number of international work camps and workshops in Germany that last for between two and four weeks. The projects include renovating educational centres, assisting with city fringe recreational activities and conservation work. They take place around Easter and from June to the end of September.

Around 1,800 volunteers take part in these schemes every year. Participants should be aged between 16 and 26, and able to do physical work. Food, accommodation and insurance are provided but participants must cover their own travel expenses.

Those interested should contact the Secretary General at the above address.

Involvement Volunteers — Deutschland
Postfach 110224, 3400 Gottingen, Germany (tel/fax 49 551 393-765).

Involvement Volunteers enables people to participate in voluntary activities related to conservation, environmental research, archaeology, history or social welfare. Individual placements or Team Task placements run for 2-12 weeks, some with free accommodation and food, others costing up to £34 per week. Volunteers need to understand and speak some English. Individual placements and/or Team Tasks are available in Germany; in addition, German applicants are placed in Australia, California, Fiji, Hawaii, India, New Zealand and Thailand.

Involvement Volunteers — Deutschland is a non profit organization which charges a fee of approximately £130 to cover administration costs. For volunteers coming to Germany, this fee includes travel and visa advice, arrival advice for suitable accommodation and transport from the airport, and a communication base for the visit.

For further information please contact K. Werner Mayer at the above address.

Osterreichischer Bauorden

Postfach 186, Hornesgasse 3, 1031 Wien, Austria (tel 0222-713 52 54; fax 0222-713 81 18).

Every June, July and August Osterreichischer Bauorden organizes around 15 projects in Austria with aims such as building homes and community centres for the handicapped, the poor, the young and the old, or constructing sports fields, etc. About 250 volunteers a year take part in the projects, which last for between three and four weeks each.   Applicants should be aged 18 — 30. They should have a basic knowledge of German and be willing to do manual work; previous experience of building work would be useful. Participants are given free board and lodging and insurance is arranged.

Those interested should contact the secretary at the above address for an application form.

PRO International

Bahnhofstr. 26A, 3550 Marburg, Germany (tel 49 6421-65277; fax 49 6421-64407).

This organization seeks to rebuild broken relationships between individuals and peoples by the promotion and encouragement of contact between young people from all over the world. To this end, workcamps, seminars and holiday courses are organized in Germany. About 500 volunteers per year participate in these workcamps. Volunteers may work as child-minders or manual workers, while others take part in activities connected with handicapped children, or the environment.

What actually happens in a work camp is dependent largely on the individual volunteer. Applicants of all nationalities are welcome as the camps are intended to be international. It is advisable, however, that applicants should have knowledge of French, German or English. Volunteers must be aged between 16 and 26, although child-minders must be aged over 18. Camps are held at Easter and between June and October and the minimum length of time for which volunteers are normally required is two to three weeks. The participation fee for 1992 was 100 DM, but meals and accommodation are free of charge. The Easter and Summer Programmes, published in February and April respectively, can be obtained from the above address at a cost of 3DM in stamps (or an International Reply Coupon).

Those interested should contact Gerd Pause at the above address.

Vereinigung Junger Freiwilliger eV (VJF)

Unter den Linden 36, Berlin, 1086, Germany (tel 20-340-386; fax 229-20-28).

VJF organizes international workcamps in the former East Germany, as well as co-ordinating exchanges with 40 partner organizations from more than 30 countries. VJF places 500 international volunteers every year, as well as 500 German volunteers.

Most of the workcamps are social or ecological projects, but there are also special programmes which focus on issues such as the history of Jewish people in Germany. In most cases, volunteers have to do easy manual work on the camps. Special workcamps might demand special skills but such requirements will be outlined in the VJF brochure. Volunteers must be aged between 18 and 30 years. Most workcamps take place between May and September and last for two to four weeks. Accommodation is provided, but no expenses are paid. Travel to the camps must be arranged and paid for by individual volunters and volunteers must pay an application fee of $120.

Applications should be sent to the above address.

Scandinavia

Atlantis Youth Exchange
Rolfe Hofmosgate 18, 0655 Oslo, Norway (tel 02-670043).

Atlantis is a non-profit making foundation for international youth exchange, recruiting about 500 young people each year to work in Norway on the Working Guest Programme. Working Guests stay with Norwegian families, and although must of the work is agricultural, volunteers may also be involved with the day to day running of the household and helping with the children. The programme is quite energetic and there are opportunities for travel to Northern Norway. The minimum stay is four weeks, the maximum three months. Families tend to prefer that the Working Guests stay for at least eight weeks.

Volunteers do not require any special skills, but farm experience is an advantage. If Norwegian is not spoken, the recruit should consider the possible problems of isolation and communication this may cause. However, most Norwegians speak English so knowledge of Norwegian is not compulsory though, of course, it is an advantage. The volunteer should be aged between 18 and 30 and will require a medical certificate and references. Board and lodging are provided, and pocket money is a minimun of Kr 500 a week.

Further details and application forms may be obtained from the Working Guest Manager, Working Guest Programme, at the above address.

Foreningen Staffansgarden
Box 66, Furugatan 1, 82060 Delsbo, Sweden (tel 0653-16850; fax 0653-10968).

Foreningen Staffansgarden is a community for mentally handicapped adults in Sweden. Between five and ten volunteers work in the community every year. A volunteer can help in many ways, including working in the bakery and the garden, weaving, farming, cooking and cleaning or merely by participating in daily life with the handicapped adults.

Applicants of all nationalities are welcome as long as they have a genuine desire to live communally with other people. The minimum age limit is 19 years and the minimum length of placement is six months, although it would be preferred if volunteers stayed for one year. For the first six months, expenses and pocket money are paid, and after that a small wage is paid. Accommodation is provided.

Applications should be made to Per Iversen at the above address.

Kansainvalinen Vapaaehtoinen Tyoleirijarjestory (KVT: Finnish Branch of Service Civil International)
Rauhanasema, Veturitori, 00520 Helsinki, Finland (tel 358 0 144 408/144 418).

The aims of KVT are, through the co-operation of young people, to contribute to international peace and friendship and to make people aware of their social responsibilities and act to abolish social injustice. To put these aims into practice KVT arranges voluntary workcamps for young people of different nationalities, runs meetings, seminars, and discussion groups and keeps in touch with organizations with similar aims in Finland and other countries. It has been the Finnish brance of SCI (Service Civil International) since 1981.

About 300 volunteers are recruited anually by the organization, of whom two thirds are Finns. Camps last from two to four weeks. The minimum age for most camps is 18 years. A basic knowledge of English is necessary and some camps may need special qualifications. All nationalities are recruited and visas or work permits are not needed. Board and lodging are always provided by KVT or the organization the work is done for, as is insurance. Travel expenses and pocket money are not paid.   Non-Finnish volunteers should apply to the SCI in their own Country. For the UK the address is IVS, 162 Upper New Walk, Leicester LE1 7QA.

Mellemfolkeligt Samvirke (MS)
Training Department, Borgergade 14, 1300 Copenhagen K., Denmark.

Besides arranging for the participation of about 900 Danes in workcamps abroad every year, MS also organizes international workcamps in Denmark, Greenland and the Faroe Islands which are open to foreign volunteers. The main objective of these workcamps is to bring participants into contact with the social problems found in every society. The camps also provide an opportunity for young people from all over the world to live and work together with the local inhabitants.

Camps in Denmark consist of an extensive range of projects such as environmental camps, nature conservation work/study camps, etc. Many camps in Denmark are open to disabled persons. In Greenland, the camps are organized in small settlements where the participants renovate buildings, build new sheep pens, etc. In the Faroe Islands the projects comprise construction of playgrounds and community centres.

The minimum age limit for participation is 18 and the volunteers must be willing to spend two to three weeks in a camp during July and August. Food, accommodation and insurance is provided but the volunteers must pay their own travelling expenses.

Applications from British people should be made through IVS.

The Swallows in Denmark
Osterbrogade 49, 2100 Copenhagen O, Denmark (tel 3526-747).

The Swallows provide financial support for organizations in India and Bangladesh by collecting old furniture and clothes and selling the goods at flea markets. During the summer, the Swallows conduct workcamps for international volunteers to assist with these tasks. Around 15 volunteers are needed each year to stay one, two or three weeks.

Volunteers must be either at least 18 years old or accompanied by an adult. English speaking volunteers are preferred. Board and accommodation and provided but volunteers must pay for their own travel expenses.

Applicants should apply to the Co-ordinator at the above address.

Nansen International Childrens Centre
Barnegarden, Breivold, Nesset, 1400 Ski, Norway (tel 02/94 67 15).

Breivold is a long term relief centre for teenagers ranging in age from 13 to 18 with deep social and emotional needs. It is situated on a renovated farm 25 km from Oslo. Help is needed in all aspects of the centre. Applicants with skills of a practical nature and with initiative to tackle and follow through ideas with the minimum of supervision are needed. Domestic and farm work is also included in the rota and all volunteers take turns with cooking. Cleaning duties and the care of the animals are part of the daily routine at Breivold. There are many opportunities for sports, hobbies, etc. and all the leaders are expected to stimulate the youths in all areas of life. The most important aspect of the work is to motivate the participation of the youths and to prepare them for the future.

Volunteers at Breivold must be prepared to work very hard, the hours being long and very tiring. Volunteers should preferably be over 22 years old, drivers and with some experience of working with young people. Volunteers receive full board and lodging and 500 NKR per week. Applicants are expected to stay for at least six months, preferably for one year. There is also a special summer programme which lasts for six weeks and for this applicants must apply before April. It takes between three and six months to process the necessary work permits.

Send an international reply coupon for all correspondence otherwise a reply cannot be guaranteed. Apply to the Director at the above address.

World Assembly of Youth (WAY)
Ved Bellahoj 4, 2700 Bronshoj, Denmark (tel 3160-7770; fax 3160-5797).

WAY promotes youth participation in all walks of life. 40-50 volunteers, of all nationalities, are provided experience in international youth work every year by becoming part of the WAY Secretariat. Knowledge of written and spoken English is essential; knowledge of Spanish and/or French is not required but would be a bonus. Applicants should also have some experience of word processing. The maximum age limit is 35. The usual length of placement is 6-12 months and volunteers are required all the year round. Accommodation is provided in a two-room apartment, to be shared with one other volunteer. An allowance of $50 per month is also provided to cover living expenses.

For further information please contact Mr Shiv Khare at the above address.

Spain, Portugal, Italy and Cyprus

Agape Centro Ecumenico
1-10060 Prali, Torino, Italy (tel 0121-80 75 14)

Agape is an ecumenical conference centre in the Italian Alps for national and international meetings. It was built by an international group of volunteers between 1947 and 1951 as an act of reconciliation after the war, and is sponsored by the World Council of Churches. Each year 12 volunteers help the permanent staff to run the centre which is especially active over the summer. The jobs to be done include working in the kitchen and laundry, cleaning, running the coffee bar and general maintenance work. Volunteers normally work six hours per day, six days per week for periods of at least one month, mostly in the summer but sometimes also in Spring and Autumn.

Applicants must be aged over 18, and would find knowledge of more than one language an advantage. Free board and lodging are provided, but participants must cover their own travel costs to and from the centre.

For further details contact the Secretary at the above address.

Centro Camuno di Studi Preistorici
25044 Capo di Ponte, Brescia, Italy (tel 364-42091; fax 364-42572).

This Centro is a research institute concentrating on the study of prehistory and primitive art, mainly in Asia and Africa. and run by a non profit making cultural association. Up to ten volunteers a year are needed to participate in the exploration of sites in surrounding Valcamonica and to help with laboratory work, research, mapping bibliographical work and computerising data in the centre both for local research work and for the expeditions abroad. The field-work in the Alpine area takes place mostly in the summer, but the centre itself is open around the year.

Volunteers are taken on for an initial period of three months. Board and accommodation are not provided but assistance is given in finding cheap basic accommodation. A few scholarships are available; candidates are selected after the initial trial period of three months. Volunteers must be aged over 18 and be deeply interested in archaeology, primitive art, anthropology or the history of religions, but formal qualifications are not necessary.

Those interested should contact the above address for further details.

Deya Archaeological Museum and Research Centre
Deya, Mallorca, Balleares, Spain (tel/fax 34 71-639001)

DAMARC has been excavating in Mallorca for the past thirty years. The 1992 season was spent at the Copper Age site of Son Ferrandell-Oleza and the pre-Roman site of Son Mas. Volunteers join a team of specialists and other participants from the US and various European countries for two-week sessions. Participants work together in the field and laboratory and live together in the Research Centre.

Accommodation is provided in dormitories of six to eight bunk beds. Meals are home-cooked and participants help in preparation and household chores on a rotational basis. Volunteers must be students of archaeology or mature persons with an interest in expanding their learning and experience in prehistory, especially that of the Balearic Islands. DAMARC is not able to pay for the volunteer's travel costs or room and board. Volunteers must pay £280 to participate in any of the two-week excavations, covering room, board and tuition, and participants should also ensure that they have medical insurance for Spain. Volunteers must also be physically fit.

Those interested should contact William H. Waldren for more information at the above address.

Gruppi Archeologici d'Italia
Via Tacito 41, 00193 Roma, Italy (tel/fax 6896981).

This organization arranges archaeological workcamps at sites in Italy. Between June and September around 1,000 volunteers of any nationality are needed to assist with the excavations. The workcamps are for a minimum of two weeks but the exact period may vary for different sites.

Volunteers experienced in the techniques of excavation work are preferred but unskilled volunteers will be accepted. A certificate of vaccination against tetanus is required upon arrival at the workcamp and volunteers should be at least 16 years old. The fee for attending the camps varies between £122 and £180 but always includes full board and accommodation at a local youth hostel.

Enquiries should be sent to the Secretary for Foreign Volunteers at the above address.

Instituto da Juventude
Av. da Liberdade 194, 1100 Lisboa, Portugal (tel 3151955; fax 3151960).

IJ organizes around 37 international workcamps in Portugal each summer. About 740 volunteers are needed to assist with construction and reconstruction work, protection of the natural environment and the protection and restoration of Portugal's cultural heritage. The workcamps last for around 2 weeks. No special skills are required to join a workcamp but volunteers must be aged 18 — 25 years old. Board and lodging are provided.

The workcamps programme is usually issued in February or March. Prospective volunteers should apply to their national branch of International Voluntary Service.

Instituto de la Juventud 'Servicio Voluntario Internacional'
Calle Orgtega y Gasset 71, Madrid 6, Spain.

This organization arranges summer workcamps in Spain which involve archaeological excavations, the reconstruction of monuments, the preservation of the countryside, building work, nature studies and community work. About 2,000 volunteers take part in the camps each year which last from two to three weeks. There are no restrictions or special skills required. Board and lodging are provided.

Those interested should apply to the address above, or if possible to an affiliated organization in their own country. These include: Mouvement des Jeunes pour la Paix, 92 rue Stevrin, 1040 Bruxelles, Belgium; Mellemfolkeligt Samvirke, Hejrevej 38, DK 2400 Copenhagen NV, Denmark; Internationale Begegnung in Gemeinschaftsdiensten e V, 7252 Weil der Stadt Marklingen, Haupstrasse 64, Germany; Concordia, 28 Rue du Pont Neuf, 775001 Paris, France; United Nations Association (Wales), Welsh Centre for International Affairs, Temple of Peace, Cathays Park, Cardiff CF1 3AP.

Turkey, Greece and Malta

American Farm School (Summer Work Activities Program)
1133 Broadway 26th Street, New York, NY 10010, USA (tel 212-463 8433).

Every summer from early June to July the farm school organizes an international group of about 20 people to help man the agricultural and maintenance programmes at the school when regular staff and students are on vacation. The work involves a 35 hour week; a small allowance is paid. Other activities include a climb up Mount Olympus, trips into Thessaloniki and the islands, as well as a short stay with a family in a rural village. Accommodation and meals are provided by the school. Participants should be 18 — 26 years of age and are expected to pay their own fare to Thessaloniki.

Further information is available from the Program Co-ordinator at the above address.

Genctur Turizm ve Seyahat Acentasi Ltd
Yerebatan Cad., No: 15/3,34410 Sultanahmet, Istanbul, Turkey (tel 1-526 54 09/1-512 04 57).

Genctur organizes international workcamps in Turkish villages involving manual work such as constructing schools, village centres, digging water trenches, forestry, etc. Study tours, camp-tours, special interest tours and Turkish language courses are also arranged. No work permits are required but volunteers from socialist countries and Sweden need visas. English is the main language in the workcamps but some German and French is also spoken.

Approximately 600 volunteers a year attend the camps, which last for two weeks between June and September. The minimum age is 18 and the maximum is 35. Board and lodging are provided but volunteers must pay an inscription fee of £30. Genctur also arranges cheap accommodation and travel for young people and students and provides a tourist information service.

Those interested should apply to the address above or if possible to a workcamp organisation in their own country.

Malta Youth Hostels Association
MYHA Head Office, 17 Tal-Borg Street, Pawla PLA 06, Malta (tel 356-239361/693957).

MYHA operates the MYHA Workcamps Scheme which gives people the opportunity to learn about the country while spending some of their time doing voluntary work. This involves spending around 21 hours a week doing office work, building, decorating and administration work in Malta's youth hostels.

There are no set hours of work, but participants are expected to put in a full 21 hours per week. They will normally work either from the 1st to the 15th or the 16th to the 31st of each month. Applicants may apply for periods of two to 12 weeks. Free accommodation and breakfast are provided. No special qualifications or experience are required, but volunteers are expected to put a reasonable amount of effort into their work.   For further details and an application form send two International Reply Coupons to the above address.

Silatur
Emek Ishani (Gokdelen), Kat: 11, No: 1109, Kizilay, Ankara, Turkey (tel 4-0418 13 26).

Silatur operate voluntary work camps in Turkey involving construction, gardening and environmental projects. The camps last for three weeks and take place in the summer, from June to September, with between 15 and 20 volunteers on each camp. Participants should be aged between 18 and 26; no particular qualifications, skills or experience are needed although good health is required. No registration fee is charged and people of all nationalities are welcome. Volunteers are also invited to help in Silatur's office for periods of three weeks at any time of year. Volunteers receive free food while on the camp, and are occasionally given some partial help with their travelling expenses.

Those interested should contact the above address for Silatur's annual workcamp programme.

North, Central and South America

The African-American Institute
833 UN Plaza, New York, NY 10017, USA (tel 212-949-5666).

There are opportunities for approximately four volunteers per year at AAI's New York and Washington offices to work with with a variety of AAI programmes including Liberia Watch, Women in Development and the magazine Africa Report.

Since AAI is a multi-ethnic, multi-racial organization, applicants of all nationalities are welcomed, but volunteers are usually students at college or university. The jobs open to volunteers depend on the applicant's qualifications and training. For further details write to Dr. Jane Martin at the above address.

Alderson Hospitality House
PO Box 579, Alderson, WV 24910 USA (tel 304 445-2980).

The Alderson Hospitality House provides hospitality to people visiting the federal prison for women in Alderson, West Virginia. The small community in the House believes in the importance of visiting prisoners and strives to encourage visitors by meeting their needs. Two volunteers are required to help with general housekeeping duties, gardening and the maintenance of the largeguest room house and its 11 guest rooms. The volunteers are responsible for making the house welcoming and attractive to guests. Assistance may be required from volunteers with the House's work on furthering human rights, writing applications for grants and raising funds

Volunteers are required for either periods of from three to six months at any time of year or for twelve months. Board and lodging are provided, along with a small monthly allowance. Applicants must speak English, and a knowledge of Spanish would be helpful; a sense of humour and a warm, outgoing personality are also essential. It is preferable that applicants should be good at house repairs, typing, cooking and working with computers. A driving licence would also be helpful. Applications should be made to John M. Parfitt at the above address.

American Friends Service Committee
1501 Cherry Street, Philadelphia, Pennsylvania, USA.

The AFSC is a Quaker organization supported by individuals who care about peace, social injustice and humanitarian service. At the moment it runs two Summer Programs in Mexico and Cuba. The Mexican Program lasts for seven weeks, while the Cuban Program lasts for three weeks. About thirty volunteers are needed in all for both camps.

On either project, participants live as a group, often in a school or unused building lent by the local community, and all share in the project's work and maintenance tasks. Work can be strenuous, and participants should be prepared to respond positively to the unexpected. For both Programs, applicants should be between 18 and 28 years old, mature, open-minded and fluent in Spanish since the project language is Spanish at all times. For the Cuban Summer Program applicants with community or church activist experience are preferred. The participation fee for the Cuban Program is $250.

For the Mexican Program, participants must pay $700 which covers orientation, food, lodging, and transportation during the project, plus insurance. For both Programs, volunteers must pay for their own travel costs.

Applications should be sent to the Personnel Department at the above address.

American Hiking Society Volunteer Programme
PO Box 20160, Washington, DC 20041-2160, USA (tel 0703-385 3252).

Thousands of volunteers are needed annually to maintain American trails, as well as helping as fire lookouts, campground hosts, historical researchers, wildlife observers, back-country guides and trail workers. Some of these jobs are especially attractive because of the scenic location or the unusually interesting work; as a result, summer positions are often filled by mid-February, however park and forest managers seek volunteers all the year round and welcome enquiries any time.

Accommodation is sometimes provided, however work is often carried out in remote wilderness areas where camping accommodation is necessary. An international driver's licence, though not necessary, can be useful. Volunteers must be over 16 years of age and prepared for hard work in isolated places. No work permits are needed by foreign volunteers. A directory, *Helping Out In The Outdoors*, listing more than 1,000 of these volunteer jobs in 42 states, is published by the AHS, at a cost of $8.

Enquiries may be sent to the above address.

American Jewish Society for Service
15E 26th Street, New York, NY 10010, USA (tel 212 683-6178).

The Society conducts voluntary work service camps for teenagers in the United States for several weeks, beginning July 1st. 40-60 volunteers are needed to work as counsellors and to help with the camps' construction work for a period of seven weeks. Volunteers of all nationalities may apply. Accommodation is provided, but pocket money is not; applicants must pay $1500 plus their travel costs.

Applications should be made to Henry Kohn, Chairman, at the above address.

Appalachian Mountain Club Trails Conservation Corps
PO Box 298, Gorham, NH 03581, USA (tel 0603-4662721).

The Appalachian Mountain Club is a non-profit-making recreation and conservation group which is responsible for over 1,200 miles of trail in the north-east of the United States, including over 350 miles of the Appalachian National Scenic Trail. Every summer the club sponsors three unique weekly volunteer based camps in NH, MA and NY, as well as ten day service projects in Alaska, Maine and elsewhere. They are are open to individuals, families and other groups. Volunteers work in teams and are given training and tools to enable them to undertake all types of trail, shelter and other work. Over 500 volunteers participate annually.

Volunteers must be at least 18 years old, in good health, willing to learn and work hard with others and have backpacking experience. All volunteers must have their own accident insurance. Room and board are provided but volunteers are charged £25-£30 or more per week towards costs.

For further information contact the Trails Program Director at the above address.

L'Arche Mobile
152 Mobile, 151 South Ann Street, Mobile, Alabama 36604, USA (tel 205 438-2094).

L'Arche is an International Federation of Communities in which people with a mental handicap and those who help them live, work and share their lives together. L'Arche was started in 1964 and there are now over ninety-five communities in over 25 countries. 12-14 Assistants are needed, annually, at the Mobile community, which consists of four homes and a work/day programme for handicapped people.

Duties of assistants include sharing with the manual labour of keeping a home together; cooking, cleaning, yardwork, repairs, etc. Assistants also help people with self-care and community living skills, as well. Shared prayer is a regular part of the life of the Community, although no-one is required to participate. Assistants work in the homes from the rising hour to 10pm, with a 3 hour break in the afternoon. (At the weekend, only a 2 hour break is possible).

Applicants need no special qualifications or professional experience, but they should be aged between 16 and 70 and in reasonably good health. Assistants generally work for 3 months to a year. Board and lodging are provided. Most assistants have private bedrooms, but otherwise share all the living conditions of the handicapped people. No pocket money is provided, but Medical Insurance is provided after one month of the three month trial period is completed. Three weeks vacation are given for the first year; one month per year thereafter.

Those interested should apply, at any time of the year, to Sr. Janet Ahler at the above address.

Association of Volunteers in Protected Areas (ASVO)
10104-100 San Jose, Costa Rica, Central America (tel 506 57-0922; fax 506 23-6963).

Volunteers are needed to live and work with the park guards in the mountains and coastal parks of Costa Rica. The work consists of maintenance (cooking, cleaning, collecting litter, repairing buildings or trails), environmental education and general vigilance and support in case of emergency. Volunteers must be at least eighteen years old and in good physical condition. Fluency in Spanish, and the ability to live in tropical conditions without the comforts of urban life, are essential, as is a respect for the culture and customs of Costa Rica.

Volunteers are needed all year round for a two month commitment. Although successful applicants must pay $350 per month plus airfare, ASVO will provide transport, food, accommodation and materials during their stay.

Applications should be sent to Karla Morales, Manager of the Volunteer Programme, at the above address.

Camphill Village Kimberton Hills
PO Box 155, Kimberton, PA 19442, USA (tel 215 935-0300).

Kimberton Hills is an international community, primarily agricultural, where about half the adults are mentally retarded; life and work in the community is nourished and inspired by Rudolf Steiner's anthroposophy. All adults residing in the community are volunteers.

Volunteers are needed to help with agricultural work of all kinds, and to work in the craft workshops, farm store, bakery, and coffee shop, as well as with housework. Volunteers trained in office and maintenance work are also needed. Almost all the work is with and alongside mentally retarded adults. Preference is given to volunteers who can stay for a minimum of six months, and volunteers are needed all the year round. Applicants may be of any nationality, but it would help to have some initial knowledge of English, plus lots of good will and enthusiasm. Basic living needs are met by the community including medical and dental coverage, as well and board and lodging, and a small amount for pocket money. Travel expenses to and from the community cannot be paid, but vacation expenses will be paid for volunteers staying longer than one year. Help will be given to overseas volunteers in obtaining the necessary visas.

Applicants for the 100 places available each year should write to the Admissions Group at the above address.

Caribbean Volunteer Expeditions
Box 388, Corning, New York 14830, USA (tel 607-962 7846).

Caribbean Volunteer Expeditions takes on between 20 and 80 volunteers a year to document, measure and photograph historic buildings in the Caribbean. The tasks normally take one or two weeks at any time of year.

For further details contact the above address.

Casa Guatemala
14 Calle, 10-63 Zona 10, Guatemala (tel 319408; fax 319408).

Casa Guatemala is a centre which cares for malnourished, abandoned and orphaned children, providing them with a school, a medical clinic and a farm. The centre needs about 100 volunteers per year to perform many different functions. In particular, the clinic needs two volunteers to act as doctor and nurse. They must be graduates in medicine and able to stay for six months. The farm has two green houses; one grows vegetables hydrophonically, the other uses organic methods. A volunteer with knowledge in these fields will be placed in charge of this project and will be in charge of some of the older children.

The school also needs between two and four volunteers to teach English and other subjects to pupils at early secondary level; the teacher for these pupils must be fluent in Spanish. Many other volunteers with experience in childcare are needed to work as nannies in the orphanage. Even though the main duties of the volunteers are very specific, they are also expected to keep an open mind and become involved in the daily life of the centre and its daily chores. This might include taking care of the chickens, pigs, and fish, or helping with the agricultural programs. In exchange for their work and enthusiasm, volunteers are provided with a place to sleep and 3 meals a day. The minimum length of placement is three months. The teachers and agronomist are required for a minimum of one year. Unfortunately, an allowance (of $100 per month) can only be paid to the doctor, teachers and agronomist.

Healthy applicants resident in the UK and over the age of 19 years should contact Michael J Upfield, c/o Caring and Sharing, Market Cottages, Market Street, Hailsham, East Sussex BN27 2AG (tel 0323-846696) for further information. Applicants must meet very strict moral criteria.

Colorado Trail Foundation

548 Pine Song Trail, Golden, Co 80401, USA (tel 303 526-0809).

The Foundation builds and maintains a 500 mile trail built across the Continental Divide which is very remote from civilization. It also recruits volunteers for 2 trail crews for the Colorado MT Club, 2530 Alameda Ave, Denver, Co 80219 USA. 300-500 volunteers are engaged in the building and maintenance of the 500 mile trail. In 1991 there were 25 crews to choose from; some are back-pack, others are 'drive-ins' or 'jeep-ins'. Each crew has a trained leader and consists of about 18 volunteers.

Volunteers are required from the middle of June until the third week in August; work is done when the snow melts in the Rockies. Most volunteers come for one week (Saturday to Saturday), unless they have come a long distance. All projects are one week in duration. Pocket money is not provided but the Foundation provides a base camp which consists of a kitchen, toilets and shower, and food plus all tools and hard hats. Volunteers must bring their own tent, sleeping-bag and pad. Applicants must be over 16 years and in good pysical health as most projects are at high altitudes.

Enquiries to the President of Foundation at the above address.

Coral Cay Conservation Limited

The Sutton Business Centre, Restmoor Way, Wallington, Surrey SM6 7AH (tel 081 669 0011; fax 081 773 9656).

Coral Cay Conservation sends up to thirty fee-paying volunteers per month on expeditions to South Water Cay in Belize. There they learn fish and marine identification in their first week and then participate in two dives a day to carry out survey work. There is no diving on Sundays. The only people sent to Belize to work specifically for CCC, usually on a 6-8 week basis, are Scientific Officers; all other volunteers pay to participate. Volunteers with medical and/or diving experience may be asked to help out as Medical/Diving Officers.

Individuals of all nationalities may apply all year round; all volunteers, whatever their nationality, must attend an interview and have a minimum diving qualification of or equivalent to BS-AC Novice. It is preferable that volunteers should be one of the following; medically trained, students in marine biology or those with marine/tropical biology degrees, carpenters, electricians or builders. All applicants must hold a current and up to date Fitness to Dive certificate or follow guidelines for fitness from a British Sub Aqua Club. Volunteers may stay for one, two or three months. CCC only provide free flight, accommodation and food to Scientific Officers, but accommodation is provided for other volunteers.

Applications to Sally Barnard at the above address.

Council of Voluntary Social Services
14 Cemetery Road, PO Box 435, Belize (tel 73712/74312; fax 501-2-74803 31474).

The Council is a co-ordinating organization serving voluntary organizations in Belize. Between 75-100 volunteers of any nationality are needed to serve on the Council's Board of Directors, as well as serve on ad-hoc and standing committees.

Applicants must have had experience in community and social work and be able to speak English. Placements are from three days to two years, depending on the volunteer. It should be noted that no expenses are paid at all, and no pocket money is provided. Volunteers also have to find their own accommodation.

Those interested should apply all year round to the Executive Director at the above address.

Cuba Solidarity Campaign
Red Rose Club, 129 Seven Sisters Road, London N7 7QG.

The Campaign organizes and selects the British contingent of volunteers for the annual 250-strong Jose Marti International Work Brigade in Cuba. The aim of the brigade is to express solidarity with and to learn about the Cuban revolution. Of the three weeks in Cuba, two weeks are spent working alongside Cubans on local construction and agricultural projects for $4\frac{1}{2}$ days a week. The rest of the time is spent visiting schools, hospitals, factories and other organizations and sightseeing to learn about Cuban society and politics. The timing of the brigade varies from year to year.

Only 25 to 30 people living in Britain and who are committed to learning about a socialist society are selected. Volunteers pay a fee of around £600 which covers the cost of accommodation, food and travel. The centre organizes the required visa.

Write to the Brigade Co-ordinator at the above address for an application form and further information by January 31st.

Fenix Language Institute
Hidalgo 204, Chalchihuites, Zac. 99260, Mexico (tel 492 292-08/287-48 288 54; fax 73 13-01-36).

Fenix is one of Mexico's oldest and most respected Spanish language and Latin American Studies Institutes. The three different campuses (Cuernavaca, Morelos; Chalchihuites, Zacatecas; and Zacatecas City, Zacatecas) offer volunteers a choice of urban and rural settings in northern and central Mexico.

Approximately 240 volunteers come to these campuses every year to participate in a variety of activities ranging from the administrative to the medical. The only qualification needed is a knowledge of Spanish. Placements are usually for a month at any time of the year, and although accommodation is provided, no other expenses are paid. Volunteers would therefore have to raise finances to cover travel and other costs. Fenix has been praised by universities, professionals and teachers for providing one of the most active and communicative approaches to learning Spanish

Applicants of all nationalities should contact Ma. Dolores Diaz at the above address.

Four Corners School of Outdoor Education
East Route, Monticello, Utah 84535 USA (tel 801 587-2156).

The Four Corners School, a non-profit making organization located in Monticello, Utah, provides outdoor education and environmental opportunities within the 160,000 square mile region known as the Colorado Plateau. Its purpose is to increase participants' awareness and sensitivity to the physical and cultural heritage of this rich and varied environment. The School teaches outdoor skills, natural sciences, and land stewardship by creating a community of individuals who share their interests through informal, relaxed, hands-on experiences.

40-50 volunteers take part in these activities every year, assisting at archaeological sites by excavating and cataloguing. Volunteers also help with the counting of Peregrine Falcons on Green River in Utah. No special qualifications are needed as instruction is given by experts in their field. Volunteers under 14 years of age must be accompanied by an adult. Volunteers stay for seven days, and the wide range of activities run through the summer months to the early autumn. Accommodation is provided in tents, and is included in the cost of the programme. No expenses are paid; participants pay a fee which covers the cost of specialist instruction, food and permits. Travel costs to Utah must also be paid.

Applicants of all nationalities should contact Nancy Carr at the above address.

Friends Weekend Workcamp Program
1515 Cherry Street, Philadelphia, PA 19102, USA.

This organization offers short term projects (2-10 days), within inner city Philadelphia which combine physical work with discussions on urban poverty.

Approximately 200-250 volunteers are engaged annually, mainly between October and May, on a variety of work projects including painting, plastering and cleaning homes, work with senior citizens and outdoor community projects. All nationalities are welcome but must speak English and be at least 15. Board and lodging are provided on the workcamps but each volunteer is asked for a donation of $35 per weekend. Opportunities are also available for long-term service, but accommodation is not normally available for these.

Those interested should apply to the Programme Organizer at the above address.

Frontiers Foundation
2615 Danforth Avenue, Suite 203, Toronto, Ontario, Canada, M4C 1L6 (tel 416-690 3930; fax 416-690 3934).

The Foundation organizes workcamps which take place mainly during the summer months. The scheme involves sending five or eight volunteers to a low income community in Canada: these tend to be Indian communities in isolated northern areas. Under the leadership of one of their number, the volunteers live together as a group, and work with the local people on the construction either of housing or community buildings. There are about 100 participants a year in these projects; they may be of any nationality, so the Foundation has adopted a policy of 'mixing' to prevent any one nationality from dominating the programme.

All applicants must be over 18, and produce a doctor's certificate which states that they are capable of performing manual work in an isolated area. The minimum period of work is 12 weeks. All living and travel expenses inside Canada are paid, and, in addition, pocket money is provided for those who serve for longer than the minimum period.

Applicants should write to Marco A Guzman, Programme Co-ordinator at the above address.

Genesis II Cloud Forest

Apdo 655, 7050 Cartago, Costa Rica, Central America.

This organization is responsible for preserving a cloud forest in the mountains of Costa Rica (altitude 2,360 metres) for bird-watching, recreation and academic research. Volunteers are needed to help with the system of trails which are continuously being expanded and improved and other related work. Tasks include trail work, gardening, reforestation, transplanting and fence construction. Volunteers work for six hours per day, five days per week.

Around five volunteers are needed annually for a minimum period of one month. Volunteers must pay a donation to the project of US$10 per week which covers cooking, sleeping and laundry facilities. Volunteers of all nationalities are welcome but a knowledge of Spanish is useful and preference is given to people experienced in construction or ecological work. Since conditions are rugged and work takes place at high altitudes, applicants should be in good physical condition with all senses intact. Accommodation is provided.

For more details contact the Co-Owner at the above address. Applicants should note that competition for places is very tough, with most places filled by March and all places filled by May.

Human Service Alliance (HSA)

3983 Old Greensboro Road, Winston-Salem, NC 27101, USA (tel 919 761-8745).

The HSA Center operates in Winston-Salem, North Carolina. Its purpose is to care for the terminally ill and, in doing so, to respond creatively to the diverse experiences of death. The newly constructed Center offers a home-like setting where guests live out their lives in a loving and supportive environment. Trained volunteers provide round-the-clock-care. The Center accepts people whose life expectancy is approximately three months or less. HSA also provides respite care for families who have a developmentally disabled child or adult living in the home. Respite care is a parent support service which offers families temporary relief from the demanding physical and mental responsibilities of caring for developmentally disabled persons. A developmental disability is a severe and chronic mental and/or physical impairment such as mental retardation, cerebral palsy, autism, vision or hearing impairment, epilepsy and spina bifida.

Approximately 200 volunteers work at the Center every year. They take direct care of the terminally ill guests, keeping them company, helping with their grooming, reading to them, or simply holding hands. They provide care for disabled children two weekends a month as well as helping with cooking, housekeeping, gardening and grounds maintenance, carpentry, general building maintenance, typing, computer work and much more. Applicants of any nationality are welcome and no special skills or qualifications are needed. However, record keeping, telephone, computer and people skills would be advantages as would be carpentry or experience of working with small machinery used in maintaining buildings and grounds. HSA welcomes individuals of any age and all backgrounds; families are also very welcome. Volunteers come and stay from one weekend to nine months and anywhere in between. It is left to the volunteer to decide what amount of time they choose to spend at HSA. HSA is a volunteer organization with no paid staff with all funds going directly to serve the community so no pocket money can be provided. Overseas volunteers must therefore pay for their own air-fares and other costs.

Applications should be addressed to Human Service Alliance at the above address.

Institute for International Co-operation and Development
PO Box 103, Williamstown, MA 01267, USA (tel 413 458-9466; fax 413 458-3323).

The IICD was founded as a private non-profit organization in 1986. The Institute now runs 'Global Education Programs' which last for between six and 12 months in Angola, Brazil, Mozambique and Nicaragua. Programs include training and follow-up periods in the US. 50-60 volunteers take part in the various programs every year. In Mozambique volunteers work in a forestry project, providing wood for construction and fuel to be used by the local community.

In Angola volunteers are required to work at a school for children orphaned by the war. In Nicaragua volunteers participate in building work in a rural community, while in Brazil volunteers help with building work in a rural co-operative. Participants must have valid passports; visa etc are taken care of during the preparatory course. Participants must complete the two-four months preparatory course in the US. No pocket money or expenses are paid, but accommodation is provided. Applicants should note that volunteers must pay a fee to cover room and board. The 1992/3 fees were; Angola, Mozambique, Nicaragua — $4300, while for Brazil the participation fee is $3200. The minimum age limit is 18 years.

For further information please write to Ester Neltrup, Administrative Director, at the above address.

Involvement Corps Inc.
15515 Sunset Blvd Suite 108, Pacific Palisades CA 90272, USA (tel/fax 1 310 459-1022).

Involvement Corps Inc. exists to give people the opportunity to participate in volunteer activities related to conservation, environmental research, archaeology, history or social welfare. Individual placements or Team Task placements run for from two to twelve weeks, some with free accommodation and food, others costing up to £34 per week. Volunteers need to understand and speak some English. Individual placements and/or Team Tasks are available in California as well as all states of Australia, Fiji, Germany, Hawaii, India, New Zealand and Thailand.

Involvement Corps Inc is a non profit-making organization which charges a fee of approximately £130 to cover administartion costs. For volunteers coming to California this fee includes travel and visa advice, arrival advice for suitable accommodation and transport from the airport, as well aas a communication base for the visit. Volunteers from overseas would have to pay for their travel costs to the US.

For further information please contact Ms Ellen Linsley at the above address.

Jubilee Partners
Box 68, Comer, GA 30629, USA (tel 706 783-5131; fax 706 783-5134).

Jubilee Partners is a Christian community based in Georgia, USA, dedicated to serving poor and oppressed people. The community's work includes several areas of service; resettling refugees, peace-making, some prison work, fund raising for Nicaraguan amputees and working against the death penalty.

Approximately 10 volunteers per session are required (about 30 per year). Volunteers are involved in a wide variety of work, such as teaching English as a second language, doing childcare, construction/maintenance of the buildings, gardening, office work, library work, etc. It is important that volunteers are flexible and willing to contribute wherever they are needed. Applicants may be of any nationality, but they must be fluent in English. Applicants with construction and/or mechanic skills are always welcome.

Volunteers must be over 18 years of age. Although Jubilee is a Christian community volunteers do not have to be Christian, but should be individuals who are searching in their spiritual life and are open to dialogue. Volunteers are expected to enter wholeheartedly into the life of the community. There are three different volunteer sessions per year: January-May, June-August and September-December. Board and accommodation, as well as a community allowance of $10 per week are all provided.

Those interested should contact Josie Winterfeld, Volunteer Co-ordinator, at the above address.

Koinonis Partners
Route 2, Americus, Georgia 31709, USA (tel 912-924 0391).

Koinonis Partners is a self-supporting Ecumenical Christian community of 25 people working with the local poor. Groups of ten volunteers are taken on for three month periods every March, June and September.

A normal week consists of about 32 hours of work alongside members of the community and six hours of seminars. Work may be in the office or involve gardening, youth tutoring, shipping and food preparation. Applicants must speak English but need not be Christians provided that they will openly consider the teachings of Jesus Christ.

Board, lodging and a small amount of pocket money for incidentals are provided, but volunteers must obtain a tourist visa for their length of stay.

Those interested should apply to the Volunteer Co-ordinator at the above address.

Latin Link (STEP Office)
Whitefield House, 186 Kennington Park Road, London SE11 4BT (tel 071 582-4952; fax 071 793-1023).

The STEP (Short Term Experience Projects) programme provides volunteers with the opportunity to carry out voluntary practical work in teams of ten to twelve people in countries including Argentina, Brazil, Bolivia, Peru and Nicaragua each year, as well as others from time to time. Most projects are community based both in rural and urban areas.

Over 150 volunteers are part of the STEP programme each year, carrying out practical work in teams in the above areas. The wide range of projects includes building and/or refurbishing schools, extending orphanages' facilities, working alongside deprived children, building/extending churches, bible schools and community/health centres. All are Christian based projects run by Latin American Christians and all applicants must be Christians.   Applicants of all nationalities are welcome, although most of Latin Link's volunteers come from the UK. However, Latin Link is happy to include any nationalities as long as visas are obtainable for them. UK citizens do not need visas to enter any of the countries listed above. 'Steppers' are not allowed to drive in Latin America. Knowledge of Spanish and/or Portuguese would be an advantage, as would any drama, music and first aid skills. Unskilled volunteers are also very welcome.

Volunteers must be aged at least 17; volunteers have been as old as 60 years, but most are under 35. As long as a volunteer is happy to fit in with the others, they are very welcome. There are few health restrictions, although it is best for asthmatics to work in lower altitudes on non-dusty projects.

The summer projects run from mid-July to early September, and Spring projects run from March to July. Medical electives can be fixed up all year round if plenty of notice is given. Volunteers have to provide all their own expenses. Summer teams must pay approximately £1,200, while Spring teams must pay £1,500 approx. This sum includes pocket money, food, accommodation, flights and insurance. Accommodation can be fairly basic as Latin Link believes in living to a standard similar to that of the Latin American hosts. Latin Link can also provide information on long-term work and 2 year placements.

Short-term applicants should contact Mrs Cathy Travis,long-term enquiries to Miss Judith Hymer, both at the above address.

Los Ninos

1330 Continental Street, San Ysidro, CA 92073, USA (tel 619-690 1437).

Los Ninos is a charitable organization founded to provide food, clothing, shelter, education and affection to children in orphanages and poor communities in the Mexican border cities of Tijuana and Mexicali. Approximately 1,200 volunteers of predominantly high school and college age take part in weekend or ten day educational workshops from October to May, as well as a six-week summer programme in July and August. Volunteers assist by undertaking jobs in education, nutrition, construction, as youth counsellors or in other areas of community development. Around 25 other volunteers help long term on the same jobs and stay for periods of over a year.

All volunteers must have a visa which allows them to cross the United States and Mexican border daily. Short-term volunteers must be at least 16 years old. Long term volunteers must be at least 18 years old, skilled in the specific areas mentioned above and hold a driver's licence. Short-term volunteers receive accommodation but must pay for their programmes while long term volunteers receive free board and accommodation and around £25 per month in pocket money. Applicants should be mature, cross-culturally aware and sensitive to the Mexican culture. All applicants should be fluent in Spanish.

Those interested should contact the Office Manager at the above address.

Lubbock Lake Landmark
The Museum of Texas Tech. University, Lubbock, Texas 79409-3191, USA.

The Lubbock Lake National Historic and State Archaeological Landmark is an archaeological preserve on the outskirts of Lubbock. The aims and activities of the Landmark are orientated toward the excavation of data and the interpretation of that data for the public through a number of public education courses. Around 50 volunteers a year are required to help with the excavation programme.

Volunteers must be able to read, write and speak English and are required to act as field and laboratory crew members during the excavations, collections workers for the care of the collections in the museum, or as leaders on tour programmes.

The minimum age for prospective volunteers is 18 years, and the period of participation is from six weeks to three months between June and August. Volunteers must pay for their own travelling and incidental expenses but receive free board and lodging in the field camp.

For further details contact the Director at the above address.

National Venceremos Brigade
PO Box 673, New York, NY 10035, USA (tel 212-246 3811).

This is a US-based solidarity and friendship organization with Cuba which focuses on education and people-to-people exchange. Between 100 and 150 volunteers per year work with the Brigade, performing some form of physical labour side by side with Cubans. The organization's multi-racial mandate means that applicants of any nationality are accepted as long as they possess a valid US passport. All applicants are screened, and, if approved, are selected by a committee.

Volunteers must be physically fit and able to perform strenuous work. The minimum age limit is 18 years. Volunteers are recruited for ten to twelve days. Applicants should note that they must assume all expenses between 950 and 1,100 US Dollars; this cost includes accommodation.

Applications should be made to Rosemari L'Mele at the above address.

Nicaragua Solidarity Campaign
129 Seven Sisters Road, London N7 7QG (tel 071-272 9619).

The Nicaragua Solidarity Campaign (NSC) and Environmental Network for Nicaragua (ENN) organise work brigades to do environmental work in Nicaragua. There are three brigades per year, each lasting for one month: one over the Christmas/New Year period and two in the summer. The brigades work for three weeks and spend the fourth week on a programme of talks and visits to organizations in Managua and around the area where the brigade is working. The programme can be varies according to the interests of the group.

Volunteers must be fit, adaptable and prepared to get involved in the work of

NSC and ENN in Britain on their return from Nicaragua. The total cost including air fares, living expenses and transport in Nicaragua is approximately £1,100. For further details contact the above address.

Nicaragua — United States Friendship Office
225 Pennsylvania Ave, SE, 3rd Floor, Washington, DC 20003 USA (tel 202 546-0915; fax 202 546-0935).

This organization is a support group for other organizations which operate in solidarity with Nicaragua. Its Technical Assistance Program, organized in conjunction with FUNDECI, enables people to do voluntary work in Nicaragua. About 75 volunteers, of all nationalities, join this program every year. Volunteers with particular skills will be assigned to a Nicaraguan community or project in those skill areas. FUNDECI will set up work assignments with ongoing Nicaraguan projects for those who have limited experience or skills. These projects usually take the form of construction. Almost all skills are needed in Nicaragua; while the mainstay of the program are the technical skills typically lacking in the third world such as hydrology, engineering, architecture and planning, some volunteers become involved in jobs as diverse as massage therapy and video production. A knowledge of Spanish is advisable, if not essential; a volunteer's overall experience in Nicaragua will certainly be enriched if he/she can be self-reliant in terms of language.

The program operates around the year and there is no limit on how long a volunteer can work under the program; it is the volunteer's decision as to how long to stay. However, one month is the usual minimum. The average is three months, while some volunteers stay for as long as one year. Volunteers usually live with a Nicaraguan family, although on some occasions volunteers may live together in a house. The program fee is $300, while monthly expenses in Nicaragua should cost a maximum of $400 per month; this covers basic expenses, as well as room and partial board with a Nicaraguan family.

Applicants of any nationality are welcome to apply. For further information, or an application form contact Stephen Poethke at the above address.

PLENTY USA
PO Box 2306, Davis, CA 95617, USA (tel/fax 916 753-0731).

PLENTY is a non-governmental relief and development organization that works with native peoples from Central and South America and Africa, as well as within the US. Recent projects ranged from community agriculture in South Dakota to building facilities for eco-tourism in Belize.

Volunteers get involved both with the fund-raising for the projects and the labour itself, which may include building structures and gardens. Volunteers can be of any nationality, and skills required depends on the projects. There are no other restrictions, and most placements are short-term. Volunteers are required all the year round, but there are more opportunities in the summer. No pocket money is provided, and no expenses are paid. Volunteers must pay their own travel costs. Accommodation is sometimes provided, but usually volunteers must find and rent their own. The organization publishes a quarterly bulletin, with up-to-date details of projects and endeavours, that may be subscribed to by sending $10 to the above address.

Those interested should contact Monica L Stoycoff at the above address.

Sierra Club
730 Polk Street, San Francisco, CA 94109, USA (tel 415 923-5527).

The Sierra Club subsidizes trips which combine wilderness outings with preservation projects in North America, although occasionally one or two trips are held in Europe. Between 1,000 and 1,200 volunteers are needed annually. Volunteers use their own camping equipment and camp out while helping to build or repair trails and restoring damaged wilderness areas. The trips last from one week to ten days with most of the trips being held in summer although some are conducted in spring and autumn, and all trips incorporate days free from work.

Volunteers must be physically fit and usually aged at least 18 years. No special skills are required but medical doctors may have their trip cost waived if they act as a staff doctor on an expedition. A typical trip costs around £125.

Contact the Publicity Manager at the above address for further information..

Sioux Indian YMCAs
Box 218, Dupree, South Dakota 57623, USA.

The Sioux Indian YMCAs organize spring and summer community projects and a summer camp in South Dakota. In the spring and summer projects the volunteers live and work in small isolated reservation communities under the direction of indigenous community YMCA organizations and help with informal recreation, leadership training and counselling. The projects last from April to June or mid-June to mid-August.

The summer camp takes place on the Oahe Reservoir of the Missouri River. It is a primitive camp without electricity or running water, and the campers are all from the small reservation YMCA's on the Sioux reservations.

Volunteers should be sensitive and mature, able to relate to people of other cultures and must like working with children. All skills are welcome especially those connected with water safety, first aid, creative arts and crafts, games and sports. Those working on the summer camp should have previous experience of camping life.

Volunteers should be in good mental and physical health and over 18. Board and lodging are provided, but volunteers are responsible for their own travel and personal expenses.

Applications should be made to the Director at the above address.

St. Jude's Ranch for Children
PO Box 60100, Boulder City, Nevada 89006-0100, USA (tel 702 293-3131; fax 702 293-7864).

St. Jude's is a children's home in Nevada. Its volunteers work primarily on a Christmas Card recycling program and the Campbell's Label Program. During summer months volunteers help with children's activities such as sports and crafts. Others open mail or help with planting and weeding.

Over 100 volunteers help annually; there are about 50 volunteers working on a regular basis. People of any nationality may apply. Special qualifications are welcome but not essential. Volunteers are welcome to stay as long as they can. Pocket money is not paid to local volunteers, but it is worked out on an individual basis for those who are not local. Accommodation is only available to long-term volunteers.

For further information write to Susan L. White at the above address.

Student Conservation Association
PO Box 550, Charlestown, NH 03603, USA (tel 603 826-4301).

This Association offers internships for students and adults to work in national parks, forests and wildlife refuges across the United States, including Alaska, Hawaii, Puerto Rico and the Virgin Islands. The High School (HS) Programme enables around 500 students between 16 and 18 years of age to work on labour-intensive projects such as trail construction and ecological restoration in groups of six to ten students. In the Resource Assistant (RA) Programme around 1,000 older students and adults work in a professional capacity alongside other staff in resource management agencies. Placements are for four or five weeks during the summer for the HS Program, or for ten to twelve weeks at any time of year in the RA Program.

All volunteers should be in good health and overseas applicants must pay for their travel to the United States. No special skills are needed for the HS Program but participants must pay for their personal equipment and transportation to the site. Financial aid may be available. The RA positions require either a specific academic background or an interest in conservation and an enthusiasm for performing this type of work. RA volunteers must be at least 18 years old and out of high school. They are paid for their travel expenses within the United States and receive accommodation and a food allowance.

For further information contact the Program Director in Recruitment at the above address.

Tahoe Rim Trail Fund Inc.
PO Box 10156, South Lake Tahoe, CA 96158, USA (tel 916 577-0676).

This volunteer organization was formed in 1983 to build and maintain a 150 mile multi-purpose trail around the ridgetops of the Lake Tahoe Basin in California and Nevada. The goal is to complete the trail by the end of 1996 and volunteers are needed for maintenance work. Between 400 and 1,000 English speaking volunteers per year are needed in all seasons for all aspects of the project, from office work and fund raising events to trail building and maintenence, but demand for volunteers is highest during the construction season which begins in May and ends mid-October. Volunteers specify the length of their service.

No special skills are necessary as training is given. Membership is not required but volunteers should be in good health and at least 16 years old. Accommodation and pocket money are not provided.

Write to the Director at the above address for an application form and further information.

United Church Board for Homeland Ministries
700 Prospect Avenue, Cleveland OH 4415, USA (tel 216 736-3266).

This Church administers three voluntary programmes which are located in the United States and Puerto Rico. Volunteers may undertake short term, summer or one year voluntary service programmes. Tasks include undertaking community service, assisting with emergency shelters, helping with programmes concerned with peace and justice, etc. Of the 90 volunteers needed each year, up to 15 of these are from overseas.

Volunteers must be at least 21 years old, English-speaking and willing to be placed by a Christian church organization. Some projects may have specific health, professional or driving licence requirements. Overseas volunteers must pay their full round trip transportation costs and have a J-1 visa. Summer service volunteers receive room and board while one-year volunteers also receive an allowance.

Those interested should apply to the Secretary for Volunteer Services at the above address.

University Research Expeditions Program (UREP)
University of California, Berkeley, CA 94720, USA (tel 510 642-6586).

UREP provides opportunities for people to participate in scientific discoveries by acting as field assistants on a University of California research expedition. Research topics offered in a large number of countries include animal behaviour, archaeology, anthropology, sociology, art, music, botany, ecology and marine studies. Over 200 volunteers are needed each year for over 20 different projects. Most projects are offered from February to September and last around two or three weeks.

Volunteers must be in good health, at least 16 years old, have a desire to learn, enthusiasm and be willing to undertake team work. Specific skills or experiences are not essential but may be an advantage. Volunteers pay an equal share to cover the project's costs, which may be anything from about £350 to about £800 depending on the logistics of the expedition. This contribution covers research equipment and supplies, preparatory materials, camping and field gear, ground transportation and meals and accommodation. Travel to the site is not included.

For more information contact the Secretary at the above address.

USDA Forest Service
Pacific Northwest Region, PO Box 3623, Portland OR 97208, USA (tel 503 326-3816; fax 503 326-5255).

The Pacific Northwest region of the US Forest Service maintains 19 national forests in Oregon and Washington. Volunteers are needed to maintain trails, campgrounds, wildlife and timber. They are also required to help with recreation, range activities, office work, interpretation and the visitor information services. There are almost no restrictions on the type of volunteers required and the organization attempts to tailor jobs to match the volunteers' skills. Volunteers must, however, be able to speak English, and be in good physical condition although the organization tries to accommodate disabled applicants.

The length of time for which volunteers are required varies, but the longer commitment (preferably between six and eight weeks) a person can make the better the chance of obtaining a placement. Volunteers are mostly required on a seasonal basis although there are some limited year-round opportunities. Food and incidental expenses are reimbursed, and lodging is provided for long-term full-time volunteers. Those interested should contact Drinda Lombardi at the above address.

Volunteers for Peace
43 Tiffany Road, Belmont VT 05730, USA (tel 802 259-2759; fax 802 259-2922).

VFP offers short-term international work exchanges in 37 different countries. The workcamps provide volunteers with an opportunity to complete meaningful community service while living and interacting in an international environment. 300-400 volunteers per year come to VFP workcamps within the USA, while 400-500 American volunteers per year are placed in other countries.

A wide range of activities are open to volunteers including environmental work, construction, work with children, the elderly and the handicapped. Applicants should note that the official language of the workcamps is English and the minimum age limit is 18 years. The programs last for two to three weeks, although multiple placements are possible. Volunteers are required between May and September. Pocket money is not paid; volunteers must pay a registration fee which covers board and lodging.

Applications should be made to Megan Brook at the above address.

The Winant-Clayton Volunteer Association
38 Newark Street, London E1 2AA (tel 071-375 0547).

This Association organizes an annual exchange between the United Kingdom and the eastern states of the United States of America for a group of 20 volunteers. Selected volunteers work on community projects which include visiting house-bound people , working with children of all ages, psychiatric rehabilitation and running lunch clubs for the elderly. The exchange lasts for three months, the last month being free for individual travel, between June and September.

In order to be selected to travel to the United States, volunteers must be resident in the UK or Eire and over 18 years old. The average age of volunteers is between 22 and 28 years old but individual volunteers may be much older. Volunteers must have some experience of community or group work, an interest in people, a sense of humour, flexibility, stamina and a satisfactory way of dealing with stress.

The Association obtains the special work permit required and provides pocket money and accommodation for the two months of work. No other expenses are paid. Interviews are held each February.

Applications should be made to the Co-ordinator at the above address.

Israel and the Middle East

American Dental Volunteers for Israel (ADVI)
108-13 67th Road, Forest Hills, NY 11375, USA (tel 718-263 4918).

ADVI is a non-profit making organization which recruits volunteer dentists and dental hygienists of all nationalities to work on kibbutzim in Israel. Volunteers undertake reparative dentistry, stress the preventative approach and train dental assistants. Between 50 and 75 volunteers are needed for placements of three or four weeks, all year round.

Volunteers must be licenced dentists or registered dental hygienists with a minimum of one or two years' experience and in good health. All volunteers are granted a temporary licence to practise in Israel upon presentation of copies of licences and diplomas to the Israel Ministry of Health. Accommodation is provided but volunteers must pay their own travelling expenses. For more details contact the Chairman at the above address.

Centre of Nautical and Regional Archaeology (CONRAD)
Kibbutz Nahssholim, Israel 30815 (tel 06-390 950).

CONRAD is located in the grounds of Kibbutz Nahsholim on the Carmel Coast, Israel. The Centre is the home base of the Museums' Maritime inspection team and the Tel Dor excavations. Volunteers are needed at all times of year to help with all projects. Field work including diving, restoration, exhibit planning, publication preparation and general maintenance of the building goes on year round. The Tel Dor excavations take place during July and August and during the autumn, spring and winter inspection diving is at its peak with underwater surveys and rescue excavations being conducted. Volunteers to act as tour guides and to assist with clerical work are always needed. Placements are for as long as the volunteer wishes but for periods longer than three months work visas may be required.

Volunteers must be in good health, over 18 years old and able to speak Hebrew or English. Diving volunteers must have diving licences. The volunteer is responsible for all costs including accommodation, meals and medical and accident insurance, although reduced rates for accommodation can be given.

Volunteers should apply to the Director at the above address.

The Church's Ministry Among the Jews
30c Clarence Road, St Albans, Herts AL1 4JJ (tel 0727-33114).

Every year the Church requires about 30 volunteers to work in its hostel in Tel Aviv, guest house in Jerusalem and conference centre on Mount Carmel for periods of three to 12 months. The work usually consists of the preparation and serving of meals for guests, housework and maintenance of the grounds and buildings. No special skills are required and volunteers may be of any nationalilty provided they are over 17 years old and in good health.

Volunteers must pay for their own travel expenses and medical insurance but receive full board and lodging and pocket money. Visas are arranged in Israel.

Further details can be obtained from the General Director at the above address.

Edinburgh Medical Missionary Society
7 Washington Lane, Edinburgh EH11 2HA (tel 031-313 3828).

This Society assists the Nazareth Hospital in Nazareth, Israel, to obtain volunteers for occasional medical, nursing, para-medical and general maintenance vacancies. Vacancies occur irregularly at any time of year. Volunteers may be of any nationality provided that they are in good health and have appropriate qualifications or experience in the relevant area. At least three volunteers a year are required for placements of one to two months, but longer stays are possible. Simple accommodation and the appropriate work visa are provided by the hospital. Travel expenses are not paid.

Write to Dr. R Martin, the Nazareth Hospital, EMMS, PO Box 11, 16100 Nazareth, Israel for further information.

Ein Yael Living Museum
PO Box 9679, Jerusalem 91094, Israel (tel 02-638421).

The Ein Yael Living Museum is situated in the Rephaim Valley of Jerusalem. The project combines experimentation in the techniques of traditional agriculture with crafts such as pottery, weaving, mosaic, basketry and construction, as practised in various historical periods. The research in these fields is an attempt to understand the way ancient man interacted with his environment. Volunteers are needed for the building of workshops, to act as guides for child visitors,and to help with research and archaeological excavations on the site. The participants will be guided by the staff and archaeologists of the institution.

Volunteers are welcome all year round provided that they are at least 16 years old and in good health. No previous experience is needed but volunteers must be prepared to work five days a week for a period of two weeks or more.

For further information wite to Gershon Edelstein, Director, at the above address.

Friends of Israel Educational Trust
25 Lyndale Avenue, London NW2 2QB (tel 071-435 6803; fax 071-794 0291).

The Trust has three basic functions. It runs the Bridge in Britain Scheme which is a school-leavers' award scheme; twelve travel awards are granted competitively each year; each Bridge group spends six months working in Israel. Travel to and from Israel and basic living expenses are provided, but not pocket money. It also organizes the Bessy Emanuel Award. One or two travel grants each year are awarded to school, undergraduate or postgraduate students planning a personal research project in Israel. Any project idea can be submitted to the academic adjudication panel. The Trust also offers placements in Israel for young artists, farmers and horticulturalists/botanists.

Further details from the Director at the above address.

Gil Tours Ltd.
16 Gloucester Place, London W1H 3AW (tel 071-935 1701).

This company arranges placements for volunteers who wish to work on moshavim and kibbutzim in Israel. Volunteers of any nationality are welcome to work in all branches of agriculture from vegetable, fruit or flower growing to poultry or dairy farming at all stages of production. The working week is six days, with eight hours work per day.

Only healthy volunteers aged 18 to 35 years old and willing to spend a minimum of two months will be accepted. Workers on Moshavim receive a number of benefits including free accommodation, social facilities and an allowance of about £160 per month. Gil Tours charges a registration fee of £30 and can provide prospective volunteers with a booklet about life and work in moshavim.

Send a SAE to the Managing Director at the above address or telephone for further information.

Hebrew Union College — Jewish Institute of Religion
One West 4th Street, New York, NY 10012, USA (tel 212-674 5300).

The Nelson Glueck School of Biblical Archaeology in Jerusalem, in co-operation with the Israel Department of Antiquities and the Semitic Museum of Harvard, has a long term ongoing programme of excavations at Tel Dan, Gilat and Shiqmim, Israel.

Around 50 volunteers per season are needed to assist with the excavation process during summer. Volunteers must be at least 18 years old with an interest in archaeology but no special skills are required. The minimum placement is two weeks and all volunteers must submit a completed medical form. The cost of around £800 excludes travel but includes room and board.

Applications to Dr Paul M Steinberg, Director, American Office, at the above address.

Institute of Archaeology, Tel Aviv University
PO Box 39040, Ramat Aviv 69978, Tel Aviv, Israel (tel 03-6409703; fax 03-6409457).

The Institute is involved with archaeological excavations in a scholastic setting. Lectures, field trips and other recreational activities are also organised outside working hours. About 300 volunteers are taken on every year, drawn from many different countries. Volunteers are mostly students or individuals interested in Biblical archaeology, field archaeology or the historical geography of Israel. There is also the possibility of work for graphic artists, surveyors and pottery restorers. Most work involves digging.

No experience is necessary, but the applicant must be in good health. English and Hebrew are the basic languages, however groups may come with an interpreter. Excavations are generally carried out in the summer months and anyone over 18 who is capable of working in outdoor conditions may apply. The minimum stay is two weeks, going up to six weeks.

Accommodation is provided in camps or in a kibbutz. Three full meals and several breaks are also provided five days a week. Expenses above this are the responsibility of the individual volunteer.

Those interested should apply to the above address.

Israel Antiquities Authority
P.O. Box 586, Jerusalem 91 004, Israel.

Israel is a country rich in history, and possessing archaeological remains from every period since prehistoric times. A number of excavations in Israel accept volunteers each year. Details of most of them cannot be given very far ahead as final plans are not usually drawn up before spring. If applicants write to the Authority early in the year they will be sent a detailed list of proposed excavations. The minimum age for prospective volunteers is 18 years, and the minimum period of participation is usually two weeks. Volunteers must be willing and able to do any work connected with the excavation. Accommodation and food are provided by the expedition, but full or part payment may be asked for this, especially if archaeological tuition is involved.

Enquiries should be sent to the Assistant to the Director at the above address.

Kibbutz Program Center
Volunteer Department, Takam-Artzi, 124 Hayarkon Street, PO Box 3167, Tel Aviv 63573, Israel (tel 03-221325, 5246156).

This organization accepts visitors, both as individuals and groups, as temporary workers on a kibbutz for a period of at least nine months. A basic knowledge of English is necessary for participation, and the age limits are 18-32 years. A working visitor on a kibbutz works an eight hour day, six days a week. Apart from Saturday, which is usually the day of rest, the visitor receives three extra days per month. As a rule, working visitors must be prepared to do any kind of work allotted to them by the work manager.

The kind of work involved is of a very diversified nature, and depends on the type of kibbutz that the volunteer is sent to. It is still mainly agricultural, but increasingly tends to be industrial as well. As the kibbutz is a self supporting community, with its own services, quite a proportion of volunteers also go into essential services. The kibbutz provides rooms (for 2-3 persons), meals in the dining hall, laundry service, work clothes, medical care, entertainment and pocket money. Travel expenses are not paid.

The best way to ensure a place on a kibbutz is by applying to a placement organization such as Kibbutz Representatives in one's own country. For the UK their address is: 1A Accommodation Road, Golders Green, London NW11 8EP (tel 071-458 9235). For the U.S.A.: 27 West 20th Street, New York, NY 10011 (tel 212-255 1338). Alternatively, volunteers who are already in Israel may apply directly to the offices at the above address, but in this case a place on a kibbutz cannot be guaranteed.

Kibbutz Representatives
1A Accommodation Road, Golders Green, London NW11 8EP (tel 071-458 9235).

Each year working holidays on kibbutzim in Israel are organized for about 3,000 people aged 18 — 32 and in good health. The work may involve physical labour in the fields, orchards, fish ponds, cowsheds and gardens; or work in the kitchens, laundry, general services or factory. Applicants must pay for their own travelling expenses and insurance for their stay lasting from two to three months with the option of extending it up to six months. A special work visa is needed and this will be arranged at the Kibbutz Representatives office. They will then receive free board and accommodation, leisure and entertainment facilities and occasional excursions, plus a small amount of pocket money.

All nationalities are welcome, except those which do not hold diplomatic relations with Israel. One can arrange to travel either as an individual or with a group of around ten people, which will be organized by Kibbutz Representatives. Prospective participants are all interviewed by Kibbutz Representatives and kibbutz life is fully explained. Kibbutz Representatives is the only official organization which represents all the kibbutzim in Israel.

Enquiries to the above address.

Laboratory of Prehistory
Haifa University, Haifa 31999, Israel.

Volunteers aged over 18 years are required to assist with archaeological excavations in caves, open air and underwater prehistoric sites in the Mount Carmel and Galilee region. They must stay for a minimum of two weeks during the summer months. Accommodation is provided and participants pay a contribution towards living expenses which vary for different projects.

For further information please contact the Director of the Zinmam Institute of Archaeology at the above address.

Lahav Research Project Phase II (1992-1994)

Cobb Institute of Archaeology, Drawer AR, Mississippi State University, Mississippi State MS 29762, USA (tel 001-601 325 3826).

The project was created in 1975 with the objective of excavating the seven acre mound-site of Tell Halif near Kibbutz Lahav in Israel and has since conducted nine summer field seasons of excavation. The site is of great historical importance, containing evidence of occupation in the Early Bronze, Late Bronze, Iron II, Roman and early Byzantine periods. Approximately 30 volunteers a year assist the staff of 20 specialists to uncover and process materials. Another purpose of the project is to allow the volunteers to gain theoretical as well as practical experience, so the daily timetable includes training sessions, supplementary lectures, and rotation of work assignments. The project lasts for six weeks each year, from mid-June until the end of July, and keeps the weekends clear to allow time for travel. Excavation seasons are planned for 1993 and 1994.

Volunteers include each year a large proportion of American students who use the dig as a means of obtaining academic credit at undergraduate or graduate level through one of several participating universities. English speaking people of any nationality are welcome to take part, but those with previous experience in this field are given priority. As the work is strenuous and in hot conditions, volunteers over 40 must produce satisfactory medical evidence of their health. The accommodation consists of a camp with five or six to a tent, and the food service at Kibbutz Lahav is said to be good (and ample: there are two breakfasts, for example, but this is something of a necessity, as work begins at 4 am). A $795 contribution is been required from each volunteer towards expenses.

Those interested should write to Dr Paul F Jacob, Co-Director, at the above address.

Project 67

10 Hatton Garden, London EC1N 8AH (tel 071-831 7626).

Project have been organisers of working holidays in Israel for the last 25 years. Project arrange for over 2,000 people a year to go on three types of working holiday, on a 'package holiday' basis; these are kibbutz and moshav holidays, which last for a minimum of two months, and archaeological digs. Departures take place arouind the year, with placement guaranteed.

Project 67 is the official UK representative of the kibbutz movement and arranges kibbutz working holidays on which volunteers receive free accommodation, meals, laundry, pocket money, recreational facilities and occasional trips in exchange for working a six day week. Age limits are 18-32.

On a moshav working holiday age limits are 21-35. Work is mainly agricultural. Free accommodation is provided (usually self-contained). In exchange for their work volunteers receive a monthly salary which may be increased if overtime is worked.

Project's archaeological digs are organised in conjunction with the Ministry of Antiquities and universities; a variety of programmes are offered on several sites throughout Israel, in which anyone aged over 18 can participate. Accommodation varies from site to site.

Project 67 has its own office in Tel Aviv which can take care of the needs of volunteers while they are in Irael. For more details those interested can visit Project's London office to watch a video, or telephone or send a sae for a brochure. See also the advertisement on the inside front cover.

Religious Kibbutz Movement
7 Dubnov Street, Tel Aviv, Israel (tel 03-6957231).

The Movement accepts a limited number of volunteers to work on its kibbutzim which are situated in many parts of Israel, including the Beit Sh'ean Valley, Ashdod, Ashkelon, and the Jerusalem and Tel Aviv areas. It should be noted however that only Jewish young people who are ready to follow an orthodox way of life are taken on as volunteers by the Movement. The minimum period of stay is two months. The volunteer works at least eight and a half hours each day, most of the work being seasonal and agricultural. The Movement also runs four Kibbutz-Ulpan programmes (five months in duration), which combine formal instruction in Hebrew with voluntary work in a Kibbutz. These programmes take place throughout the year.

Volunteers must be at least 18 years of age, and in good health. No special qualifications are needed, but people with diplomas in life-saving are appreciated. All nationalities are welcome. Accommodation and food are provided, and moderate pocket money is paid. Expenses are not paid, including those arising from travel. A tourist visa is required but no work permit is needed.   Applications should be sent to: Bnei Akiva, 2 Hallswell Road, London, NW11 ODJ or to Kibbutz Representatives, 1a Accommodation Road, London NW11 8EP.

Tel Aviv University — Classics Department
c/o Kibbutz Palmahim, DN Emek Sorek 76890, Israel.

The Tel Aviv University Classics Department, in collaboration with the Kibbutz Palmahim, is conducting an archaeological excavation at Yavne Yam, situated on the Mediterranean coast, about half an hour's drive from the city of Tel Aviv. The site is mentioned in ancient sources, and was known as an important port, as confirmed by recent underwater excavations. Interest in the site was increased by an inscription revealed there accidentally several years ago which has been dated to the Hellenistic period.

Up to 40 volunteers are required every year between July and August for three two-week periods. Volunteers of all nationalities are needed to assist with general archaeological work on the site. As the work is moderately strenuous, good health is important. Volunteers work six days per week, with Saturday free. Applicants should have knowledge of English, French or German.

Yavne-Yam is situated near Kibbutz Palmahim which will serve as host to the volunteers, who are given accommodation in tents and receive all their meals in the kibbutz dining room. There are also a laundry, first-aid services and a shop, open several days per week, where the volunteers can purchase things for their daily needs. Volunteers must pay for their accommodation, board and services, as well as for their air fares and travel costs. The cost of room and full board will be about £200/US$400. It is also necessary for each volunteer to arrange complete insurance coverage.

For further information write to Batya Dashti at the above address.

UNIPAL

33A Islington Park Street, London N1 1QB (tel 071-226 7997; fax 071-226 0880).

UNIPAL, the Universities Educational Fund for Palestinian Refugees, sends volunteers each year to work on short-term projects during July and August in the Israeli-occupied West Bank and Gaza Strip, and with Palestinian communities in Israel and Jordan. Most projects involve teaching English or work with children. There are also opportunities to teach English for a minimum of one year. TEFL qualifications, experience of teaching English or working with children is essential.

Short-term volunteers are provided with food and accommodation but pay their own air fares and insurance. Long-term volunteers receive pocket money and may be given assistance in paying fares etc.

Send SAE for application form before the end of March. Interviews in April with a briefing in June for those selected.

The Workers' Moshav Movement in Israel (Volunteers Dept)

19 Leonardo da Vinci Street, Tel Aviv 64733, Israel (tel 03-258473).

Moshavim are agricultural communities where almost all farms and homes are privately owned. There are about 450 Moshavim in Israel, and over 100 of these participate in the Moshav volunteers scheme. Volunteers must be aged between 18 and 35 with a clean bill of health and prepared to work for at least two months. Accommodation varies from moshav to moshav, but there is generally a self-catering volunteers' house next to the farmer's home with a shower, kitchen, cooking facilities, etc. There is also a club for the volunteers with facilities for sport and social activities.

The working week is eight hours per day, six days per week with one day off extra per month. Any overtime is paid over and above the allowance of about $320 per month. After two months, volunteers get a trip bonus of $45. Volunteers must pay their own air fares. Unlike kibbutz work, moshav work is mainly agricultural.

For more information contact the above address.

WST Ltd.

Israel-Egypt Dept., Priory House, 6 Wrights Lane, London W8 6TA (tel 071-938 4362).

WST organize a programme called 'In for a Dig' which is a working holiday of two weeks on various archaeological sites in Israel. Applicants must be over 17 years of age and in good physical condition. No visas are needed for British volunteers.

Enquiries may be sent to the above address.

Africa

Les Amis des Chantiers Internationaux de Meknes
BP 08, Ville Nouvelle, Meknes, Morocco (tel 5268-63; fax 5118-29)

ACIM runs summer camps in Meknes between July and September. It also arranges voluntary exchanges between other countries and recruits Moroccans for voluntary placements abroad. For the summer camps, ACIM requires about 60-80 volunteers from abroad to work with children and to do some ecological, agricultural and building work. Applicants must be aged 17 or over. No pocket money is provided, but while working on the camp, accommodation is arranged. For more information on the summer camps, contact Boucetta Bouzerki, General Secretary, at the above address.

ASTOVOCT (Association Togolaise des Volontaires Chretiens au Travail)
BP 97, Route de Stet-Hanyigbu, Kpalime, Togo.

ASTOVOCT is a non-profit making Christian organization, dedicated to the improvement of the standard of living in rural areas of Togo. Work undertaken by ASTOVOCT includes the building of health centres and schools, and tree planting. One hundred volunteers are engaged per year to spend three or four weeks on a summer workcamp, where they take part in construction and agricultural work. As Togo is a French-speaking country, a good knowledge of French is advisable. Volunteers must pay their for their lodging, board and travel expenditure.

UK applicants should contact UNA (Wales), Temple of Peace, Cathays Park, Cardiff CF1 3AP for further details.

Chantiers Sociaux Marocains
BP 456, Rabat, Morocco (tel 07-79 13 70).

CSM organizes workcamps in Morocco which concentrate on projects intended to benefit the local community. About 300 volunteers a year are involved, spending two or three weeks of the summer on the sites with fellow workers from many European and African countries.   Applicants should be between 18 and 30 years old, and in good health. Food and accommodation are provided, but the volunteer is responsible for all his personal expenses.   Those interested can either apply through their national branch of the CCIVS (which is IVS in Britain), or directly to the President at the above address.

Club Unesco Au Monde des Lecteur (CUML)
BP 4671 Kinshasa 2, 7 Rue Meteo No. 7, Djelo Binza (Delvaux), Zone de Ngaliema, Kinshasa Zaire.

Founded in 1983, CUML is a non-governmental organization concerned with voluntary services committed to improving the standard of living in Zaire. Its voluntary workers are active in every sphere of life; health, agriculture, the environment, social issues, education, the economic and the cultural.

Around 150 volunteers of all nationalities are needed to help in the above areas, and with rural community activities and building programmes. Volunteers are also needed for other long-term projects. No special skills, qualifications or training is needed. Applicants must be aged between 18 and 35 and be in very good health, and are needed all the year round for periods of between 3 weeks and a year. Food, accommodation and pocket money are provided and some travel expenses are paid.

To apply, or for further information, please write to Mr Atumanu Mbanza at the above address.

Corps Volontaires Zairois au Developpement (COVOZADE)

Rue Meteo No. 7, Binza-Delvaux, Zone de Ngaliema, BP 3410 Kinshasa/Gombe, Zaire.

The primary purpose of this voluntary association is to heighten awareness of the social problems of Zaire and to help particularly deprived areas.

Over 120 volunteers between the ages of 18 and 55 are needed each year to help in many areas including health, education, agriculture, the environment, literacy and rural development. Applicants should have at least two years' practical experience in their chosen field; they can be of any nationality, but they should know French and/or English. Volunteers can stay for six months, a year or two years. Participants receive pocket money, food and accommodation, travel expenses and free time. COVOZADE also recruits for many other voluntary organizations within Zaire.

Those interested should apply to the above address.

Eclaireuses et Eclaireurs du Senegal

5 rue Pierre Millon, BP 744 Dakkar, Senegal (tel 221 21 73 67; fax 221 22 88 73).

This organization needs volunteers to help on the following projects. They are needed to carry out a survey in Senegal on health problems and to work both in the national headquarters and at local or district level. Volunteers are needed to lead training courses for scouts' unit leaders and other commissioners, and to train young people in agriculture, mechanics, wood craft and to give advice to adolescents on sex education. A voluntary Deputy Director is also needed for a community Development Project in a rural area, who will be able to oversee an agricultural training programme.

Applicants may be of any nationality, but it would be preferable if applicants were able to speak French. Applications are welcome at any time of the year; the length of placements depends on the availability of volunteers. Accommodation is available in both urban and rural areas, but volunteers must make a financial contribution towards costs. Pocket money is not provided and volunteers must pay for their own travel expenses to and from Senegal.

Those interested should apply to the national Commissioner for Administration at the above address.

FOCUS, Inc.

Department of Opthalmology, Loyola University Medical Centre, 2160 South First Avenue, Maywood, Illinois 60153, USA (tel 312 531 3408).

FOCUS recruits opthalmologists as short term volunteers for eye clinics in Nigeria where they provide medical and surgical eye care services. Around 15 volunteers are needed for placements of three weeks or longer, all year round.

Applicants must be certified opthalmologists and need to obtain a Nigerian visa. Usually a US medical licence is required but this would be waived for UK opthalmologists. Board, lodging, laundry services and transportation within Nigeria are provided but volunteers pay for their own international travel.

Write to the President of FOCUS at the above address for more details.

Gormogor Agricultural Development Organisation (GADO)

c/o Njala University College, Private Mail Bag, Freetown, Sierra Leone, West Africa.

GADO's primary concern is to promote community development in the 100 or so villages within the Dasse chiefdom of Sierra Leone. Most changes and improvements are needed in agricultural related areas but opportunities also exist for other community work such as conducting educational courses for various groups within the communities. Around five volunteers are needed each year with the volunteer specifying the length of service. Tasks for volunteers involved in agricultural work will vary according to the season but on-going tasks include conservation projects and erection of fences and huts. Other volunteers may teach, work in creches, undertake administrative work, etc.

All volunteers must be at least 15 years old and able to communicate in English. As volunteers live in remote African villages they should also be in good mental and physical health. No special skills are required but volunteers with agricultural experience will be welcomed. Accommodation in huts is provided but volunteers must pay their own travelling expenses and contribute towards the food which is provided for them. A timetable of work will be prepared to suit both the volunteer and the needs of the community.

Those interested should write to the Programme Director at the above address for more information.

Health Projects Abroad

HMS President, Victoria Embankment, London EC4Y 0HJ (tel 071 583-5725; fax 071 583-2840).

HPA works on health projects to support governments in developing countries; it currently works in Tanzania, having completed a pilot project in Cameroon in 1990, and provides funding and expertise and voluntary labour for the construction of health centres, water storage tanks, sanitation facilities and renovation of existing hospital wards.

45 volunteers are engaged by HPA each year, but this figure is by no means fixed. Professional volunteers — experienced engineers and nurses — are needed to work alongside Tanzanian counterparts and help run a project, as well as co-ordinating volunteer input and health. Volunteers are also required to work alongside local villagers in building, painting, and renovation. Applicants of all nationalities are welcome, but successful volunteers have to be present in the UK for an assessment weekend and two training weekends prior to departure.

Volunteers should be aged between 18 and 28, but otherwise there are no specific requirements. Volunteers must be open, able to benefit from experience and sensitive to host communities and other members of the team. Projects last for three months; HPA's current projects run from May to November. No pocket money is provided. Each volunteer has a personal fund-raising target of £2,450 (1993 figure). Over half of this is for personal expenses, including food, travel, medical insurance and approximately £1,000 for project costs.

Those interested should write to Andrew Webb at the above address.

Lesotho Workcamps Association
PO Box 6, Maseru 100, Lesotho (tel 050-314 862).

This Association organizes workcamps within Lesotho for volunteers of all nationalities. Volunteers are needed to work in co-operation with local communities on manual tasks including soil conservation, afforestation, installing water supplies and building roads, foot bridges and latrines. Held in June, July, December and January, the camps last for two or three weeks and consist of up to 20 people from Lesotho and abroad who are prepared to work seven or eight hours a day for five days a week.

Volunteers must be at least 18 years old, physically fit and prepared to do any amount of physical work, as well as being able to communicate in English. Transport to the workcamps, accommodation and food are provided during the work camps.

Write to the Director at the above address for more information.

Mouvement Twiza
Maison des Jeunes, Zerktouni, BP 77 Khemisset, Morocco.

Mouvement Twiza organizes weekend and summer work camps for volunteers in Morocco. It recruits about 500 volunteers per year to participate in a range of socio-cultural activities including work in the slums and in schools and construction work.

Applicants of any nationality are accepted, but volunteers must speak French and English, and preferably be outgoing and sociable. The minimum age limit is 18 years of age, and applicants must be healthy, willing and able. Volunteers are required in the summer for a maximum of three weeks. Accommodation is provided but pocket money is not.

Those interested should contact Lahcen Azeddou, Studio 7ieme 'ART', Rue Chakib Arsalane, Khemisset, Morocco.

Nigerian United Voluntary Association (NUVA)
107 Herbert Macauley Street, Ebute, Metta, Lagos, Nigeria.

The Association's activities include the organization of voluntary manual labour for the benefit of Nigeria's rural areas and communities. NUVA also organizes work camps, seminars and conferences. Over 100 volunteers per year are engaged in activities such as building, painting, construction of roads and drainage systems, and, occasionally planting or harvesting. Some volunteers also help working with NUVA's self-help services for the disabled.

Applicants of all nationalities are accepted, but all volunteers must speak fluent English and be over 18 years of age. Participants should also ensure that they are vaccinated against cholera and yellow fever etc., and that they are in general good health. Volunteers are needed for a maximum of 3-4 weeks on a seasonal basis. Participants must pay a registration fee but food and accommodation are provided. Those interested should contact David T Whesu at the above address.

Nyanyahn (Women) Agricultural Development Association (NADA)
Kowa Chiefdom, Mayamba District, c/o Mr Joseph S M Saffar, Faculty of Education, Njeila University College, Private Mail, Freetown, Sierra Leone.

NADA is a non-governmental organization dedicated to the improvement of the standard of living of poor women in rural areas of Sierra Leone, particularly those in the Kowa Chiefdom in the Mayamba District. It is a pilot scheme which could be extended to other parts of Sierra Leone. The major activities include farming, household sanitation, etc. As yet (1992) NADA has not engaged volunteers on a regular basis, but between three and four are required to co-ordinate the Association's activities. NADA organizes the following activities; non-cash crop farming in crops like groundnut, cassava, pepper and beans, family life and health programmes including personal child health care hygiene and nutrition, adult education, basic literacy programmes and community development projects.

Applicants of any nationality are welcome. Those experienced in community projects, especially in rural Africa are particularly welcome. Applicants should be aged between 20 and 40, healthy, disease-free and able to work with women of the similar age. NADA's recruitment starts in January of every year; the first batch of volunteers arrive in January and stay until June, while another batch arrive in July and stay until December. Long-term volunteers wishing to stay for an entire year are also welcome. Accommodation and insurance will be provided at a small cost, but volunteers must pay for all other expenses, including travel. Volunteers live with the people and are expected to become part of the community.

Those interested should contact the Project Co-ordinator for NADA at the above address.

Pa Santigie Conteh Farmer's Association (PASCOFAAS)
PMB 686 Freetown, Republic of Sierra Leone, West Africa.

PASCOFAAS is centred around Makarie and over 20 neighbouring villages in the Bombali district, and was founded in 1982 to promote increased agricultural productivity for food production and income generation in order to improve the living conditions of its approximately 2,000 members with special attention to women, children and young people.

Activities undertaken include agriculture, the planting of rice and trees, construction of houses, roads and so on. Opportunities open to volunteers include secretarial work in the head office, agricultural and construction work and training local people in different skills.

All nationalities may apply as long as they speak English. They are required all year round for periods of two weeks to two years. About ten international volunteers are taken on each year. Preference will be given to volunteers who are wiling to help programmes either financially or with materials. The minimum age is 17. Expenses and pocket money are not paid but accommodation is provided.

The Association also supplies information to anyone interested in farming in rural areas of Sierra Leone. For further details about this or the voluntary work, contact Andrew Conteh, the Director, at the above address.

Pensee et Chantiers
B.P. 1423, Rabat R P, Morocco (tel 07-73 44 59).

Pensee et Chantiers organize international work camps in Morocco for international volunteers. The work camps last for 21 days during August and projects include forest management, gardening, construction and maintenance work. Volunteers need no special skills but the minimum age accepted is 18 years. Sleeping bags and tools used in the projects are provided. Volunteers must pay a registration fee of around £30, provide their own meals, and pay for their own travel expenses.

For further information write to the President at the above address.

Right Hand Trust
Gelligason, Llanfair Caereinion, Montgomeryshire SY21 9HE (tel 0938-810215; fax 0691-778179).

Each year the Trust places around twelve young Christian people in their gap year between school and university on Anglican missions in Zimbabwe and Uganda. The positions normally involve teaching, but there are occasional paramedical placements. The placements are usually from January to August. Training is given in the UK before departure.

For details contact the above address.

Tanzania Youth Organization
PO Box 19989 DSM, Tanzania (tel 24176-7-8).

The Tanzania Youth Organization runs work camps in Tanzania. 200 volunteers every year work on these camps in a variety of ways including farming and building for schools. Applicants of all nationalities are welcome, as long as they can speak English. The usual length of placement is one month, and volunteers are required seasonally. Accommodation is provided but volunteers must pay for all other costs, including air fares and a contribution towards costs.

Applications should be made to the Secretary General at the above address.

Union Marocaine Des Associations De Chantiers (UMAC)
BP 455, Rabat, Morocco (correspondence); or 37 Rue Al Hind, Immeuble Chandouri Maison No.; 3, Rabat, Morocco.

Morocco is a country with a young population: three out of four Moroccans are under 30 years of age. Workcamp organizations have come to play an important part in mobilizing the energies of Moroccan youth, and encouraging a positive attitude to the problems of a developing country. The Moroccan workcamp movement grew out of local organizations and the first major project the latter undertook was helping with the construction of 'La Route de l'Unite' joining the North and South of the country. This was shortly after independence. In 1960 six regional organizations were founded in Meknes, Rabat, Fez, Sale, and Safi. Then a national co-ordination committee was founded in 1961, which became UMAC in 1963. It organizes weekend camps throughout the year and about 15 summer camps lasting three weeks to a month in July and August. About 500 volunteers are recruited each year.

The summer camps are international, and all nationalities are welcome. No special qualifications are needed. Volunteers should however speak Arabic, French or English, and enjoy good health. The age limits are 18 — 35. A participation fee of about £40 is payable. Board and lodging are free and work insurance is provided. No pocket money is paid, however, and volunteers pay their own travel expenses.

Applications should be made to the individual organizations directly. Some of these are: Amis des Chantiers Internationaux de Meknes, BP 8, Meknes, RP; Association des Chantiers de Jeunes, BP 171, Sale; Jeunesse et Co-operation, BP 19, Safi; Chantiers Sociaux Marocains, BP 1423, Rabat; Mouvement Twisa, BP 77, Khemisset; Association de Travail Volontaire et Culturel, BP 4537, Casablanca, Morocco.

Voluntary Workcamps Association of Ghana (VOLU)
PO Box 1540, Aacra, Ghana (tel Accra 663486).

VOLU organizes international workcamps in the rural areas of Ghana for international volunteers. Tasks involve mainly manual work; construction projects, working on farm and agro-forestry projects, tree planting, harvesting cocoa and foodstuffs, working with mentally retarded people, teaching, etc., Around 1,500 volunteers are needed for workcamps at Easter, Christmas, and from June to October. Volunteers can stay throughout each period.

No special skills or experience are required but volunteers should be over 16 years old and fit to undertake manual labour. Volunteers pay their own travelling costs and a £50 registration fee but accommodation and food are provided at the camps. VOLU supplies offical invitations to enable volunteers to acquire visas before leaving for Ghana.

Those interested should apply either through Service Civil Internationnal member organizations in their own country or directly to the National Organising Secretary at the above address.

Voluntary Workcamps Association of Nigeria
PO Box 2189, Lagos, Nigeria (tel 01-961290 or 821568).

VWAN organizes workcamps centred around community projects for youths of different cultural backgrounds and nationalities throughout Nigeria. Between 120 and 150 volunteers per year participate in the workcamps; the work is mainly unskilled manual labour, but can also include bricklaying, carpentry, sport, games, excursions, debates and discussions.

Applicants of any nationality are welcome, but a knowledge of English is required. Volunteers must also be physically fit. The usual length of placement is between one and two months between July and September. Volunteers must pay a registration fee of $100 and provide for their own upkeep apart from board and lodging.

Applications should be made to the Secretary General at the above address.

YMCA (Union Chretienne de Jeunes Gens)

Secretariat General, 18, Bd. Mobutu Sese Seko, BP 02 Lome, Togo.

UCJG-TOGO is an international Christian voluntary organization dedicated to improving the standard of living in Togo. The organization is involved in a wide range of activities offering many opportunities for volunteers. As well as organizing summer workcamps, the organization runs education and training programmes, community development programmes, environmental projects, cultural programmes and biblical study retreats. The usual maximum length of placement is one month. Participants must pay a fee of $300 which covers board and accommodation. They must also pay for their own air fares and travel costs.

For further information contact the above address.

Asia and Australia

Australian Trust for Conservation Volunteers (ATCV)
PO Box 423, Ballarat, Victoria 3353, Australia (tel 053-32 7490; fax 053-332 290).
ATCV is a national non-profit making community based organization which acts as a link between concerned people, landholders and community organizations with expensive or potentially expensive environmental problems. Much of the essential work required to repair damage and restore land stability can only be achieved by the use of volunteers ATCV undertakes projects with a wide range of landholders and government departments, working in national parks and in rural areas throughout the country. ATCV also assists a wide range of community based groups such as Water Authorities and landcare groups. ATCV projects include tree planting, walking track construction, protection and monitoring of endangered flora and fauna, fencing, seed collection and wildlife surveys.

ATCV organizes short and long term placements for volunteers. The short-term placement of six weeks costs $AUD600 which provides accommodation, food and travel whilst working with the Trust in Australia (it does not cover the fare to Australia). ATCV has offices in all states, except Western Australia. For further information and an application form, write to the Executive Director at the above address. An International Reply Coupon for return postage should be included.

Bharat Sevak Samaj
Nehru Seva Kendra, Gugoan Bye Pass Road, Mehrauli, New Delhi 30, India (tel 4852215).
The Samaj was founded by Shri Jawaharlal Nehru, the first Prime Minister of India, as a non-political national platform for mobilizing people's spare time, energy and resources for national reconstruction as a part of the first Five Year Plan. It has a network of branches all over the country, with a membership of over 750,000, 10,000 members working on projects, and about 50 foreign volunteers helping each year. Any person who offers his services for a minimum of two hours a week can become a member of the Samaj.

Its normal programme includes the organization of urban community centres in slum areas, night shelters, child welfare centres, nursery schools, training camps for national reconstruction work, family planning camps and clinics, and publicity centres for the Plans. The work also encompasses relief and reconstruction work after natural calamities, such as famine, drought, cyclones and earthquakes as well as the construction of houses for the Schedule Caste (lowest caste) and tribes and low cost latrines in villages.

Both skilled and unskilled workers are welcomed. Foreign volunteers, who can serve for between 15 days and three months, should be prepared to live in simple accommodation and respect local customs and traditions. They must finance their own stay, and it is preferred that they speak English.

Applicants should contact the General Secretary at the above address for further details.

Bombay Sarvodaya Friendship Centre
Friendship Building, Kajupada Pipeline Road, Kurla, Bombay 400072, India (tel 511-3660; 513-7398)

The Friendship centre in Bombay consists of two adjoining flats near the airport providing a homely and informal base for visitors from India and overseas where an exchange of ideas, experience and information on social and cultural issues can occur. The centre also works with students' groups, women's groups, Gandhian workers etc. The centre's library includes a collection of rare books. Projects undertaken include visits to slums through grassroot contacts in Bombay, work in rural areas, and non-violent action against the slaughter of bullocks.

One or two volunteers are needed every year for a minimum commitment of six months to help with a wide variety of tasks at the centre and other related projects; voluntary co-ordinators are also needed for several peace-related and development activities. Applicants should be experienced in organizational work; a main task would be stimulating awareness of the centre and its resources through efficient publicity and the editing of a newsletter. The volunteer would be expected to look after and liaise with any guests or visitors, and also to help with general domestic and maintenance chores. Other activites open to volunteers include village development and other awareness-building work. Fluency in English and one Hindi language is essential, as is a belief in non-violence, and a willingness to do all kinds of work. Communal accommodation is available, but an allowance is not; volunteers should be prepared to share the cost of food.

Open-minded applicants should contact Daniel Mazgaonkar at the above address.

Calcutta Rescue Fund
PO Box 52, Brentford, Middlesex TW8 0TF (tel 071 701-2765).

The Fund recruits suitable volunteers from the UK to work exclusively at the Calcutta clinics for destitute people founded by Dr Jack Preger. Volunteers help with the day to day running of two street clinics. Duties include diagnosis and treatment of patients, record keeping, accounting, general administrative tasks, the ordering and administering of medication and the regular dressing of wounds.

No experience is essential, but preference will be given to those with medical, administrative and accounting knowledge. There is no age limit but it is important that applicants are in good health; it is advisable that all volunteers obtain all the recommended vaccinations as well as an adequate supply of malaria tablets. Volunteers stay for a minimum of two months. The maximum stay is usually six months due to visa restrictions. It must be emphasised that participants must pay for their travel expenses. Accommodation is not provided but cheap accommodation is readily available in the area.

Applicants may apply all the year round for the 150 places available each year. Those interested should write to Simon Nicholls at the above address.

The Cambodia Trust
PO Box 14, Woodstock, Oxon OX20 15H (tel 0993 811674; fax 0993-813244).

The Cambodia Trust was formed to provide emergency aid to Cambodia's 8.5 million people. The Trust organizes medical aid programmes, specializing in prosthetics, physiotherapy, counselling and the rehabilitation of the war wounded and amputees. It also organizes rural banks and runs a Centre for Sustainable Industry which advises the Cambodian government and investors on suitable areas of industrial enterprise.

Individuals experienced and qualified in prosthetics, physiotherapy and orthopaedic surgery are needed. General Practitioners are also needed to work as voluntary sessional doctors in support of the Trust's Limb Project. Knowledge of both French and Khmer (Cambodian) is necessary, as is a drivng licence and the ability to live in rugged conditions. Volunteers must be aged between 30 and 55. Placements could be as short as six weeks or as long as three months and applications are welcome at any time of the year. Board and accommodation are available at the Trust's villa and basic living expenses, airfare and pocket money will be paid.

Full details can be obtained from Ms. Jean Hollis, 21 Union Street, Woodstock, Oxon OX20 15H (tel 0993-811674; fax 0993-813244).

FEBA Radio
Ivy Arch Road, Worthing, West Sussex BN11 2DT (tel 0903-237281).

FEBA (Far East Broadcasting Association) is a Christian Mission organization which broadcasts from its own radio station in the Seychelles to countries around the Indian Ocean; it currently operates in some 40 languages.

Opportunities occur from time to time for one or two short-term student assignments in the field of electronic and electrical engineering, or radio programme production. Applicants should be committed Christians with experience and background in one of the above fields. Volunteers must raise their own funds for travel and living expenses. Accommodation is provided. A work permit is required.

For further information contact the Associate Director for Personnel at the above address.

Indian Volunteers for Community Service
12 Eastleigh Avenue, Harrow, Middlesex HA2 0UF (tel 081-864 4740).

This organization seeks to motivate anyone over the age of 18 who is keen to go to India and learn about Indian culture, and be more than just a volunteer. Each year, people are sent as Project Visitors to different rural development projects in North India for two weeks as a paying guest. They must pay for their own airfares and personal sightseeing expenses. No skills are required.

Volunteers are going primarily to learn, to have a unique and rewarding experience and to see a very different way of life. If a volunteer would like to stay on for longer than two weeks, the director will decide if he is happy for that person to stay on. Volunteers can stay on for six months with board and lodging free if they volunteer in an area of activity in which they would be happy and useful.

For more details contact the General Secretary at the above address.

International Study & Service Exchange (India)

Vakil House, II Floor, Sprott Road, Ballard Pier, Bombay 400 038, India (tel 2614359)

The Exchange organizes workcamps, job training programmes, community centres, seminars, conferences, AIDS advice, health clinics, social forestry, publications, environmental and training programmes, etc. Around 100 volunteers per year take part in the running of these various programmes.

Applicants of all nationalities are welcome, but for volunteers other than those involved with the workcamps knowledge of local Indian languages is essential. Also specific jobs require specific skills. Volunteers are needed from June to March; the workcamps last for two to four weeks but other volunteers are needed for a minimum of 6 months. Unfortunately, no expenses or pocket money are provided. Volunteers must also arrange for their own accommodation. Air fare costs must also be met by the volunteers.

Those interested should write to K. R. Patankar at the above address.

Interserve

325 Kennington Road, London SE11 4QH (tel 071-735 8227; fax 071-587 5362).

Each year approximately 40 volunteers participate in the On Track Programme in Pakistan, India, Nepal and the Middle East. Generally volunteers become involved in medical, educational and technical projects which last from two to three months. This is a self-financing scheme.

Volunteers must be committed Christians who have a desire to share their faith as well as their skills.

Further information may be obtained from the Personnel Director at the above address.

Joint Assistance Centre

H-65, South Extn-1, New Delhi 110049, India

The Joint Assistance Centre is a small voluntary group concerned with disaster preparedness. Volunteers from abroad can belp by participating in workcamps held all over India, undertaking office, editing and library work or developing useful training resource materials. Workcamp projects may involve road repair, construction of community centres, replanting forests and conservation projects, etc. Around 100 volunteers are needed each year, all year round, although workcamps are held intermittently. Placements vary from four to 26 weeks long.

Volunteers may be of any nationality provided that India has diplomatic relations with their country. All volunteers must be at least 18 years old and English-speaking. Very basic accommodation with elementary facilities is provided but volunteers must pay a contribution of around £60 per month of their stay.

For more information write to the Convenor at the above address, enclosing three International Reply Coupons. Alternatively, those in the UK can contact Mike Hicks, 15 Burkes Road, Beaconsfield HP9 1PB, while those in the USA and Canada can contact K Gopalan, PO Box 14481, Santa Rosa, CA 95402, USA.

Lanka Jatika Sarvodaya Shramadana Sangamaya (Inc)

98 Rawatawatta Road, Moratuwa, Republic of Sri Lanka (tel 507159/505255).

The ideals on which this organization is based are contained in its name: 'Sarvodaya' means the awakening of all, and 'Shramadana' means the sharing of labour. For over 30 years the movement has sought to improve the quality of life of those who live in the most deprived areas of Sri Lanka, placing as much stress on the spiritual and cultural elements of life as on purely material development. Construction work is undertaken in 8,000 villages around the country with about 30,000 volunteers lending their services every year. Small numbers of helpers are taken from those countries with which Sri Lanka has diplomatic relations, and those with qualifications in tropical agriculture and technological skills are preferred. Any familiarity with the fields of health, nutrition, education, and social welfare would also be useful.

Volunteers should be young and in good health. The usual period of service is three months or more but it depends on the visa extensions given by the authorities concerned. No expenses are paid. Limited accommodation is available in dormitaries. Volunteers are recruited according to the availability of vacancies.

Those interested should write to the Co-ordinator, International Division.

The Leprosy Mission

Goldhay Way, Orton Goldhay, Peterborough PE2 5GZ.

The Mission sponsors about ten medical students each year to spend an elective period of a minimum of eight weeks at one of its centres in Southern Asia. They receive a substantial grant towards travelling costs and free board and lodging at the centre, but no pocket money. Students must be in their final year of training, in good health, and practising members of one of the Christian churches.

Applications should be made to the Executive Director at the above address.

The Samanvay Ashram

Bihar, Northern India

The Samanvay Ashram takes on volunteers to help with their programme of educating some of the poorest children in India. Volunteers with mechanical, electrical or agricultural skills are especially welcome, although those without these skills will be considered. The personality and attitudes of applicants will be taken into consideration when selecting participants. Accommodation and vegetarian food are provided at minimum cost.

Initial applications should be made to: The Friends of the Children of India, 4 Willow Close, Saxilby, Lincoln LN1 2QL.

Samasveya

National Secretariat, Anuradhapura Road, Talawa NCP, Sri Lanka (tel 025-6266).

Samasveya works for peace in Sri Lanka and has five main projects including an educational programme with the emphasis on self-reliance, a programme for women, a national harmony educational programme, an environmental education programme and a programme for children. About ten volunteers per year work with Samasveya's local groups in the areas of agriculture, animal husbandry and health, as well as helping with marketing and fundraising.

Applicants of all nationalities are welcome and no special skills and qualifications are required. The minimum age limit is 16 years, and volunteers must possess a health certificate. The length of time for which they are normally recruited varies from one month to two years; volunteers are needed at all times of year. No pocket money is provided, but accommodation is provided free of charge.

Those interested should apply to Samson Jayasinghe at the above address.

Trekforce Expeditions
58 Battersea Park Road, London SW11 4JP (tel 071-498 0865; fax 071-498 1503).

Trekforce is the expeditionary arm of the International Scientific Support Trust, a registered charity. Expeditions to Indonesia provide physical and logistical assistance to scientists undertaking biogeographical and ecological research in general conservation and the regeneration of the rainforest, as well as giving trekkers the opportunity for adventure and exploration in remote parts of Indonesia. All trekkers undergo an intensive four days of jungle training where they learn about the local culture and are taught the basics of jungle living. All expeditions are for six weeks.

Each year between 150 and 200 trekkers act as willing pairs of hands to help the scientists in the field on their projects. There are many ways in which a volunteer can help including tagging trees, taking soil specimens, trapping vertebrates, questioning local Indonesians, catching grasshoppers and generally helping the scientists carry out their projects. Though the expeditions are primarily scientific, they are also as much an adventure with trekking, living in and seeing at first hand a third world culture, as well as experiencing an understanding of themselves and others. Anyone can be a trekker, as long as they are over 18 years of age, can speak English, and can swim 500 metres. Volunteers must possess a willingness to contribute and undertake their share of the expedition, as well as being physically fit and able to take part in a sometimes testing environment. Volunteers may be 16 years of age if part of a school group.

The length of time for which volunteers are recruited is six weeks with an extra two weeks to stay in Indonesia at their own cost. Longer stays of up to three months can be arranged. Expeditions mainly run from July to November, but also sometimes also in March/April and May. Trekkers have to raise £250; this is their contribution to the overall cost of the expedition and covers all food, accommodation, airflights, land-based travel, insurance, guides, porters, radios and staffing.

Those interested should contact Lizzy Ellis at the above address.

Youth Charitable Organization (YCO)
20-14 Urban Bank Street, Yellamanchili-531 055, Visakhapatnam DT, AP, India (tel 51122/51077).

YCO is a non-profit making, non-political, secular, voluntary rural development organization working with the rural poor for their all round development in six Mandals of the Visakhapatnam district. YCO's activities include non-formal education, children's and women's welfare, health, forestry, water resources development and housing development for 8,800 families in 30 villages mainly in Andhra Pradesh. YCO also recruits for other similar organizations.

20-30 volunteers per year help in many community development programmes. Activities include nursery raising, watering, planting, soil conservation, land development and rural housing activities, as well as the activities mentioned above. Applicants of all nationalities are welcome, but volunteers must be prepared to learn the regional language — Telugu — during their stay. Preference will be given to young people and/or students. The minimum period of work is 15 days, the maximum is six months and volunteers are needed at all times of the year. Volunteers must pay a fee of about £3.50 per day for food and accommodation, as well as their airfares and travel costs.

Those interested should contact M S R Prem Kumar at the above address.

Other Short Term Opportunities

The following organizations are mostly concerned with long term voluntary work, but they also cater to some extent for volunteers for periods of under a year. They will be found listed in the *Long Term* chapter above.

ATD Fourth World Voluntariat
Escuela de Enfermeria — Stella Maris
Habitat for Humanity
International Liaison of Lay
  Volunteers In Mission
Missions to Seaman
Peace Brigades International
Christian Welfare and Social
  Relief Organization

Daneford Trust
Boys Hope
International Health Exchange
Benediction Lay Volunteers
Catholic Medical Mission Board
Christians Abroad
Christian Foundation for Children
  and Ageing
Visions In Action

Non-Residential Work in the United Kingdom

Glancing over some of the headings in this non-residential section, which indicate that it gives details of working with *The Sick and Disabled*, *Elderly People*, *Prisons and Probation*, or *Hospitals*, may give the impression that goverment cuts have meant that volunteers are now needed to perform tasks formerly undertaken by the welfare state. Tempting though some would find it to make such a case, this impression would not be accurate: few, if any, of the voluntary opportunities described below involve doing work formerly done by paid professionals.

It is rather the case that volunteers can be of their greatest use when they are complementing existing statutory services, not replacing or competing with them. One of the volunteer's greatest assets is that they are volunteers, that it to say, they are doing whatever their chosen task may be because they want to, not because it is their job. One of the most extreme examples of this is in the case of working with prisoners: it can make all the difference to a prisoner to know that whoever they are speaking to is there because they genuinely desire to help, not because they are part of 'The system'. Volunteers are also able to devote a period of time to helping and befriending an individual, whether it involves visiting an old person or going shopping with someone with learning difficulties, that would be prohibitively expensive were they doing so as paid professionals.

Another advantage possessed by the voluntary sector is that it can react to events in a far quicker manner than the statutory authorities, which may have to drag a new idea through levels of bureaucracy before it can take a new course of action. The most conspicuous example of this involves AIDS: the Terence Higgins Trust, a charity, was using volunteers to take positive action to help sufferers from AIDS long before the Social Services had adjusted to its existence.

Volunteers are also, of course, able to involve themselves in activities that most people would accept are not the responsibility of the state; examples in this book range from promoting vegetarianism to campaigning against nuclear weapons. People can also pursue their own interests through voluntary work; dog lovers can work in an animal sanctuary run by the

National Canine Defence League, or those with equine interests can help the Riding for the Disabled Association.

The work listed in this section may often be pursued on a full-time basis, but since few of us are lucky enough to have no other commitments, the majority of opportunities described below are more of a part-time nature. Some of these part-time duties involve a fairly heavy time commitment of several hours a week; others merely require a degree of regularity or consistency. Some may continue for several years; others may last only for a weekend or for a couple of weeks during the summer.

In attempting to categorize the different types of voluntary work available in the UK, it has not been possible to draw distinct dividing lines, although it is to be hoped that the classification system we have used will act as a useful guide. There are obvious overlaps, for instance between the section on *Disease and Disability* and the sections of *Children* and *The Elderly*. At the beginning of several sections, an attempt is made to cross-refer readers to other relevant sections, but it is assumed that the general areas of overlap will be easily deduced from a glance at the table of contents. It should also be mentioned that several sections, notably National and Local Volunteer Organizations, Community Projects and Fund Raising and Office Work describe organizations that cut across the general classifications system.

National and Local
Volunteer Organisations

Unbeknown to the general public, the UK's voluntary resources are carefully monitored by several complex and overlapping networks of official and semi-official organizations. At the national level, these organizations are concerned with collecting and interpreting data, and producing new plans and programmes in response to both national and local needs. The local offices are in charge of implementing these plans, and acting as recruitment and referral agencies on behalf of the prospective volunteers, and of the local bodies that require volunteers.

As far as individual applicants are concerned, the national offices that are described below are of little practical value, other than as a source of information and referral to the appropriate local office. Local branches — whatever title they adopt — act more or less in the same way as labour exchanges. However, they vary a great deal in their policies, and some are more actively involved in recruitment than others. All can at least offer information on local volunteer needs, and can refer enquiries to the appropriate local organizations.

The people who run local volunteer bureaux should be in touch with all nearby organizations and institutions concerned with voluntary work, and be aware of the type of help that they need. For example, a conservation group may need people with a knowledge of architecture, an old people's home may want car drivers with their own cars, or a youth club may require a bricklayer to help build a new clubhouse.

There is normally a short informal interview before a volunteer is sent on to an agency. This is to make sure that the volunteer will be used in a situation where his interests and abilities will be put to the greatest use, and to tell him what exactly his job will entail. There is a big difference between vaguely wanting to 'do something useful', and being prepared, for example, to give up every Monday evening for an indefinite period in order to drive people to and from a hospital. Of course, not all voluntary work involves a regular commitment of time, but there are many cases, especially those which concern befriending people, where some degree of regularity is essential.

National Associations

National Council for Voluntary Organizations
8 Regents Wharf, All Saints Street, London N1 9RL.

NCVO was established in 1919 as the representative body of the voluntary sector. It is a membership-based organization, including some 600 national voluntary organizations. Through its wide-reaching activities, NCVO is also in touch with thousands of other voluntary bodies and groups, and has formed close links with government departments, local authorities, the European community, statutory and public bodies and the business sector.

NCVO can provide prospective volunteers with information sheets on employment opportuniuties in the voluntary sector, both paid and unpaid. It also produces factsheets listing the major national voluntary organizations which work in the Uk and overseas.

For any of the above please contact the Publicity and Enquiries Officer at the above address.

National Youth Agency
17-23 Albion Street, Leicester LE1 6DG (tel 0533-471200).

The National Youth Agency provides information and support for all those concerned with the informal and social education of young people. It provides information about voluntary work opportunities for young people in England and Wales. This list of voluntary work placements is available from the Agency's Information Services, price 50p.

The Volunteer Centre UK
29 Lower King's Road, Berkhamsted, Herts. HP4 2AB (tel 0442-873311; fax 0442-870852).

The Volunteer Centre UK is a national agency looking critically and constructively at current practice in volunteer involvement. It gives information and advice to people working with volunteers in both voluntary and statutory sectors. The Centre is an independent charity funded by the Voluntary Services Unit of the Home Office and by charitable trusts.

The Volunteer Centre UK operates an enquiry service (there is an information bank of 10,000 items on volunteering), a consultancy service, runs training courses, and produces publications and case studies on the policy, theory and practice of volunteering, plus regular publications including a quarterly journal. These services are aimed not only at voluntary service co-ordinators, but also paid workers working alongside volunteers (for example, social workers, nurses, teachers) and policymakers and managers in central and local government and voluntary organizations.

If you wish to get involved in voluntary work locally, contact your volunteer bureau, or contact the Centre's information unit at the above address.

Local Volunteer Bureaux and Councils

Prospective volunteers are recommended to consult one of their local volunteer associations or councils for advice on voluntary work opportunities within their area. Not all local associations are actively involved in recruiting volunteers, but all should be prepared to at least refer applicants to an appropriate local recruiting body.

A few of the more active local volunteer bureaux and councils are described below, but it must be emphasized that these are only included as examples, and their activities are typical of many such bureaux up and down the country. The Volunteer Centre UK (entry above) should be able to advise you of your nearest bureau or council.

Bournemouth Voluntary Workers Bureau
East Lodge, 80 Gloucester Road, Boscombe, Bournemouth BH7 6JB (tel 0202-304400).
The Bureau interviews, recruits and places volunteers with the many voluntary organizations in the Dorset area. Almost every type of work is catered for and there are usually some 100-200 different types of job available.
Those interested should contact the Bureau at the above address.

Clywd Voluntary Services Council
Station Road, Ruthin, Clywd, North Wales LL15 1BP (tel 082 42-2441).
The Clywd Voluntary Services Council collects information about the opportunities for voluntary work that exist within the county of Clywd. Potential volunteers are given advice and information before being referred to appropriate organizations. Volunteers are recruited to help with people with learning difficulties, clerical work, sporting and church activities, holiday play projects, animals, etc.
Those interested should apply to the Director at the above address.

Gwent Volunteer Bureau
8 Pentonville, Newport, Gwent (tel 0633-213 229).
This Bureau recruits, places and provides support for volunteers in Gwent. There are around 200 mostly non-residential positions offered each year. The minimum age for volunteers is usually 14 — 15 years and special or useful skills such as having a driving licence may be required for some jobs, but are not necessary not for most. The length of time for which volunteers are required varies widely.
Those interested should contact the Volunteer Bureau Organizer at the above address.

Leeds Volunteer Bureau
229 Woodhouse Lane, Leeds L2 9LF.
Leeds Volunteer Bureau recruits volunteers for all types of voluntary work in the Leeds area and also supplies information on voluntary work opportunities in other areas. Around 1,000 volunteers are recruited each year usually for placements of a month or more. Volunteers must normally be over 16 years old and most jobs do not require any special skills. Many organizations pay for volunteers' expenses but accommodation is not usually provided.
Prospective volunteers should apply to the Organizer at the above address.

Leicester Volunteer Bureau
171 Granby Street, Leicester LE1 6FE (tel 0533-553333).
Leicester Volunteer Bureau recruits for both statutory and voluntary organizations in the Leicester City area. Opportunities are available during the daytime, evenings and weekends and are both long and short term. As with other Volunteer Bureaux there is a wide variety of openings available, ranging from helping with children in playschemes through to elderly people at Lunch Clubs, or to local groups on outings and holidays. Practical help is also needed from drivers with their own

cars, people to help with basic woodwork, metalwork or painting at a workshop or to serve in charity shops and so on.

Special qualifications may be needed for some jobs, but not for most. The minimum age is normally 14. Organizations recruiting volunteers are encouraged to pay expenses. The length of time for which volunteers are required varies widely. Applications should be sent to the above address.

Rochdale Voluntary Action
158 Drake Street, Rochdale, Greater Manchester OL16 1PX (tel 0706-31291).

The Council for Voluntary Service for Rochdale Metropolitan Borough co-ordinates the work of over 360 local organizations involved in voluntary activities with disabled, elderly, young or disadvantaged people, etc. It also represents the interests of the voluntary sector and seeks new initiatives in voluntary work such as a silk screen workshop.

The Council has an extensive library with a computer, and provides a limited duplicating and typing service for member organizations.

Further information may be obtained from the General Secretary at the above address.

Scottish Community Education Council
West Coates House, 90 Haymarket Terrace, Edinburgh EH12 5LQ (tel 031-313 2488).

The Scottish Community Education Council aims to provide a national focus point for community education in Scotland. It provides an information service on topics related to community education and refers volunteers to appropriate agencies and organizations. The council also issues an annual information sheet *Summer Opportunities* which lists addresses of voluntary work programmes in Scotland.

For more information or referral, contact the Information Officer at the above address.

Service 9
66 Gloucester Road, Bishopston, Bristol BS7 8BH (tel 0272-662676).

The aim of Service 9 is to promote, support and develop opportunities for people to become involved in their community through voluntary work. Service 9 advertises and recruits for approximately 150 organizations throughout Avon by keeping on file details of the work they do and their requirements for volunteers.

For more information contact the above address.

Strathclyde Regional Council: Community Education Department
218 Ayr Road, Newton Mearns, Glasgow (tel 041-639 7160).

Around 20 volunteers are needed to help run holiday playschemes which take place in July. Non-local volunteers can be found accommodation in local student halls of residence if they can pay for their own food, etc.

Those interested should contact the Area Community Education Officer at the above address to learn how they can help.

Voluntary Service Belfast
70-72 Lisburn Road, Belfast BT9 6AF, Northern Ireland (tel 0232-32499; fax 0232-321797).

VSB only operates in the Belfast area; it recruits and places 320 volunteers every year in all types of voluntary work including childcare, work with the elderly or disabled, befriending, counselling, clerical work, fundraising, decorating, horticultural work and mechanics. In addition, VSB refunds out-of-pocket expenses, and provides training and support to all volunteers. The length of time for which volunteers are normally required depends on the type of voluntary work chosen.

Those interested should contact Alan Hanna at the above address.

West Kent Voluntary Services Unit
St James Centre, Quarry Road, Tunbridge Wells, Kent (tel 0892-531584).

VSU recruits volunteers aged between 14 and 18 in the West Kent area and aims to give them the opportunity to initiate, organize and implement projects and activities with the elderly, handicapped, children, conservation, fund raising, etc.

Those interested should contact the above address for further information.

Other Nationwide Organizations

The organizations listed and described above, whether at the national or local level, are all inter-related through official and semi-official networks. The entries below refer to organizations and schemes that are nationwide in their scope and also cover such a wide spectrum of voluntary work opportunities that they defy classification elsewhere. Other national bodies that are more specific in their activities and volunteer needs will be found under the other divisions of this chapter.

Association for Jewish Youth
50 Lindley Street, London E1 3AX.

The Association for Jewish Youth is the umbrella organization for Jewish Youth Clubs in the UK. It is also the parent organization for the Jewish Youth Voluntary Service which operates a number of schemes throughout the country in which teenagers and young adults work for the disadvantaged. Volunteers act as helpers in youth clubs, with senior citizen's groups and the Meals on Wheels service.

Applicants should contact the Executive Director at the above address.

British Association of Settlements and Social Action Centres
13 Stockwell Road, London SW9 9AU (tel 071-733 7428).

This Association unites 63 member organizations around the country doing many types of local community work. These need volunteers to work with young people, the mentally and physically handicapped and the elderly.

A list of the member organizations can be obtained from the above address and applications should be made direct to them.

Christian Service Centre

Holloway Street West, Lower Gornal, Dudley, West Midlands DY3 2DZ (tel 0902-882836).

The Christian Service Centre acts as an information centre and advisory service for people wishing to undertake voluntary work, whether short or long-term, with Christian organizations and missionary societies both in Britain and abroad. Among its various publications it produces *Time to Give*, a catalogue of short-term opportunities with over 30 different Christian organizations.

For more information contact the above address.

Family Service Units

National Office: 207 Old Marylebone Road, London NW1 5QP (tel 071-402 5175/6).

The aims of Family Service Units are to undertake intensive and comprehensive welfare work among families who require special assistance, and to develop community resources. The contribution of voluntary workers has had a far-reaching influence on the work of Family Service Units, as the genesis for the organization was the activities of a group of volunteers during the Second World War. Today there are at least three times as many volunteers, including committee members, as paid staff in the 20 Units in England and Scotland.

There are five broad categories of volunteers working in the units: (1) committee members who manage local and national business; (2) those who provide services to clients, such as transport to clinics or holiday homes, running children's groups, playschemes and mothers' groups; (3) those who bring practical skills such as fund raising or decorating, and who usually are not in direct contact with clients; (4) those who give free advice to Unit committees and staff, based on their professional experience, e.g. teachers, doctors, psychiatrists and social workers; (5) clients and ex-clients who are able to offer practical help to either a Unit or to other clients.

Those who would like to help should contact their local Unit; the address should be in the telephone directory.

League of Jewish Women

5th Floor, Woburn House, Tavistock Square, London WC1H OEZ (tel 071-387 7688).

The League of Jewish Women is the leading national Jewish Women's Voluntary Service organization in the UK. It provides all types of service to the whole community regardless of race, colour or religion. Membership is approximately 6,000 and almost 75% of these actually carry out voluntary work such as working with the young, in hospitals, for the physically and mentally handicapped, the elderly, and with and for other organizations including the WRVS, the Red Cross, Adult Literacy, Relate, and the Council of Christians and Jews.

Membership is open to all Jewish women resident in the UK who are over 15 for a minimal annual subscription. There are groups throughout the UK which meet regularly. No special skills are required, all are welcome and expenses are paid where necessary.

Applications for membership whould be made to the General Secretary at the above address and will be forwarded to the relevant Group Secretary.

REACH
89 Southwark Street, London SE1 OHD (tel 071-928 0452; fax 071-928 0798).

REACH finds part-time, expenses-only jobs for retired business or other professional men and women who want to use their skills to help voluntary organizations with charitable aims. This free service is available for jobs anywhere in Britain.

For further information contact Jill Munday, the Director, at the above address.

Willing Hands Service
W H Smith Limited

The WHS consists of the distribution of leaflets at branches of WH Smiths in the UK describing the possible range of local voluntary work and giving the address of a local volunteer bureau to contact. The scheme has proved to be a great success; it is estimated that since it began in 1972 it has introduced almost 23,000 people of all ages to voluntary work. Volunteers need no formal qualifications to take part and there is a wide range of jobs open to them.

Willing Hands leaflets, describing local volunteer opportunities are distributed from special dispensers located at cash tills in selected W H Smith shops.

Women's Royal Voluntary Service
234-244 Stockwell Road, London SW9 9SP (tel 071-416 0146).

The WRVS assists Government Departments, Local Authorities and other voluntary bodies in organizing and carrying out welfare and emergency work for the community on a nationwide network operated through area, county, district and London Borough organizers.

Activities include work for elderly and handicapped people: residential/day clubs, meals on wheels, books on wheels, visiting schemes; for young families: children's holidays, playgroups, mother and baby clubs; for offenders and their families; non-medical work in hospitals including shops/canteens and trolley services; clothing stores which provide clothing for distribution to the needy; drivers for rural transport; welfare work for HM Forces and for Service families; trained members to assist local authorities in emergencies including food, rest centres and information services.

Women and men of all ages, who can provide a few regular hours of help are welcomed. Local office addresses are in telephone directories, or for further information write to the above address.

Advice and Counselling

Below are listed several organizations that need help from volunteers to offer the general public advice and support with their problems. To offer direct help the volunteer needs more than a sympathetic ear and a liking for the sound of their own voice; they need to be mature enough to cope with serious problems, intelligent enough to offer appropriate advice, and discreet enough to respect their clients' confidence. Of course, no organization will place a volunteer in a position of responsibility without giving them during due preparation: for example RELATE (the former Marriage Guidance Council) gives its advisors full training, and in exchange expects them to give a regular commitment of their time for at least five years.

Those who are not willing to become so deeply involved can still be of use by helping with the administration and office work involved with running such large national organizations. Obviously those who know how to type or have experience of office procedure can be of the greatest use here, but there may still be scope for those whose main qualification is enthusiasm.

Blacklines
Eurolink Business Centre, 49 Effra Road, London SW2 1BZ (tel 071 738-5274).

Blacklines provide counselling, advice, information, buddying/befriending, housing advice and a drop-in centre for black people of African, Asian and Caribbean descent in South London who are HIV positive. Volunteers, preferably black, are needed to man the drop-in centre and the Helpline, to do 'outreach' work and to help with the buddying/befriending scheme.

Those interested should contact Trisha Plummer, the Director, at the above address.

CARA
178 Lancaster Road, London W11 1QU (tel 071 792-8299).

CARA is a pastoral ministry offering care and resources for people affected by HIV/AIDS. CARA also visits religious organizations and orders, helping to inform, educate and increase awareness of the issue of HIV/ AIDS.

Volunteers are needed all year round to help for one day per week with an assortment of jobs including catering, hospitality, office work and word processing. After training, volunteers can help with home and hospital visiting, and also massage and alternative therapies. Applicants of all nationalities are welcome to apply, but all applicants must have knowledge of the issues surrounding HIV and AIDS. Travel fares will be paid, and a meal will be provided after five hours' work.

Applicants can apply for the 40 places by contacting the Volunteer Co-ordinator at the above address.

CRUSE — Bereavement Care
Cruse House, 126 Sheen Road, Richmond, Surrey (tel 081-940 4818).

Cruse was founded in 1959 to help widows and their children, and extended its service to widowers in 1980 and now offers help to all bereaved people. It provides counselling support by trained and selected counsellors, advice on practical problems and opportunities for social contact. There are now 183 branches in Britain which are normally run entirely by volunteers. Each branch offers counselling and social contact.

Those who would like to help should contact the Information Officer at Cruse

House for details of their nearest branch.

Family Planning Association
27 — 35 Mortimer Street, London W1N 7RJ (tel 071-636 7866).

The FPA is a charity whose role is to promote sexual health and family planning through information, research, education and training and publicity. Expenses and training are provided.

The FPA welcomes volunteers who would like to work in any of the four centres in the UK which are in London, Glasgow, Cardiff and Belfast.

Further details from the above address.

FWA(The Family Welfare Association)
501-505 Kingsland Road, Dalston, London E8 4AU (tel 071-254 6251).

FWA is a national charity that offers emotional and practical support to families and individuals living in poverty. Volunteers are needed both to offer assistance to social workers in local projects and also to take part in fundraising activities. Expenses are paid.

Further information from the above address.

Lesbian and Gay Switchboard
BM Switchboard, London WC1N 3XX (tel 071-837 7324).

Lesbian and Gay Switchboard provides a 24 hour telephone information, advice and support service for gay men and women. As well as having detailed information on clubs, pubs, discos, befriending and counselling organizations in London and UK (including information on specialist groups such as disabled and married gays); they also operate an accommodation service for those gay people seeking somewhere to live as well as those wishing to let, within the Greater London Area. They have about 120 volunteers to answer the telephone lines, produce publicity, carry out fund raising, administration and training.

Volunteers are of either sex and are welcomed on the basis of being lesbian or gay and willing to undertake a short, supervised training aimed at expanding their knowledge of the London gay scene, AIDS and the law. Travelling expenses are reimbursed for unemployed volunteers.

Applications initially to the Training Group at the above address.

Marriage Counselling Service
24 Grafton Street, Dublin 2, Eire.

The service offers relationship counselling to couples and individuals, and operates a sex therapy clinic. The service also provides trained counsellors to run workshops for related agencies, schools and business organizations. All counsellors are carefully selected and professionally trained over a three year training period.

Further information can be obtained from the above address.

National Association of Citizens Advice Bureaux
115/123 Pentonville Road, London N1.

The Association is the central servicing body for the 1,346 Citizens Advice Bureaux outlets throughout the UK. These provide information, advice, guidance, support and representation to any individual on any subject. Many Bureaux have special legal and/or financial advice sessions with experts on hand; all help is supplied free and in complete confidence. Over 90% of the 13,000 people working in the bureaux are volunteers. Some of these have special skills, such as legal or financial knowledge or experience of administration or social work, but they should all be mature, understanding and sympathetic. The range of jobs to be done include interviewing, tribunal work, secretarial, clerical, filing and organizing. Each interviewer is asked to work for at least four hours a week.

Skills are developed by training and in-bureau experience. All new workers are required to undergo a ten week course of information sessions, practical work and visits for one day a week which should provide a basic knowledge of procedure. After this course trainees are generally offered a three month probationary attachment to a bureau. Training is a continuing process and all workers are expected to attend courses for experienced workers, refresher courses, training on new legislation, and special courses on particular topics. The service expects an equal quality of work from paid and unpaid workers. Any travelling or personal expenses incurred by voluntary workers in attending courses are reimbursed.

Those interested in offering their services should contact thier local bureau: the address should be under 'C' in the telephone directory.

Planning Aid For London
100 Minories, London EC3N 1JY (tel 071-702 0051).

This organization provides free and independent advice on town planning matters to both individuals and communities that cannot afford professional fees. Operating in the London area, their office provides written and telephone advice, while a network of over 100 volunteers works closely with individuals or communities on more detailed cases.

Approximately 30 volunteers per year help, but there is no restriction on the numbers that can be taken on. Volunteers in their own time assist members of the public, with town planning problems in various ways including representing the public at local inquiries, advising on town planning laws and procedures and developing communities' awareness of and involvement in town planning. Applicants may be of any nationality, but previous experience and/or qualifications in town planning are essential. Experience/qualifications in architecture, surveying or planning law are also desirable. There are no restrictions whatsoever on the length of time for which volunteers are normally recruited, and they are needed all the year round. Expenses on voluntary casework are payable.

To apply, or to send for a fact sheet on volunteering, please contact Sorwar Ahmed at the above address.

RELATE, National Marriage Guidance
Little Church Street, Rugby, Warwickshire CV21 3AP (tel 0788-573241).

Counselling is skilled work demanding much warmth, tact and perseverance, but it can be done very well by part-time volunteers. Men or women who wish to work as marriage and personal relationship counsellors for RELATE have to undertake a part-time training course and commit at least seven hours of their time per week for 40 weeks in the year. The timing of the work and the training can to some extent be adapted to meet the volunteer's own circumstances. An informal commitment to work for RELATE for five years is looked for. Volunteers are not normally accepted if they are under 25 years of age.

Out-of-pocket expenses are paid, and in many RELATE centres some payment is made to counsellors who work substantially more than the basic voluntary commitment.

Local RELATE centres are happy to give more information to interested people; their addresses are listed in telephone directories under RELATE, National Marriage Guidance.

Children and Youth

Voluntary work with young people can mean far more than working with those who are from disadvantaged backgrounds or suffer from some physical disability. For example, the hundreds of thousands of members of the Girl Guide Association depend upon the assistance of thousands of adult volunteers to keep the movement going, not only to act as leaders but also to provide transport, deal with paperwork and so on.

Indeed, many of the opportunities in this section are to do with helping young people to make constructive use of their time, which can also be of great assistance to hard-pressed mothers, who have their offspring taken off their hands for a while. Not listed here, however, are the untold number of children's playschemes operated by local authorities during the school holidays which keep children aged up to thirteen occupied during the week while their parents are at work. These playschemes are normally staffed by paid workers but additional assistance from volunteers will normally be greatly appreciated, whether it is offered on a regular or irregular basis. People with artistic, musical or sporting abilities will normally be especially appreciated. For further information contact the Recreation Department of your local authority, which will be co-ordinating playschemes in the area.

The subject of child abuse has been much in the news in recent years. Anyone volunteering for a job which involves direct contact with children must be prepared to be carefully vetted before their services will be accepted.

Other voluntary opportunities connected with child care and youth work will be found under *Sick and Disabled People, Hospitals* and *Education*

Army Cadet Force Association
E Block, Duke of York's Headquarters, London SW3 4RR (tel 071-730 9733).

The ACF is a national Voluntary Youth Organization committed to developing confidence, self-discipline, self-respect and health in 13-18 year olds so that they can gain employment and take their place in society as responsible, contributing young citizens. It achieves this through a challenging structured programme of military, adventurous, sporting and citizenship training. Adult volunteers are needed to conduct this training. They should be in good health, aged between 18 and 55 and British citizens. Training is given to them at the Cadet Training Centre in Surrey.

Those interested should contact the General Secretary at the above address.

Barnardo's

Tanners Lane, Barkingside, Ilford, Essex IG6 IQG (tel 081-550 8822; fax 081-551 6870).

Barnardo's, the UK's biggest children's charity, works with 20,000 children, young people and families a year. 155 community projects provide a range of services from under fives day care to work with young people with severe physical and learning disabilities. Volunteers are needed for both child care work and fund raising activities.

Those interested in child care should contact their nearest Divisional Office, while those interested in fund raising their nearest Regional Office:

Divisional Director, London Division or Regional Appeals Director, London and East Anglia Region, Tanners Lane, Barkingside, Ilford, Essex IG6 IQG (tel 081-551 0011 (Child Care) or 081-550 8822 (Appeals)).

Regional Appeals Director, Southern England Region, Summerfold House, 152 Leylands Road, Burgess Hill, West Sussex RH15 8JE (tel 04446-43489).

Divisional Director, Midlands Division or Regional Appeals Director, Midlands Region, Brooklands, Great Cornbow, Halesowen, West Midlands B63 3AB (tel 021-550 5271/6).

Divisional Director, North East Division, Orchard House, Fenwick Terrace, Jesmond, Newcastle-upon-Tyne NE2 2JQ (tel 091-281 5024).

Regional Appeals Director, North East England Region, Four Gables, Clarence Road, Horsforth, Leeds LS18 4LB (tel 0532-582115).

Divisional Director, North West Division, 7 Lineside Close, Liverpool L25 2UD (tel 051-487 5313).

Regional Appeals Director, North West England Region, Golden Hill, Leyland, Preston, Lancs. PR5 2NN (tel 0772-453929).

Divisional Director, Yorkshire Division, Four Gables, Clarence Road, Horsforth, Leeds, West Yorkshire LS18 4LB (tel 0532-582115).

Divisional Director, South Wales/South West Division or Regional Appeals Director, South Wales/South West England Division or Regional Appeals Director, Wales and the West Country Region, 11-15 Columbus Walk, Brigantine Place, Atlantic Wharf, Cardiff CF1 5BZ (tel 0222-493387).

Divisional Director, Scottish Division or Regional Appeals Director, Scottish Region, 235 Corstorphine Road, Edinburgh EH12 7AR (tel 031-334 9893).

Divisional Director, Northern Ireland Division, 114 Holywood Road, Belfast B14 1NU (tel 0232-672366).

Regional Appeals Director, Northern Ireland, Carrickfergus Industrial Centre, 75 Belfast Road, Carrickfergus, Co. Antrim BT38 8PH.

Bristol Association for Neighbourhood Daycare
Barton Hill Settlement, 43 Ducie Road, Bristol BS5 0AX (tel 0272-54128/556971).
BAND was formed in January 1978 with three member groups. These groups arose
in response to the Finer Joint Action Committee Report (1976) which recognized
that one of the most fundamental needs of a working single parent was a facility
for school age children during holidays, and after school. Such a facility would
enable parents to work full-time and the family unit to become stable and financially
independent. BAND currently has 36 member groups with six more either newly
opened or still in development. Volunteers are needed to help with the above groups
carry out their aim.

For further information contact the above address.

Children's Country Holidays Fund (Inc.)
First Floor (Rear), 42-43 Lower Marsh, London SE1 7RG (tel 071-928 6522).

Every year the Fund provides holidays in the country, at the seaside, in private
homes or established camps, for almost 3,500 disadvantaged London children.
The arrangements for the children's holidays are undertaken by voluntary workers,
under the umbrella of a small administrative staff in Head Office. Volunteers are
also needed to act as train marshalls supervising the children's travel to and from
London.

There are no special requirements for camp supervisors, beyond a minimum
age of 18, good health, and the ability to supervise children aged between nine
and thirteen. The holiday periods vary between ten to fourteen days, and holidays
always take place during the six weeks of the school summer holidays. The Fund
much regrets that it can no longer accept applications from outside the UK.

Those interested should write to the Director at the above address to find out
how they can help.

Children North East
1a Claremont Street, Newcastle Upon Tyne NE2 4AH (tel 091-2323741).

The organization was founded in 1891 and its main concern is the welfare of children
(and their parents) in the North East of England, principally the Tyneside area.
It runs six home visiting scheme with more than 200 trained volunteer parents
who befriend families in their own homes, a Family Centre and a home for six
adults with severe learning difficulties and some physical handicaps.

Any volunteers interested in helping with these activities and generally being
of help and support to families, should apply to the Director at the above address.

The Children's Society
Edward Rudolf House, Margery Street, London WC1X 0JL (tel 071-837 4299).

Originally founded as the Waifs and Strays Society in 1881, the Children's Society
has developed; as social problems have changed, so has the care it provides for
children and families. Through its projects the work of the Society is now aimed
towards addressing those injustices where children or young people are denied
choice and control, impoverished, exploited and abused, grouped together or locked
away.

Alongside qualified practitoners, volunteers play an important role developing projects and activities and working with children, young people and parents.

Anyone wishing to volunteer their services should write to the Social Director at the above address, who will put them in touch with their nearest office.

City of Bradford Playscheme Association
c/o Community Recreation Office, Baildon Recreation Centre, Green Lane, Baildon, Bradford, W. Yorks (tel 0274-593234).

At present the Association organizes playschemes throughout the whole of the Bradford district which operate during the summer holidays for children aged between 6 and 15. There are about 90 schemes in operation, many of which include children from different racial backgrounds. Most of the schemes run for around three weeks. Volunteers must be 16 or over, and like hard work and children. A small sum is usually paid to cover expenses.

Applicants should write to John Bedford, Community Recreation Officer, at the above address.

Contact a Family
16 Strutton Ground, Victoria, London SW1P 2HP (tel 071-222 2695; fax 071-222 3969).

Contact a Family is a national charity which supports families who have children with disabilities or special needs. It brings families with a disabled child together through local mutual support and self-help groups. It advises parents who wish to start a group in their neighbourhood for parents of children with disabilities and offers nationwide support to families where the child has a rare syndrome or handicap.

For more information contact Harry Marsh at the above address.

Duke of Edinburgh's Award
Gulliver House, Madeira Walk, Windsor, Berkshire SL4 1EU (tel 0753-810753).

The Award is a programme of adventurous, cultural and practical activities undertaken voluntarily by young people; it is now operating in over 50 countries. All participants are required to complete a Service Section which is intended to encourage them to realise that as members of a community they have a responsibility to others and that their help is needed. This Service Section involves practical work in one of the following fields (after some initial training): first aid; coastguard service or mountain rescue; work with the WRVS; or care of the mentally handicapped. For the Gold Award this participant must give practical service over a minimum period of 12 months, as well as reaching the required standard in the course of instruction and the service to which it is related. The scheme relies on an estimated 40,000 adults in the UK, who assist as leaders, organizers, instructors, fund raisers and committee members.

The Award programme is open to all young people between the ages of 14 and 25. Adults who help as instructors and assessors must be qualified persons nominated by the appropriate bodies.

Applications should be made to the Operations Officer at the above address, who will pass them on to the appropriate Regional Officer.

Endeavour Training
17a Glumangate, Chesterfield, Derbyshire 54D 1TX (tel 0246-27301; fax 0246-203828).

Endeavour runs courses and programmes to support its network of Local Volunteer Groups around the country. The training opportunities and Local Groups provide opportunities for personal development and enjoyment. Endeavour takes up where traditional education leaves off, by drawing out untapped reserves of personal resource. As a culmination to a person's progression through Endeavour's developmental curriculum opportunities for expeditioning are provided combining adventure with service to the host country/community.

Volunteers can work alongside or become part of a Local Endeavour Group and join in whatever community service is being undertaken. Endeavour's 'target' group are 16-26 year olds from disadvantaged backgrounds or who are considered to be at risk. Volunteers are required for a week at a time to help run summer camps for disadvantaged 8-14 year olds. Those wishing to take up the Endeavour challenge can be associated for as long as they wish. Applicants can be of any nationality but they should be resident within the UK at the time they wish to participate in the programme. The minimum age limit is 16 years. Accommodation is provided for volunteers helping on the summer camps. Expenses may be paid; this is looked at on a case by case basis.

Applicants should contact John Bell at the above address.

Gingerbread: The Association for One Parent Families
35 Wellington Street, London WC2E 7BN (tel 071-240 0953).

Gingerbread was founded in 1970 by a woman who was experiencing difficulties in keeping a home together for her sons and herself. The authorities told her that the boys should be taken into care whilst she found a home, which would not only have been far more expensive for the state, but would also have broken up the family. The organization grew as a result of the initial publicity, and there are now more than 300 self-help groups operating throughout England and Wales, with separate organizations covering Scotland and Ireland.

Although the organization runs largely on a self-help basis, volunteers are also needed, especially to assist with child care. This ranges from baby sitting for individuals to running full and part-time holiday playschemes and after school care for 5 — 11 year olds. Help may also be needed by lone parents who are ill and therefore unable to take their children to school, go shopping, or perform household jobs.

Those interested should contact the national office at the above address, who will put them in touch with their local branch.

Girl Guide Association
17-19 Buckingham Palace Road, London SW1W OPT (tel 071-834 6242; fax 071-828 8317).

Guiding aims to help girls to learn self-reliance and self-respect; it teaches them to be resourceful, responsible and to think for themselves, and develops their sense of tolerance, kindness, justice and honour and shows them the importance of family and community values.

Guiding offers fun, friendship and adventure. The eight-point programme is tailored to age groups, which are:Brownies 7-10; Guides 10-14; Rangers 14-25; and Young Leaders 15-25. The programme provides a framework within which a young girl can, by setting her own goals and working at her own pace, pursue new interests, show personal initiative and generally broaden her horizons.

Membership of the GGA is voluntary and open to any girl over the age of seven provided only that she is willing and able to make the Guide Promise of Service to God, the Queen and other people and to accept the code of living embodied in the Guide Law.

There are 778,131 members in the United Kingdom and $8\frac{1}{2}$ million Girl Guides and Girl Scouts in more than 100 countries. Guiding depends on volunteer adults.

Women, especially those who have been Guides themselves, are always needed to run units. Men and women who are able to give occasional or regular help with the paperwork, fund raising, transport, publicity, training and badge testing are also welcomed.

To make contact with Guiding in your area contact Communications at the above address.

Handicapped Adventure Playground Association Ltd
Fulham Palace, Bishop's Avenue, London SW6 (tel 071-736 4443).

There are five adventure playgrounds for disabled children in London maintained by this association. Each has four full time paid playleaders with extra temporary workers in the Easter and Summer holidays. Volunteers are also welcomed to help both with caring for the children and the playground. Charity shops in Fulham and Wandsworth run entirely by volunteers raise money for the playgrounds. Volunteers can also help with administration, office work, etc. They are needed all the year round and all skills and experience can be put to good use. Travelling expenses are given to regular volunteers if necessary.

Those interested should apply to the Administrator at the above address.

Hawksworth Hall School: The Spastics Society
Guiseley, Leeds, West Yorkshire. (tel 0943-870058)

This is a residential school for severely disabled children with multiple learning difficulties which uses many part-time volunteers each year for care and classroom work and taking the children on outings. Volunteers are needed all the year round except in the main school holidays, and there are no restrictions except that they should be in good health and physically strong.

Those interested should write to the Headmaster at the above address.

Holicare (Northbourne, Central and Southbourne Schemes)
c/o Mrs Tina Sartain, 125 Mossley Avenue, Poole BH12 5DB (tel 0202-535488)

Holicare is a playscheme for children aged between five and eleven with working parents that is operated during all school holidays in three areas of Bournemouth.

It provides supervised activities in small groups, with a varied programme that includes craft work, games, outings and trips to the beach, and swimming. Around five volunteers are needed to help run each playscheme. The schemes operate from 08.45 to 15.45. Applicants must be aged over 18; the possession of a driving licence by people aged over 25 would be an advantage. For further details contact Mrs Muriel Field, Chairman of the Management Committee, at the above address.

Hospitals for Sick Children
Great Ormond Street, London WC1N 3JH (tel 071-405 9200, ext. 5528)

The Hospitals for Sick Children organize non-residential voluntary work at two children's hospitals in London. The hospital has a minimum age limit of 18 and asks for a commitment of one day per week for at least six months.

For further details, please contact the Voluntary Services Organizer at the above address.

Lothian Play Forum
c/o Betty Kennedy, Regional Organizing Secretary, Room 9, Dalry Primary School, Dalry Road, Edinburgh EH11 2BU (tel 031-337 6208).

About 150 volunteers are needed each year, mainly in the summer, to organize such activities as outings, camping, games, painting, etc. for children of primary school age. Volunteers should be at least 16, preferably have some experience in helping with children and be prepared to work for three to six weeks. Expenses are provided but no accommodation is available.

Those interested should write to the above address.

Meldreth Manor School
Meldreth, Near Royston, Hertfordshire (tel 0763-260771).

Meldreth Manor is a residential school for physically disabled young people with severe to profound learning difficulties. Pupils may also have additional sensory impairments. The aim of the schools is to maximize the communication, physical and intellectual abilities of each pupil.

Volunteers are required to help with a wide range of activities from feeding to physiotherapy. Expenses are sometimes paid and accommodation may be provided if necessary.

Those interested should apply to the Co-ordinator of Volunteers.

National Association of Young People's Counselling and Advisory Services
Magazine Business Centre, 11 Newarke Street, Leicester LE1 5SS.

NAYPCAS is an independent association of individuals and agencies providing counselling, advice and information for young people. Anyone interested in volunteering for this type of work with young people should contact the Association which can forward their enquiries to the relevant address.

National Playbus Association/Mobile Projects Association
Unit G, Arnos Castle Estate, Junction Road, Brislington, Bristol BS4 3JP (tel 0272-775375).

Playbuses and mobile community resources are any vehicle, normally double decker buses, which provides a range of services in isolated areas, both rural and urban. These resources include playgroups for the under fives, holiday playschemes and afterschool work, youth club work, exhibition and welfare rights work, education and health projects and work with pensioners. The Association provides information, publications and support services to the 500 projects operating in the United Kingdom.

Anyone interested in helping with one in their area or seeking advice on how to organize one should contact the headquarters at the above address.

The Prince's Trust Volunteers
8, Jockey's Fields, London WC1R 4BW (tel 071-430 0378; fax 071-404 5339).

The Prince's Trust Volunteers was founded at the instigation of the Prince of Wales with the purpose of providing young people from widely different backgrounds the opportunity of coming together in a team for voluntary work in the community, and in so doing to grow in maturity and self confidence. Between 750 and 1,000 volunteers are expected to participate in the scheme in 1993.

The Trust provides a 60 day development programme for volunteers aged between 16 and 24, who are placed in teams of 12-15 people under the guidance of a team leader. A major part of the programme is a 40 day placement where the team provides voluntary assistance; this may involve community care or environmental work. Teams operate all over Great Britain and around the year. Employed participants continue to receive their salary from their employer, and those without a job still receive unemployment benefit: others may receive a small amount of pocket money.

Those interested should contact the above address for further information.

The Rathbone Society
The Rathbone Society, 1st Floor. Princess House, 105/107 Princess Street, Manchester M1 6DD (tel 061-236 5358)

At the beginning of the century, Elfrida Rathbone was a pioneer in providing care for educationally disadvantaged young people. In 1919 she set up an occupational centre in North London for children excluded from special schools, and worked until her death in 1940 to prove that these children could be helped to lead active and useful lives. The Society has branches throughout the country which organize Youth and Training Workshops, Residential Services, family support schemes in Leicester and a national advice and information scheme.

Volunteers are seen as having a unique contribution to make. They bring fresh ideas, new skills and a non-professional friendliness to people. Using volunteers involves the community in supporting children and young people who can feel alienated and lack confidence. Volunteers are needed all year round to give one to one support in social and communication skills and literacy and numeracy and help with the advice scheme. Only a few hours a week are needed but a regular commitment is important. No accommodation is provided.

Enquiries for the Manchester area may be sent to the Volunteers' Organizer at the National Office as above. For details of how a volunteer can help elsewhere ring the Information Department on the above number for details of local opportunities.

Play Matters (National Toy Libraries Association)
68 Churchway, London NW1 1LT (tel 071-387 9592).

Play Matters is the parent body for over 1,000 toy libraries in the United Kingdom; it is a registered charity. The first toy libraries were set up by parents to loan toys to children with physical and/or mental handicaps. Now a growing number of toy libraries (over 50%) are open to all children in the community. Many toy libraries are run wholly by volunteers; those which have a paid organiser are also dependent on voluntary help. There are toy libraries in schools — nursery, infants' and junior — attached to public libraries and some loan to groups such as childminders and play groups.

Each toy library is autonomous and the need for voluntary help can vary from one to another. Anyone wishing to offer their services should contact Play Matters who will put them in touch with the nearest toy library. if there is not a toy library in your area, help and advice is available to anyone wanting to start one. Please write to the Director at the above address.

Sailors' Families Society
Newland, Hull HU6 7RJ (tel 0482-42331/2).

The Society cares for the children of seafarers from all parts of the country. Up to 48 children and young people are in residential care at the Newland Homes in family groups of not more than eight. A further 550 are supported with their widowed mothers in their own homes in different areas around the country. As well as its work for children the Society provides or supports homes for aged seafarers or their widows in Hull and South Shields. The Society has a number of fund raising committees in various parts of the country, staffed by voluntary helpers.

Those interested in helping should contact the General Secretary at the above address.

Saturday Venture Association
66 Clarendon Road, London W11 2HP (tel 071-727 0670).

This association is concerned with the provision of activities for deprived, disabled or terminally ill children. It works with councils to ensure that the most is made of entertainment and sports centre facilities and supports Saturday clubs for the children and their friends. The Saturday Venture Association supports various charities and furniture projects. Volunteers are needed to assist with the various projects; surveying areas to establish local needs and then setting up autonomous clubs, working in the charity furniture shops, helping with Saturday activities in the clubs and helping on holiday projects which occur during Easter, Christmas and summer vacations. Any commitment, from one month to 12 months will be accepted.

Volunteers should be non-smokers and preferably have a driving licence.

Typing and other skills are useful. Depending on the project accommodation may be provided but pocket money is always paid.

Those interested should contact the Chairman at the above address.

St Basil's Centre

Heath Mill Lane, Deritend, Birmingham B9 4AX (tel 021-72 2483).

This youth organization based in the city centre of Birmingham needs about 50 volunteers to help in the running of night shelters, hostels, information and housing aid and counselling services. Most of the young people who seek assistance are aged 16 — 25, and come from backgrounds of tension, frustration, fear and violence. They need to be helped in finding accommodation, and in learning to adjust to a more stable environment through acquiring appropriate social skills.

Applicants of all races and nationalities are welcome, provided they speak fluent English and are over 23 years of age. Experience of working with youths in informal settings would be an asset, although not essential.

Enquiries and applications may be sent to Mr Les Milner, Warden and Team Leader, at the above address.

Scout Association

Baden-Powell House, Queen's Gate, London SW7 5JS (tel 071-584 7030; fax 071-581 9953).

The Scout Association aims to prepare young people to take a constructive place in society by providing interesting and enjoyable activities under voluntary adult leadership. Scouting began in 1907 based upon Lord Baden-Powell's ideas and book, *Scouting for Boys*. The Movement quickly spread and the world Scout population is now 16 million in 150 countries. In the UK there are some 658,000 members — Cub Scouts (ages eight to ten and a half), Scouts (ten and a half to fifteen years) and Venture Scouts, which includes young women (fifteen and a half to twenty years). There is a pre-Cub facility, Beaver Scouts for those aged from six to eight years. All offer a progressive training scheme which encourages personal development as well as collective and individual achievement. There is an emphasis upon outdoor activities. Scouting in the UK is committed to offering its services to young people in ethnic communities and in remote and inner-city areas.

Long-term voluntary opportunities are available with Scout Groups throughout the country and there is the possibility of occasional paid jobs at activity centres during the summer. Similar opportunities are also available in some other countries, notably the USA and Switzerland, for suitably qualified and experienced adults.

Those interested in helping can obtain the address of their local branch from the above address.

Surrey Docks Play Association

Trident Street, London SE16 (tel 071-232 0846)

The Play Association offers safe play facilities, both indoors and outside, for able-bodied and disabled children aged up to 19 years old in south-east London. There is a wide range of activities open to volunteers including fundraising, arts and crafts workshops with the children, working on a one-to-one basis with children, driving the mini-bus and carpentry. Applicants of all nationalities are welcome.

Volunteers are recruited for an unlimited period of time if they prove satisfactory. Up to £5.00 pocket money per week is paid.

Applications should be made all the year round to S. E. Comber, the Co-ordinator, at the above address.

Youth Clubs UK
Keswick House, 30 Peacock Lane, Leicester LE1 5NY (tel 0533-629514).

Youth Clubs UK (formerly the National Association of Youth Clubs) provides a range of services to support youth club work throughout the UK. There are over 45,000 youth workers including part-time workers and volunteers, involved in over 7,500 affiliated clubs. Volunteers are welcome, whether they bring a specific practical skill or simply enjoy working creatively with young people.

Prospective volunteers should contact their local youth club or Local Association of Youth Clubs, or the Publications and Information Officer at the above address.

Community Projects

Community projects can take many forms and have many functions: they may exist to run a drop-in centre for local unemployed people or elderly people, to provide a local base for arts and crafts, or to run a toddlers playgroup. What they all have in common is that they are all run by the community for the community. Sometimes local authorities may provide some funds or premises to assist a community project, but most depend for their existence on the time and energy of volunteers.

Anyone thinking of starting a community project in their own area should first contact the National Federation of Community Organizations (see entry below). The first problem will be finding suitable premises from which to operate, preferably with a telephone. With the right array of talents, skills and ehthusiasm, it should be possible to start and run a successful community project. Most projects find that, after slow beginnings, their schemes snowball and their range of activities multiplies. Publicity is one of the keys to the success of this type of project: once a scheme is established and proves to be useful, it will generate its own publicity. Local press coverage and distribution of leaflets in public places (libraries, information centres, citizens advice bureaux, etc.) are invaluable in the early stages.

Many community projects exist in towns and cities up and down the country but they need not be solely in urban areas: for example. residents of country villages isolated by reductions in bus services may now legally pool their resources and share car journeys, on an organised basis, for example. The best community projects depend on an individual spotting some local need, then setting out to meet it.

Action With Communities in Rural England (ACRE)
Somerford Court, Somerford Road, Cirencester, Gloucestershire GL7 2LJ (tel 0285-653477).

ACRE works to support rural community life by aiding a network of member organizations across England. Volunteers are required to work for the 38 Rural Community Councils, who make up ACRE. Opportunities for volunteers vary, but they include working in the offices, driving community minibuses and helping with rural research projects. The RCCs may also be able to refer volunteers onto approppriate community and voluntary groups in their local area.

Volunteers are required all the year round, for varying lengths of time,according to the nature of the task undertaken. Accommodation is not available, though most RCCs would pay for expenses.

Those interested should write to Ro Lyon at the above address, who will then forward enquiries to the relevant RCC.

Free Form Arts Trust
38 Dalston Lane, London E8 3AZ (tel 071-249 3394).

Free Form is a registered charity which promotes the use of arts, crafts and decoration to improve the environment and develops opportunities for the participation of community groups and individuals in school and local projects around the country. Work may be either interior or exterior and examples are mosaic wall panels, landscaping and planting and decorative wall murals. For school projects every attempt is made to organize the work so that children, teachers and parents all have a chance to help. Depending on the project work, around 10 to 20 volunteers are needed per year to assist with all aspects of environmental regeneration from workshop activities to the production of written information material. Projects begin at Easter and may last through to October.

Volunteers must speak basic English, have writing, creative, architectural, landscaping or planning skills. Drivers are preferred. Reasonable expenses or pocket money may be paid.

For further information apply to the Administrator at the above address.

Fulham Good Neighbour Service
378 Lillie Road, London SW6 (tel 071-385 8850/8308).

The Service provide assistance through volunteers to those who need it and supplements statutory services in Fulham. Volunteers are used in a variety of ways: driving, shopping, gardening, decorating, pushing wheelchairs, doing household jobs, escorting, etc. There are no restrictions or special skills required. Travel, expenses and on-the-job expenses are paid.

Anyone interested in helping should contact the Volunteers Organizer, Les Tostevin, at the above address.

International Flat
20 Glasgow Street, Glasgow G12 (tel 041-339 6118)

The International Flat is a community centre situated in a multi-racial area of Glasgow that aims to bring people of different races and cultures together. It contains a common room/library, working room,dining area, kitchen and office in addition to accommodation for four overseas students. There are various activities such as weekly sewing, cookery and keep fit classes, overseas wives' group, monthly meetings intended to help people share their religious faiths, and an annual playscheme for children in July, for which voluntary help is required.

Help is needed from volunteers either for one or two hours per week around the year or for three weeks in July while the playscheme operates. Basic accommodation can be provided for volunteers on the playschemes. For further details contact the Community Worker at the above address.

London Diocesan Board for Social Responsibility (formerly Wel-Care)
30 Causton Street, London SW1P 4AU (tel 071-821 0950).

The Board, a Church of England voluntary agency, employs professional social work staff in 12 local offices across London north of the Thames. There are specialist residential and day care projects, and they assist over 2,000 people each year, dealing with family and personal problems arising from homelessness, inadequate housing, unemployment, poverty, family conflicts, bereavement, addiction, loneliness and difficult personal relationships.

Voluntary help is needed by local committees in management of practical projects, fund raising, book-keeping, typing and advertizing. Volunteers who help with home visiting and counselling are given training and supervision.

Those interested should contact the Director of Social and Community Work.

The National Federation of Community Organizations
8/9 Upper Street, Islington, London N1 OPQ (tel 071-226 0189).

The Federation exists to provide advice and information to local community organizations on running voluntary organizations, managing community centres, identifying and meeting community needs, working with statutory authorities and other voluntary organizations, etc. Help is needed from volunteers who are able to conduct research, do general clerical work or provide legal advice.

Some volunteers give regular help perhaps once a week, others just occasionally to help with specific jobs such as mailings. Expenses are covered where necessary.

Applications should be sent to the Information Officer at the above address, who can also advise on the addresses of community organizations around the country.

St. Mark's Church Kennington
St. Mark's Office, Montgomery Hall, 58 Kennington Oval, London SE11 5SW (tel 071-735 4609).

St. Mark's Church organizes community work with the young, senior citizens, and a playgroup in the Oval area of London. It also organizes food for the homeless community of that area. About 20 volunteers help regularly every year, but even more do so on an occasional basis. Volunteers do kitchen work, work with children, youths and the elderly as well as helping with general duties.

Applicants of all nationalities are welcome. Generally volunteers should be committed Christians with trustworthy reputations, and, if possible, members of St. Mark's Church. though anyone would be considered. The length of time for which a volunteer is recruited will be mutually agreed; volunteers are needed all year round. Pocket money is by arrangement. Accommodation is a possibility depending on the availability of church property.

Those interested should contact Stephen Roe at the above address.

Student Community Action Development Unit (SCADU)
Oxford House, Derbyshire Street, London E2 6HG (tel 071-739 9001).

The Unit encourages, promotes and develops the voluntary community work of students through approximately 100 local Student Community Action Groups in Great Britain. Altogether there are some 15,000 volunteers involved with these autonomous local groups which have different priorities, perhaps concentrating on work with the mentally handicapped, children, young people, the disabled, welfare rights, women's centres, etc.

These groups are not volunteer bureaux; most members are students who become involved with the groups attached to their place of study and who state the level of involvement they are able to give to its activities over the academic year. It would be helpful if the area of the country in which involvement is wanted could be stated. There is no payment for this voluntary work; arrangements for travel expenses, board and lodging will depend upon the individual groups.

Those interested should send a stamped addressed envelope for a list of Student Community Action Groups in Britain.

Conservation and the Environment

Since the first edition of this book was published over a decade ago there has been a massive increase in public awareness of environmental matters. Concern for the environment was once regarded by many as the preserve of cranks: now it has become a selling point in car advertising.

The organizations in this section share the goal of preserving the environment against the ravages of progress. They have different objectives, and use voluntary help in many different ways: for example, Butterfly Conservation aims to preserve both common and rare butterflies by getting volunteers to study the affect of habitat and climate on their survival, while the Commonwork Land Trust needs voluntary assistance for hands-on conservation work on 500 acres of land, including coppicing and bridge building.

The largest voluntary body concerned with nature conservation is the RSNC Wildlife Trusts Partnership which consists of 47 Wildlife Trusts and 44 Wildlife Groups in the UK. The Partnership's national office itself has only a limited need for volunteers, to perform clerical and administrative work in its offices at The Green, Witham Park, Lincoln LN5 7JR. The regional Wildlife Trusts, however, have wide needs for skilled and unskilled volunteers to perform practical conservation work on nature reserves and other land of conservation interest, to work as wardens on the reserves and to help with their office work. Each Trust recruits its own volunteers, and needs may vary from region to region: addresses of individual Wildlife Trusts are available from the national office (tel 0522 544400).

Those who find that voluntary work in this area whets their appetite for environmental work can consult a new book, *The Environmental Careers Handbook*, (£9.95) published in 1993 by Trotman & Co., 12 Hill Rise, Richmond, Surrey TW10 6UA.

British Naturalists' Association
23 Oak Hill Close, Woodford Green, Essex

The Association was founded in 1905 (as the British Empire Naturalists' Association) in order to bring nature lovers in all parts of the UK and from overseas into contact with each other. It encourages and supports schemes and legislation for the protection of the country's natural resources, and organizes meetings, field weeks, lectures and exhibitions to extend and popularise the study of nature. The Association does not supplement the activities of local and regional bodies, some 150 of which are at present affiliated to it.

Volunteers who wish to offer practical help on such projects as clearing a village pond should join their local branch, if possible. These are at present operative in the following areas: Buckinghamshire, Dorset, Essex, Hampshire, Hertfordshire, Kent, Lancashire, London, Greater Manchester, Middlesex, Norfolk, Shropshire, Somerset, and Surrey. The subscription rate for members is at present £10 per annum, which includes three issues of the Association's Journal *Country Side*, and the *British Naturalist*, which provides details of branch activities.

Applications for membership should be sent to the Hon. Membership Secretary at the above address.

Butterfly Conservation
PO Box 222, Deedham, Essex CO7 6EY (tel 0206-322 342).

Various projects devoted to the conservation of both common and endangered species of butterfly are carried out with the help of volunteers. They are needed to work on butterfly habitat surveys, over a period of five years, in order to discover how habitat and climate affect certain breeds.

Participants with a considerable knowledge of British butterflies, larval food plants, wild flowers and trees are needed to carry out the work of the Society. Surveys are organized between April and October each year.

Enquiries may be sent to the Director, at the above address.

Canterbury Oast Trust
South of England Rare Breeds Centre, Highlands Farm, Woodchurch, Ashford, Kent TN26 3RJ (tel 0233 861494).

The trust offers work for 20-30 volunteers throughout the year at the Centre, which is a commercial tourist attraction run by a charity for adults with learning difficulties. Jobs are open to volunteers in various areas. In the restaurant, servers are needed and volunteers are needed to prepare food in the kitchen. Car park supervisors are required, as are volunteers to help in the shop and entrance kiosk. On the farm, volunteers are needed for a variety of jobs ranging from general farm work and basic maintenance to tractor-driving.

Applicants can be of all nationalities, but they must speak English and have their own transport. It is essential that they are capable of working with mentally handicapped adults. The minimum age is 16, and applicants must be in good health. Disabled applicants are welcome to apply, although individual cases would have to be discussed.

Volunteers are required all the year round, but demand is highest in the summer when the minimum stay would be one month. Accommodation is not provided, but camping space may be available. No pocket money can be paid. Enquiries and applications should be sent to the Volunteers Co-ordinator at the above address.

Commonwork Land Trust
Commonwork, Bore Place, Chiddingstone, Edenbridge, Kent TN8 7AR (tel 0732-463255; fax 0732-740264).

Commonwork requires 50+ conservation volunteers to work on 500 acres of the Kent Weald at Bore Place. Activities open to volunteers include coppicing, bridge building, field trail maintenance and gardening. Volunteers are required to fit the specific volunteer days offered by Commonwork. Applicants of any nationality may apply, but accommodation and pocket money are not provided.

To apply, or for a copy of Commonwork's annual Broadsheet, please contact Richard King at the above address.

Council for the Protection of Rural England
25 Buckingham Palace Road, London SW1W 0PP (tel 071-976 6433; fax 071-976 6373).

CPRE fights for a living and beautiful countryside. It is active locally, nationally and internationally. As a registered charity, CPRE relies upon volunteers for the achievements of its objectives. Membership is open to all.

Enquiries to the above address.

Henry Doubleday Research Association
Ryton Organic Gardens, Coventry CV8 3L9 (tel 0203-303517; fax 0203-639229).

The Gardens, which are open to the public, need about 15 volunteer guides each year. At present, these are only needed in Ryton Gardens, but there will shortly be a similar need in new gardens in Kent. These organic and environmentally friendly gardens are designed to educate and give pleasure. There might also be opportunities for volunteers in the organic cafe/shop and also to help in the office. Applicants of all nationalities are welcome, but some knowledge of gardening, conservation, organic growth and the environment is needed. Volunteers are required to work on a part-time basis, usually all the year round. Expenses will be paid.

Those interested should apply to the Executive Director at the above adress.

London Wildlife Trust
80 York Way, London N1 9AG (tel 071 278-6612/3; fax 071 837-8060).

The Trust was founded in 1981. It is an independent voluntary organization without charitable status which operates throughout the Greater London area and is affiliated to a national organization, the Royal Society for Nature Conservation (RSNC). The LWT has the following aims and objectives; to positively promote an interest in wildlife to members of the public to encourage them to support the work of the Trust as members or supporters, to protect identified sites of wildlife interest, to promote positive management of those sites, thereby conserving or enhancing the wildlife interest of those sites and to encourage local community involvement and volunteer support.

Approximately 500 volunteers per year help the Trust with practical conservation work, wardening, educational activities, publicity, campaigning, local group work, monitoring and surveying wildlife and visitors to reserves. Volunteers of any nationality will be accepted but fluent English is essential. It would also be useful if volunteers have had previous experience in any of the above areas, especially in ecological surveying. Volunteers must also be reasonably fit. The length of time for which volunteers are recruited is dependent on the project, but the usual minimum commitment is 2 months, although this is not necessarily on a full-time basis. Lunch and travel expenses are available.

Those interested should contact Graham Turnbull, the Director, at the above address.

Marine Conservation Society
9 Gloucester Road, Ross-on-Wye, Herefordshire HR9 5BU (tel 0989-66017; fax 0989-67815).

The Marine Conservation Society is the only environmental organization which works exclusively to safeguard the marine environment across the whole range of conservation issues. The Society is a registered charity with an expanding membership which encourages members to take part in projects to help provide a sound research base for campaigns. The Society is a limited company and has two associated companies which support its work. One deals with the sales of MCS goods and related products and the other with marine biological consultancy.

Up to 100 volunteers per year work with the Society, but this number is variable. Volunteers assist with beach surveys and clean-ups, measuring the impact of human activity and waste by surveying and recording specific marine animals. Volunteer divers are also needed to help with underwater surveys of coastal waters. Volunteers may also be needed to assist at shows and exhibitions. Applicants of any nationality may apply and no special qualifications are needed, except for the diving-related activities. The length of time for which volunteers are recruited depends on the task, but volunteers are usually required between May and October every year. Applicants should note that no accommodation is provided for volunteers, and no expenses are paid.

For further information contact Gordon Clark at the above address.

North York Moors National Park
The Old Vicarage, Bongate, Helmsley, York YO6 5BP (tel 0439-70657).

The North York Moors National Park covers 555 square miles in North Yorkshire. Between Easter and October of each year, 150 volunteers are needed to act as rangers throughout the park. Tasks include providing information to visitors, patrolling the park and carrying out both conservation work and improvements to the public rights-of-way network. Weekend and day-long training sessions for prospective rangers are held during winter. Voluntary rangers are required to work a minimum of 12 sessions each lasting for six hours between 10am and 5pm during the opening season.

Volunteers should be between 18 and 65 years old, able to get on well with people and reasonably fit. Applicants with a knowledge of the area and driving licences are preferred. No accommodation is available but a mileage allowance is paid.

Applicants should apply to the Principal Assistant in Land Management at the above address.

Peak Park Conservation Volunteers
Peak National Park Office, Aldern House, Baslow Road, Bakewell DE4 1AE (tel 0629-814321; fax 0629-812659).

Each year thousands of volunteers help to protect the wildlife habitats and areas of outstanding natural beauty in the Peak District National Park over weekends, bank holidays and during school and college holidays around the year. Types of work to be done include building and repairing footpaths, stiles, steps, footbridges, fencing, walling, hedgelaying and tree planting, pond clearance and collecting litter.

No specific requirements are expected of volunteers except that they be between 14 and 65 years old. No accommodation is available so applications from local volunteers are preferred; but tools, materials, training and drinks are provided. Individuals outside the UK should not apply until they are in the country and have accommodation arranged.

Those interested should contact the Volunteers Organizer at the above address.

Plants For A Future
The Field, Higher Penpoll, St. Veep, Nr. Lostwithiel, Cornwall PL22 0NG (tel 0208-873554)

This organization specializes in the growing of unusual and useful plants. In a world that is increasingly beset with environmental problems it is becoming clear that unless changes are made to the way the planet is treated, it will become less and less capable of supporting life. Plants For A Future attempts to address this problem; it is their belief that plants can provide people with the great majority of their needs, and in a way that works for the planet's health rather than against it.

Volunteers of all nationalities are required to help with all forms of horticulture from seed sowing to harvest, and everything in between (including weeding, rotovating and grass cutting). Volunteers need to speak English or Portuguese reasonably well. Short-term volunteers can be accommodated, but volunteers who live locally are welcome to make a long-term commitment. No expenses are paid, and no pocket money is provided.

For further information please contact Ariadne Morais at the above address.

River Thames Society
Side House, Middle Assendon, Henley-On-Thames, Oxon RG9 6AP (tel 0491-571476).

This registered charity has, over its 30 years existence, assumed the role of the voice for the whole river. The Society has been active in protecting the Thames as a public amenity, for effective commercial use, an area of conservation and natural beauty. Using volunteers the Society has been very successful in surveillance of such matters as planning consents, pollution and navigation while undertaking surveys of banks and paths. In association with local authorities and organizations such as the Thames Heritage Trust, the Society actively manages restoration projects.

Opportunities exist for volunteers to learn something of riparian management, local government negotiations and charity funding.

In the first instance applications should be made to the Administrator at the above address giving personal details and suggested availability and type of work sought.

Tree Council
35 Belgrave Square, London SW1X 8QN (tel 071-235 8854; fax 071-235 2023).

The Tree Council promotes and co-ordinates the Tree Warden Scheme, sponsored by British Gas, which was launched in September 1990. The Scheme is a national initiative to enable people to play an active role in conserving and enhancing their local trees and woods. Between 2,000 and 3,000 volunteers per year act as tree wardens and gather information about their local trees, give advice on tree matters, protect threatened trees and encourage local projects to do with trees and woods. Trees are a precious part of the national heritage and action must be taken now if future generations are to enjoy the beauty and variety of British landscapes. To be most effective, this action should be taken by people on the spot; the people who know their own localities intimately and have most to gain from the protection and enhancement of their immediate environment. The Tree Council is working closely with local authorities and voluntary organizations to set up schemes in town and country throughout the British Isles.

Anyone can become a Tree Warden as long as they are enthusiastic about trees; volunteers are needed all the year round. Tree Wardening can often happily be combined with other activities such as taking the children to school, exercising dogs and family walks. Some wardens have demanding jobs; others are unemployed or retired.

Applications to the above address will be forwarded to the relevant local organizations, or write for a list of these organizations.

Education

For one reason or another large numbers of people in Britain manage to slip through the state education system without managing to learn basic skills, for one reason or another: it is estimated that there are two million adults who can barely read, and half a million who are totally illiterate. There are many more who do not reach their full potential in the education system, and volunteers can provide invaluable help in amending this situation by acting as tutors with, for example, the Marine Society, which helps seafarers to continue their education to secondary and tertiary levels.

There is also a large number of immigrants living in ethnic minority communities around Britain who have little or no knowledge of English, which can lead to immense problems in coping with day to day life. Volunteers are greatly needed to act as language teachers with them: the job requires patience and a sympathetic approach, but no formal qualifications.

This section also includes details of ways in which volunteers can help other organizations whose aims are educational, although not necessarily to do with fundamentals such as literacy or speaking English.

The Africa Centre
38 King Street, Covent Garden, London WC2E 8JT (tel 071-836 1973).

The Africa Centre functions as an education centre, which gives information about Africa and its culture. The Centre requires 10 volunteers per year to work mainly as administrative and secretarial assistants in its office, but also as Programme assistants, who will help in the running of a variety of activities from Film Festivals to workshops on African culture.

Volunteers, of any nationality, are required all the year round and can work for up to twelve months. Volunteers can be of any age, and no special qualifications or experience are needed. Although the Centre does not provide accommodation for its volunteers, it will pay for any travel expenses.

Applications should be made to the Director, Adotey Bing, at the above address.

Commission for Racial Equality
Elliot House, 10/12 Allington Street, London SW1E 5EH (tel 071-828 7022).

There are nearly 100 Racial Equality Councils in the UK, many of which can use voluntary help in such areas as running youth clubs, arranging publicity, and language tuition. The most important of these is teaching English, especially to Asian women, as many Asians are unaware of their rights simply because they cannot speak English. A regular commitment, even of only a few hours a week, is essential in this field as those learning English may forget what they have learnt or simply become disillusioned if their tutors arrive irregularly or simply give up.

The needs of Councils vary from area to area; prospective volunteers should contact their local Councils directly, either by finding their address from the phone book or through the Information Officer at the above address.

GLOSA Education Organization (GEO)
PO Box 18, Richmond, Surrey TW9 2AU (tel 081 948-8683).

GLOSA's aim is the organization of 1,000 international Latin and Greek roots into an expressive and euphonious International Auxiliary Language (IAL). GEO aims to publicize this language, to provide information about it among the public, pupils and educationalists world-wide and to encourage the teaching of GLOSA in educational establishments.

In 1990-91 between 20 and 30 volunteers helped with the above aims. Volunteers are urgently needed world-wide to help publicize GLOSA via the writing of articles for journals and newspapers. Voluntary translators are needed to translate many GLOSA publications, especially the central vocabulary, as are people to teach

GLOSA either in their school etc via letters and cassettes or small groups/individuals in their own town. Applicants of all nationalities accepted. Knowledge of a second language is preferable, but motivation is the main qualification as GLOSA can be mastered in just a few days. Volunteers are needed all the time, and can help for as long or short a time as they want. Funds are limited but paper/ink expenses can sometimes be paid.

Those interested should write to Wendy Ashby at the above address.

The Hornsby International Centre
71 Wandsworth Common Westside, London SW18 2ED (tel 081 871-2691; fax 081 877-9737).

The Hornsby International Centre runs a preparatory school in England, and also provides, on an international basis, teacher training in specific learning difficulties and individual educational/speech therapy as well as individual tuition.

Two or three volunteers are engaged annually by the Centre to help with a number of tasks including general secretarial work, word processing, envelope stuffing, driving the school minibus, gardening, delivering leaflets, carpentry and general repairs, cleaning and the moving of furniture. Applicants from overseas may apply, but they must speak good, clear English. A clean driving license and the ability to type or use a word processor would be useful. Volunteers should be aged between 25 and 55, and they must be agile, strong and in good health. Volunteers are required on a termly basis unless they prove to be particularly satisfactory when this period could be extended indefinitely. Alternatively, volunteers can just work during the holidays. The Centre pays volunteers a small amount of pocket money, plus travelling expenses if they live locally. It is preferable that volunteers live in London.

Applicants should contact Dr Beve Hornsby, the Principal, at the above address.

The Marine Society
202 Lambeth Road, London SE1 7JW (tel 071-261 9535).

The Marine Society provides libraries for merchant ships and educational facilities for merchant seamen. About twenty teachers a year act as voluntary tutors by correspondence. One or two other volunteers are also used at the London office. Tutors can work either for short periods or indefinitely all the year round.

Postage for their correspondence is paid for and sometimes pocket money can be given to to office volunteers. There are no restrictions except that volunteers should be fluent in English.

Enquiries should be sent to the General Secretary at the above address.

Elderly People

As standards of medical care and nutrition have steadily increased over the course of this century so has life expectancy, and Britain now has rapidly growing numbers of people aged over 85. Parallel with this has been an increase in the average age of the population as products of the post World War Two 'baby boom' grow older without having replaced themselves with equal numbers of children. The result of these factors is growing pressure on the stretched resources of the social services to cope with the frailties of an increasingly large proportion of the population, and the activities of the voluntary organizatiuons described below are becoming more and more needed. Although the state can take care of an old person's physical needs, volunteers can be of invaluable assistance in helping their mental well-being.

It can make an immense difference to the life of an old person if they are visited by a volunteer, even if it is for only an hour a week. There are many simple practical jobs which a volunteer can do to improve the quality of life of an old person, from shopping, gardening or going to the library, to simply changing a light bulb, but the most important job that the volunteer can do is simply to provide companionship, whether the old person lives alone or in a home or hospital: this is a job at which the young are particularly successful. For many housebound people the volunteer is their only visitor, someone to talk to over a cup of tea, and someone who is there because they care, not because they are just doing their job.

There are many ways of entering this field of voluntary work: Age Concern, the British Red Rross and the WRVS are the principal national organizations which are active on a local scale. If none of the opportunities listed in this section appeal you can simply phone up the officer in charge of a local old people's home and ask if you can help in any way.

Apart from the entries below, other voluntary work concerning elderly people is discussed in the sections on *The Sick and Disabled* and *Hospitals*.

Abbeyfield Society

186-192 Darkes Lane, Potters Bar, Hertfordshire EN6 1AB (tel 0707-44845).

The Abbeyfield Society is a national voluntary organization which provides a special type of accommodation for lonely elderly people. Ordinary domestic properties are purpose-built (or existing properties are converted) to provide communal facilities and 7-12 bed-sitting rooms which are furnished and looked after by the occupants. A resident housekeeper cooks and serves two main meals of the day. There are about 960 such houses throughout the UK, together with 40 others providing 24 hour personal care for very frail elderly people. Houses are purchased, converted and managed by some 600 local Abbeyfield Societies all over the UK; members of local societies are al voluntary workers, with the exception of the resident housekeepers.

Abbeyfield Societies need a wide range of skills from volunteers in order to function effectively. Executive Committees usually have a solicitor, an accountant and a doctor to liaise with the medical profession and advize on medical matters generally. It also needs several members who are available during the day to be responsible for the day-to-day administration of the Society's houses. Besides these voluntary committee members, whose responsibilities require fairly specific amounts of time, there is also always a need for volunteers whose time cannot be given on such a regular basis. These contributions may take the form of visiting, taking the residents on outings, gardening, organizing jumble sales or coffee mornings, or deputising for the housekeepers on their days off.

Those interested should contact the Chief Executive at the above address for the address of their nearest local Society.

Age Concern England

Astral House, 1268 London Road, London SW16 4ER (tel 081-679 8000; fax 081-679 6069).

The Age Concern movement is a confederation of over 90 national and 1100 regional and local UK organizations which exists to promote the well-being of older people, helping to make later life a fulfilling and enjoyable experience. Established in 1940 as the National Council on Ageing, Age Concern England is a central co-ordinating body for those other organizations concernedd with older people and our ageing society.

The 1,100 regional and local Age Concern organizations rely upon over 180,000 volunteers to provide a wide and varying range of services and opportunities appropriate to the needs of older people in their area. These can include running day centres, lunch clubs, transport schemes, home visiting, and providing practical advice and assistance, and can extend to the provision of intensive care for mentally and physically frail elderly people in some areas. The time and skills of volunteers are highly valued — everyone should have something to offer their local Age Concern organization.

Details of the nearest Age Concern Group can be discovered from the telephone directory.

Age Exchange Theatre Trust Limited

The Reminiscence Centre, 11 Blackheath Village, London SE3 9LA (tel 081 318-9105; fax 081 318-0060).

Age Exchange aims to improve the quality of life for older people by emphasising the value of their reminiscences for old and young. To this end the Reminiscence Centre was founded in 1987 to provide creative activities for older people. 30-50 volunteers are recruited annually to staff the Centre and to help in the Cafe. This is done on a rota of morning and afternoon sessions.

Duties are varied, ranging from clerical work to welcoming visitors to the Centre. Applicants can be of any nationality, but must be able to speak good English. Pocket money is not provided, but some expenses can be reimbursed.

Apply to the Administrator, P. Rossiter, at the above address.

Counsel and Care

Twyman House, 16 Bonny Street, London NW1 9PG (tel 071-485 1566).

Counsel and Care is a registered charity that offers a free advisory service, particularly concerning care, for those of pensionable age who are facing problems, and provides advice on finding and paying for care in a registered home.

Some help is available for single needs payments for people living in their own homes for items such as telephone installation, clothing, etc. Volunteers help to send out factsheets.

Enquiries to the above address.

Help the Aged
St James's Walk, Clerkenwell Green, London EClR OBE (tel 071-253 0253).

Help the Aged offers a variety of opportunities for voluntary work throughout the UK. Most of these opportunities are in fundraising and may involve organizing or participating in a local event, giving talks to publicize local appeals or with a collection. Committees made up of influential people in a county or region organize programmes of high-profile fund-raising events each year. Volunteers are also always needed to help in the Charity's shops.

Other opportunities include research work, home-based secretarial and clerical work and helping with administration at Head Office or one of the three Regional offices.

All volunteers receive full training and support. For further information please contact the Volunteer Co-ordinator at the above address.

Jewish Care
Stuart Young House,221 Golders Green Road, London NWll 9DQ (tel 081-458 3282; fax 081-455 7185).

For over 125 years Jewish Care (formerly the Jewish Welfare Board), a voluntary organization, has served the Jewish Community in London and South England. Their objective is to meet the needs of elderly people and their families by maintaining elderly people in the community, supporting and encouraging families and the community to care for their elderly, reducing isolation and loneliness, and helping people prepare for and adjust to old age.

Volunteers are needed to assist Social Workers by providing a back-up service, which involves visiting and befriending people in their own homes. Other ways of being of service include driving, escorting and shopping. There are no recruitment restrictions; however volunteers of the Jewish faith will be preferred.

Enquiries may be sent to Mrs Rachel Frankel and Mrs Betty Young, Voluntary Services Co-ordinators, at the above address.

Pensioners Link
284 Harrow Road, London W2 5ES (tel 071-289 1849).

Pensioners who are frail or differently abled and living alone often have to rely on volunteers for even very simple odd jobs. This may be gardening, decorating, small repairs or moving furniture. Pensioners Link organizes volunteers to do these jobs for pensioners living in Westminster. A drop-in centre is also open three days a week for friendship and information.

Outings, socials and the Christmas day party always need plenty of support from volunteers. This challenging work with an equal opportunities collective can be very rewarding. Out of pocket expenses are paid.

Enquiries to the above address.

Tooting Neighbourhood Centre
28 Glenburnie Road, Tooting, London SW17.

The Centre runs a luncheon club for the elderly on Tuesdays, Wednesdays and

Thursdays, a community care for the elderly project and two youth clubs. 30-40 volunteers are engaged annually by the Centre; there is a wide range of activities open to them including preparing meals and work in the luncheon club, visiting housebound, frail and isolated elderly people in their homes and providing recreational activities for the young people. Volunteers can also work on the playscheme, attend regular meetings, escort the elderly to and from the Centre and accompany them to the doctor, shops or on outings.

Applicants of any nationality are welcome as long as they possess a driving licence and can speak English. They must also be aged over 18 years and in fairly good health. The length of time for which volunteers are recruited varies from three months to as much as three years. Volunteers are needed all the year round, although the playscheme operates on a seasonal basis. Lunch money and, sometimes, travel expenses are paid.

Those interested should contact Rose Powell at the above address.

Fund Raising and Office Work

Fund raising has always been one of the most important activities of any charity or voluntary body, but in the past it has tended to suffer from a less than glamorous image; people have tended to associate it with rattling collection boxes in the high street on damp Saturday afternoons. This has in recent years changed with the help of the media: both one-off events like Live Aid or annual appeals like the BBC's Children in Need or ITV's 'Telethon' have added a veneer of show-business to this essential activity. Such media-generated appeals are not, however, covered in this section, as the regular ones tend to be seasonal in their operation and they generate their own publicity at the appropriate time.

There is hardly an organization in this book that would turn down an offer of either money or administrative help from a volunteer. The organizations in this section have many different specific objectives, but all have in common the fact that their greatest need for voluntary help is with raising money and doing office work.

It must be stressed that the list of organizations requiring this type of help is almost endless, and the few entries below are merely given as examples. If a volunteer wishes to help a specific organization, then he should find the address of the local branch from the phone book and offer his services. Alternatively, many organizations advertise in local and national newspapers for help with some specific project; for example the British Legion appeal for poppy sellers in early autumn. Most good causes have some established machinery for fund raising, such as flag days or jumble sales, but they should also welcome new ideas, such as an offer from a school to organise a sponsored swim. The most dramatic fund raising schemes, such as wind surfing around Britain or running across the Himalayas, are normally the result of individual enterprise, someone feeling that he or she has some special way of attracting the attention of the public. It is always advisable to contact the relevant organization before arranging any project, as it may be possible to link it with some publicity material such as leaflets or T-shirts to increase its impact.

Clerical and administrative work are equally essential in any organization whether commercially or voluntarily run. The examples of office work included below range from routine filing and letter-writing to organizing complete surveys and investigative research studies. Although it may seem mundane, it is work that must be done if the organization's overall aims are to be successful.

Action Aid

Hamlyn House, McDonald Road, Archway, London N19 5PG.

This charity aims to improve the quality of life in some of the poorest parts of the world. Although Action Aid does not operate an overseas voluntary programme, volunteers are required all the year round to help with regional fundraising all over the UK. Volunteers are also needed at Action Aid's Chard office in Somerset to do administrative work. Applicants can be of any nationality, but they must speak English. Pocket money is not provided, but Action Aid may pay for travel to the Chard Office if volunteers live outside the immediate Chard area.

Those interested in the regional fundraising should only apply to the above address if Action Aid is advertising for such volunteers in The Guardian on Wednesdays. Those interested in voluntary work at the Chard office should apply to Mrs Felicity Rowe, Tapstone Road, Chard, Somerset TA20 2AB (tel 0460-62017).

Action Resource Centre (ARC)

1st Floor, 102 Park Village East, London NW1 3SP (tel 071 383-2200; fax 071 383 3332).

ARC acts as a broker for the placement of volunteers with business and professional skills in community organizations. In 1991/92 150 volunteers were recruited for community organizations throughout the UK for a variety of jobs using business, professional, or managerial skills. A volunteer could find him or herself as an adviser, a member of a management committee or carrying out market research.

Volunteers are recruited at various times of the year, and will work for three hours (or more) per month. It is essential that applicants possess business and management skills; they should be at supervisory or management level. Other qualities necessary include the willingness and capacity to adapt to different working environments and a capacity to learn as well as give. Expenses will be paid. As ARC's remit is for the UK only, the organization rarely deals with foreign nationals (though there are no explicit restrictions on nationality).

Those interested should contact David Hemsworth at the above adress.

Akina Mama Wa Afrika

London Women's Centre, 4 Wild Court, London WC2B 5AV (tel 071 405-0678; fax 071 831-3947).

Akina Mama wa Afrika means 'Solidarity among African women'; AMWA is a voluntary development organization for African women based in the UK, providing support services for them. This includes advice, information, counselling, the publication of a journal called *African Women*, and a project for African women in prison. Up to thirty volunteers, preferably black females, are required all the

year round to help with a wide variety of tasks such as filing, mailing, typing, research, prison visiting and helping in reception. Volunteers are welcome for any length of time, and travel expenses will be paid.
Volunteers should apply to Bisi Adeleye-Fayemi at the above address.

Aklowa

Takeley House, Brewers End, Takeley, Bishops Stortford, Herts (tel 0279-871062; fax 0279-871256)

Aklowa is a charitable organization established in 1977 with the overall aim of promoting understanding of African culture and society through the study and participation in the music, dance and the arts of Africa, all in the setting of an 'African Traditional Heritage Village'. A voluntary receptionist and volunteers with secretarial skills are needed to help at Aklowa.
Applications to Celia Daniels at the above address.

Association of Medical Research Charities

Tavistock House South, Tavistock Square, London WC1H 9LG (tel 071 383-0490; fax 071 383-0507).

The Association's aims are the advancement of medical research in the UK and, in particular, the advancement of the collective effectiveness of those charities for which a principal activity is medical research. The Association aims to represent charities supportive of medical research through membership or affiliation. One volunteer is needed for approximately one day per month to do payroll and pensions and assist with book keeping; experience in all the above areas is essential. Applicants of all nationalities are welcome, but it must be emphasised that this is a long-term commitment. The Association will pay for any expenses.
Those interested should apply to Diana Garnham, General Secretary, at the above address.

Azimuth Adventure and Education Afloat

Mrs C. Mason, 46 Vicarage Meadow, Fowey, Cornwall PL23 1EA (tel 0726-833750).

Azimuth is an association of adults and young people sharing the aim of education and personal development through the medium of adventurous and self-reliant expeditions, usually by sea in a sail-training vessel. In 1992 it embarked on a 2-year project consisting of four expeditions of a five month duration, taking 11-16 year olds to Mauritania, Guinea Bissau, French Guiana and Panama, in co-operation with the French organization 'Archipel' and their boat.

Opportunities for volunteers on expeditions are fairly limited, but anyone interested in the project is welcome to volunteer to help with fund-raising and keeping the interest in the organization alive while the boat is on expedition. One young person is required to join an expedition in 1993-4; a research background in marine studies, and an interest in anthropology is preferable. Sailing qualifications for the adults on the boat are necessary, but for the 11-16 year olds all that is needed is commitment and enthusiasm. Volunteers can join for at least a year, but longer if the project succeeds. Volunteers to help with the fund-raising are required all year round. Accommodation is obviously provided on board a boat on expedition, but volunteers have to pay for their keep. Otherwise, only expenses incurred on Trust business will be reimbursed.

Anyone interested should contact Mrs Chris Mason, 46 Vicarage Meadow, Fowey, Cornwall PL,23 1LX (tel 0726 833750)

The Balmore Trust
Viewfield, Balmore, Torrance, Glasgow G64 4AE (tel 0360 20742).

The Balmore Trust is a small grant-giving Trust funded largely by its shop, The Coach House Charity Craft Shop, which is run by volunteers. Related activities include a branch of Tools for Self-Reliance and occasional hyperactivity in 'material aid' both in Glasgow and also in the shipment of hospital and educational supplies to parts of the Third World.

Volunteers are needed to work in the shop, to help with work servicing the shop (especially baking), to refurbish tools for export to developing countries and also to help with the collection and distribution of goods as 'material aid'. Applicants of all nationalities will be accepted for the 100 places available each year, but accommodation and expenses cannot be provided except in special circumstances.

Those interested should contact Rosalind Jarvis at the above address.

Birth Control Trust
27-35 Mortimer Street, London W1N 7RJ (tel 071-580 9360).

The principal aim of the Trust is to advance medical and sociological research into contraception, sterilization and legal abortion and to publish the results of this research. Volunteers normally help at the above address, filing and sorting press cuttings, once per week or per fortnight.

Applications should be made to the Information Officer at the above address.

The British Association of the Experiment in International Living
Otesaga, West Malvern Road, Malvern, Worcs. (tel 06845-62577).

The Association exists to promote understanding between people of different cultures and countries throughout the world. It does this by enabling anyone over the age of 17 to stay as a member of another family in over 45 countries. In becoming part of that family they learn something of the customs and culture of that country. Host families are volunteers as are the local representatives who administer the programmes in each country. The National Office with 11 paid staff recruits volunteers during busy periods. In addition, volunteers are always needed to meet Experimenters arriving in this country at a variety of airports, and to act as advisors on how to recruit outbound participators.

There are no restrictions or special requirements and the period for which volunteers are recruited depends upon the job. Host families receive expenses as do local representatives. Travelling and out of pocket expenses are provided for London work and generous expenses are given to recruiters of outbound participants. Further information can be obtained from the National Director at the above address.

British Heart Foundation Appeal
14 Fitzharding Street, London W1H 4DN (tel 071-935 0185; fax 071-488 5820).
Volunteers are always needed to help with fundraising events throughout the United Kingdom.
Enquiries should be made to the nearest Regional Office which is listed in all telephone directories.

BUFORA (British UFO Research Association)
The Leys, Suite 1, 2c Leyton Road, Harpended, Herts AL5 2TL (tel 0582-763218).
BUFORA depends entirely on the voluntary participation of its members for its research, investigations and administrative activities. The association, founded in 1964, aims to encourage, promote and conduct unbiased scientific research of UFO phenomena in the UK. It also co-operates with other researchers throughout the world. The research findings and theories are published in the bi-monthly *UFO Times* and presented in a series of monthly lectures in London.
Volunteers who are both sufficiently interested and informed are needed to carry out, collate and document research. Voluntary help is also required in editing reports, summarising news, writing articles, translating relevant foreign journals and letters, and interviewing eye-witnesses, where the qualities of tact, perseverance, initiative and common sense are essential. BUFORA publishes an Investigator's Manual for instruction in researching and interviewing techniques. Some form of transport is usually needed by volunteers, since sightings can be reported in remote areas of the country. Sometimes expenses are reimbursed, although the majority of investigators bear their own expenses.
Enquiries, enclosing a medium-sized self-addressed envelope, may be sent to the Honorary Secretary at the above address.

Cancer Research Campaign
Cambridge House 6-10, Cambridge Terrace, Regents Park, London NW1 4JL(tel 071-224 1333).
As the largest single supporter of research into forms of cancer, including leukaemia, in the UK, the Cancer Research Campaign needs an unlimited amount of help with fundraising activities. There are 1,000 local committees throughout the UK who co-ordinate the efforts of several thousand volunteers every year. The money they raise is used to support over 700 projects in universities, medical schools, and hospitals throughout the country. It is impossible to do more than generalize about the range of fundraising activities which are organized, as volunteers are encouraged to use their initiative to find original means of attracting money.
Any questions please contact Linda Stanwell, Appeals Office Manager, at the above address.

CARE Britain
35 Southampton Street, London WC2E 7HE (tel 071-379 5247).
CARE Britain is a Third World development agency operating in 40 countries

but voluntary positions are only available within the London office. Volunteers are needed to assist with fund raising activities wuch as mail-outs and special events at various times.

Volunteers are normally recruited for periods of one to four weeks, all year round. No special skills are required and volunteers may be of any nationality. Reasonable travel expenses within London and lunch are provided.

Those interested should contact the Director of Fund Raising at the above address.

The Cats Protection League
17 Kings Road, Horsham, West Sussex RH13 5PN (tel 0403-261947).

The objects of the League are to rescue stray, unwanted and injured cats, to provide information on the care of cats and kittens, and to encourage the neutering of all cats not required for breeding. The practical work of the League and fund raising are carried out by voluntary workers through a system of over 200 local branches and groups, with some 30,000 members.

For further information those interested should contact the above address.

The Centre for Accessible Environments
35 Great Smith Street, London SW1P 3BJ (tel 071-222 9780).

The Centre provides guidance to architects and planners of buildings on how they can take into account the needs of disabled people. Voluntary help is needed with routine office work, such as answering enquiries, ordering publications, filling envelopes and filing. The hours of work depend both on the volunteers circumstances and the requirements in the office. Travel expenses are reimbursed to volunteers.   For further information contact the Information Officer at the above address.

CHANGE
PO Box 824. London SE24 9JX (tel/fax 071-277 6187).

CHANGE researches and publishes reports on the condition and status of women all over the world, organizes exhibitions, meetings and book stalls and lobbies the Government.

Around six volunteers are needed to help with all aspects of this work; basic administration, book production, writing press releases or other materials, organizing meetings, exhibitions and book stalls and research. The duration of particular projects can vary from one month to one year.Volunteers of any nationality with skills in any of the above areas are welcome.

Contact the Director at the above address for more information.

Common Ground
45 Shelton Street, London WC2H 9HJ (tel 071 379-3109; fax 071 836-5741).

Common Ground is a small environmental/arts charity which publishes a variety of books, leaflets, cards and posters. The main need for volunteers is in dealing with requests for these. One or two volunteers at any time are needed to perform various clerical jobs ranging from photocopying to updating computer files using Amstrad PCWs and an Apple Macintosh. Occasionally, volunteers may have to help with special events.

Applicants may be of any nationality, but they must all speak and read English. Volunteers are required for 1-2 days or more per week. As the office is on the second floor with no lift, applicants who have difficulty climbing stairs should not apply. Reasonable travel expenses will be paid.

Apply to Jane Kendall at the above address.

Commonwealth Institute

Kensington High Street, London W8 6NO (tel 071 603-4535; fax 071 602-7374).

The Institute is a London based education, exhibition and cultural centre with the objective of increasing knowledge and understanding of the British Commonwealth, its nations and people. A variety of activities are open to volunteers, linked to marketing and publicity, exhibitions, events and the performing arts, visual arts and administration. Applicants of any nationality are accepted as long as they possess the capacity to 'do the job' and can speak and write English. Short and long term placements are available, but the Institute's needs vary. There is no pocket money, but travel expenses within the London area only might be paid.

Applications should be sent at any time of the year to Paul Kennedy at the above address.

Dial UK

Park Lodge, St Catharine's Hospital, Tickhill Road, Balby, Doncaster, South Yorkshire DN4 8QN (tel 0302-310123; fax 0302-310404)

Dial UK provides an information service to DIAL and other local disability, information and advice services. It also co-ordinates a network of over 100 disability advice centres in England, Wales, Scotland and Northern Ireland.

Approximately 1,000 volunteers work for Dial UK, both at the Doncaster headquarters and with local DIAL groups, every year, engaged in a variety of functions including writing, clerical work, information officers and disability advice workers. Applicants may be of any nationality, but good English is essential and volunteers must have direct experience of disability. Volunteers are required to work full and part-time all year round and the usual length of placement is one year. Local travelling expenses are normally paid.

Those interested should contact Mrs D. McGahan, Information Manager, at the above address.

Environmental Investigation Agency

2 Pear Tree Court, London EC1R 0DS (tel 071 490-7040; fax 071 490-0436).

EIA, founded in 1984, is an independent non-profit group working to protect the natural environment and the species that inhabit it. The Agency has a very small but dedicated team of staff and volunteers. Dubbed the 'Eco-detectives' by the press, EIA has built up a reputation for in-depth research and undercover investigations. EIA teams gather unique film footage, interviews and information from across the world, often at considerable personal risk. The results of EIA's research are used for their campaigns and to brief other conservation and animal welfare organizations, as well as governments and intergovernmental organizations.

EIA works through international conventions to develop workable and effective solutions to environmental abuses, and to implement changes which will protect exploited species.

Regular volunteers are required mainly to help in EIA's London office. Duties may include opening the post, computer input onto a Paradox database, posting merchandise, replying to queries from members, banking cheques, organization of press cuttings and releases, working with staff on various projects such as fundraising, corporate sponsorship, PR, membership, office management and accounts. EIA has room for, and need of, many volunteers. All volunteers will be trained in the relevant areas. Applicants are required for anything from a few hours per day to full time all year, or longer. Travel expenses are paid after the volunteer has been into the office five times. Applicants should note that there is no wheelchair access to the office.

Those interested should contact Richard Cavaliero at the above address.

Global Partnership
PO Box 1001, London SE24 9NU (tel 071 924-0974; fax 071 738-4559).

Global Partnership works to increase public awareness of third world and environmental issues by holding an annual event with the same name in London. A variable number of volunteers are needed to work in the London-based office at intervals throughout the year, and also at the event itself which takes place every year at the end of November. Volunteers are needed to help with direct mailing, filling envelopes and other tasks according to experience. At the November event volunteers act as stewards manning the ticket gates etc. Expenses will be paid.

Applications to Benny Dembitzer at the above address.

The Haemophilia Society
123 Westminster Bridge Road, London SE1 7HR (tel 071-928 2020; fax 071-620 1416)

The Society was established in 1950 to serve the needs of people with haemophilia and similar blood disorders. The Society represents the interests of people with haemophilia by providing help, information and advice to them and their families. Volunteers serve the Society at all levels (the Executive Committee, Chairman and Vice-Chairman are all volunteers) and all its 26 local Groups are all staffed and run by volunteers. Volunteers of all nationalities are welcome to serve the Society in any way they can whenever they can spare the time.

For a complete and up-to-date contact list for local groups please write to the above address.

HEADWAY: National Head Injuries Association
7 King Edward Court, King Edward Street, Nottingham NG1 1EW (tel 0602-240800; fax 0602-240432).

HEADWAY offers advice and support to individuals who suffer the devastating effects of accquired brain damage following head injury, and helps families to come to terms with the enormous responsibility of home care and rehabilitation. HEADWAY is very much involved in fund-raising to enable this work to continue.

The Nottingham centre also recruits for almost 100 local HEADWAY support groups and 25 HEADWAY day care centres throughout the UK. The Nottingham centre has about 3 or 4 volunteers working at any one time. Locally, there are unlimited opportunities for volunteers, according to local need. In the national office, volunteers are required to give general assistance or to work on specific projects related to office administration, fund-raising, groups and membership or information and services. Overseas volunteers are welcome, but special skills or qualifications may be needed for various jobs. Volunteers are required all the year round; placements will be by negotiation. Out-of-pocket expenses will be reimbursed.

Those interested should contact Gloria Morgan at the above address.

Heritage Ceramics
Unit C16, Charles House, Bridge Road, Southall, Middlesex UB2 4BD (tel 081-843 9281; fax 081-813 8387).

Heritage Ceramics, founded in 1984, is a small collective of artists who work in the area of ceramics and pottery with the aim of exploring and producing work with themes that spring from the African experience. The UK based organization provides basic and advanced training in all aspects of ceramics and pottery, as well as providing input in arts and crafts education in schools through outreach workshops.

Six volunteers work with Heritage every year mainly contributing to and assisting in administrative management, but also in technical/practical operations in the workshop. Applicants may be of any nationality and no special qualifications are necessary apart from a basic command of the English language. Volunteers usually work for one year on a full or part-time basis. In most cases Heritage pays for travel and subsistence.

For further information contact Mr Tony Ogogo at the above address.

Imperial Cancer Research Fund
PO Box 123, Lincoln's Inn Fields, London WC2A 3PX (tel 071-242 0200).

The Fund operates throughout the United Kingdom and recruits volunteers to help with all aspects of fundraising. Hundreds of volunteers are needed annually to assist with the Fund's administration and to help run the Fund's network of charity shops. Volunteers of all nationalities are needed around the year for varying lengths of time. Expenses may be offered to key volunteers.

hose interested should apply to their nearest regional office.

Index on Censorship
Writers and Scholars Educational Trust, 32 Queen Victoria Street, London EC4N 4SS (tel 071-329 6434).

The Trust is a charity that publishes manuscripts that have been banned and gives details of writing that has been censored anywhere in the world. There is a constant need for help in the office both with research and general clerical work. Volunteers are needed to work on a regular basis even if only for half a day per week.

For further details contact the editor at the above address.

International Institute for Environment and Development
3 Endsleigh Street, London WC1H 0DD (tel 071 388-2117; fax 071 388-2826).

This organization is a policy research institute working on Third World environment issues in development. Volunteers are required to help with general office work and administration, to work in reception and to do any odd jobs. Applicants may be of any nationality, but they must have had previous experience of office work. They must also be in good health, as provisions for handicapped people are limited. Volunteers would be needed for a few days per week, or more, all the year round. Travel and lunch expenses will be paid.

Those interested should contact the Personnel Officer at the above address.

The International Shakespeare Globe Centre Limited
Bear Gardens, Bankside, Southwark, London SE1 9EB (tel 071-602 0202).

This Centre is an educational and cultural centre with a small theatre and museum containing a permanent exhibition on the Elizabethan Theatre. The Centre is involved in fundraising in order to rebuild Shakespeare's Globe Theatre at Bankside, Southwark. Several volunteers are needed each year to help with public events or fundraising and to assist the Educational and Events Officer or Development Officer. Work project continues all year round but the length of each varies.

Volunteers may be of any nationality provided they have education and interest in the Arts. Young students and retired persons are preferred. Accommodation is not provided but volunteers are reimbursed for any expenses incurred while working on a project.

Applicants should apply to the Administrator at the above address.

Jewish Child's Day
Sixth Floor, 707 High Road, London N12 0BT (tel 081-446 8804; fax 081-446 7370).

This organization needs occasional clerical help with its fund raising. With the money it raises it provides equipment for a wide variety of children's houses, mostly in Israel, but also in the UK, France, Yugoslavia, Morocco and Tunisia.

Applications should be sent to the Director at the above address.

Kids Clubs Network
279-281 Whitechapel Road, London E1 1BY (tel 071 247-3009; fax 071 247-44 90).

Kid's Club Network is a national children's charity based in the UK which supports school age children after school and in the school holidays. Volunteers have the opportunity to help at an administrative level or the organization can put them in touch with members of KCN who do face-to-face work with children.

One and two volunteers help in KCN's London based office each year; they assist with general administrative duties including photocopying, word processing, reception work and filing, as well as helping with the preparation for training events and seminars. Applicants may be of any nationality but they should speak fluent English, particularly for such tasks as reception and telephone work. The KCN building is not accessible to wheelchair users. All volunteers must abide by an Equal Opportunities policy. Volunteers will be expected to work for KCN on a fairly flexible basis; the office needs help all the year round. Expenses will be paid subject to negotiation with the volunteer.

Those interested should contact Colette Kelleher at the above address.

Kurdish Cultural Centre
14 Stannary Street, London SE11 4AA (tel 071 735-0918; fax 071 582-8894).
The Centre gives assistance to Kurdish refugeees and asylum seekers in the UK,

promotes Kurdish culture and is involved in relief work in Kurdistan.

Approximately 100 volunteers of all nationalities work for the Centre every year, helping with office work, translation, relief work, and work with refugees in London. Help is needed all the year round and volunteers are welcome to work with the Centre as much as possible. Travel and lunch expenses are paid.

Those interested should apply to Sarbast Aram at the above address.

Life Education Centres
115-123 Baynham Street, London NW1 0AG (tel 071 267-2516; fax 071 267-2044).
Life Education Centres provide positive and innovative drug prevention programmes for children and young people aged from three to fifteen via mobile classrooms which travel to schools throughout a region. The 11 mobiles are equipped with audio-visual and advanced teaching aids and the programmes are run by specialist educators. Life Education also produce materials for use in following up the messages of the programmes for schools.

Three or four volunteers are engaged by the organization each year. Volunteers are usually sporadically involved in fund-raising or awareness raising events in London, although the organization does have a part-time volunteer accountant and there may be occasions when a suitably qualified volunteer might become involved in education work with children. Usually, no qualifications or skills are needed but volunteers must have had either teaching qualifications or experience if they are to be involved in any education-based activities. Out-of-pocket expenses are usually reimbursed.

Applications to Jane Goodwin at the above address.

LINK — Global Book Aid (Books Abroad)
Richmond Avenue, Rhynie by Huntly, Aberdeenshire AB54 4HJ (tel 046 46-446).
This registered charity sends carefully chosen five kg parcels of gift books direct to the places of greatest need worldwide. It was founded in 1982 with the aim of joining the battle against illiteracy in needy parts of the world. Two volunteers per year work in their HQ in Scotland helping with book sorting and selection, and performing general clerical tasks. Applicants of any nationality are welcome. Knowledge of school text-book requirements and the abiltiy to lift boxes of books are needed.

Volunteers are needed every year for the six week period between the beginning of July unti the 20th August (approximately). Expenses may be negotiable.

Applications should be sent to Keith Brunskill at the above address

Live Music Now!
15 Grosvenor Gardens, London SW1W 0BD (tel 071 828-7073).
Live Music Now! is dedicated to taking live music to disabled and disadvantaged people throughout the UK. Two volunteers per year help with book-keeping and typing in their London office. Volunteers are wanted all the year round for indefinite periods of time. Minimal travel expenses are paid.

Apply to Virginia Renshaw, the Director, at the above address.

National Asthma Campaign
Providence House, Providence Place, Islington, London (tel 071-226 2260; fax 071-704 0740).
The National Asthma Campaign is the major charity in the UK funding research

into asthma and allergy in hospitals and university departments throughout the country; it strives to improve the treatment and management of asthma and ultimately to find a cure. The Campaign also provides information for doctors and nurses, sponsors activity holidays for children and provides help and advice for all people with asthma and their families.

About 12 volunteers per year are needed to help in the London office with clerical work, data entry and typing and filing, etc. Volunteers of all nationalities are accepted; it would be useful if applicants have knowledge and/or experience of asthma. The office is without disabled access. Volunteers are needed for any length of time all the year round. No expenses are paid.

Applications should be made to Lynne Elliot, Voluntary Personnel Officer, at the above address.

National Canine Defence League
1-2 Pratt Mews, London NW1 OAD (tel 071-388 0137).

Although volunteers are needed at rescue centres for mistreated and abandoned dogs throughout the country to help with the exercising of the dogs their help is especially needed to help raise funds to keep the centres open, running coffee mornings and stalls at local venues, etc. In addition, clerical help is always welcomed at the head office in London. Volunteers should be at least 18 years of age.

A list of centres is available from the above address.

National Society for the Prevention of Cruelty to Children
67 Saffron Hill, London EC1N 8RS (tel 071-242 1626).

Although the society's active work is conducted only by professionally qualified staff, volunteers are always needed to start fund raising groups or join in existing groups. The society has around 4,000 branch and district committees that raise money through house to house collections, organizing eventss and flag days, etc. Many individuals and groups of people help by running their own fun activities in aid of the Society.

Those willing to help should contact the Appeals Dept. at the above address.

New Consumer
52 Elswick Road, Newcastle-upon-Tyne NE4 6JH (tel 091-272 1148; fax 091-272 1148).

New Consumer is a charitable membership-supported public interest research organization; by evaluating and comparing the social and environmental policies of Britain's biggest companies, New Consumer enables consumers to apply their own values to the choices they make on their everyday shopping trips. The organization also plans suitable economic development projects of an environmental or social nature. Three or four volunteers per year are required to work in the New Consumer office, carrying out policy and issue research with UK and international companies. Volunteers have the opportunity to work on high level reports and publications, and get credited. As well as meeting a social objective the work provides excellent experience of corporate policy.

Volunteers may be of any nationality, but they must be over the age of 21, have at least a first degree in an honours subject (with a first or 2:1), and be computer literate. Unfortunately, the office does not have wheelchair access. Volunteers stay for 3-6 months, possibly longer, and are required all the year round. New Consumer pays travel and subsistence expenses and it might be possible to provide accommodation.

Those interested should apply to Richard Adams, the Director, at the above address.

Nicaragua Health Fund

83 Margaret Street, London W1N 7HB (tel 071-580 4292).

The Fund aims to raise awareness and raise money in Britain to support primary health care projects and the provision of medical supplies in Nicaragua. It also promotes and supports visits to Nicaragua by British health professionals.

Volunteers are needed to help in the Fund's London office; about 30 volunteers help every year. They assist with clerical work such as updating membership files on computer, desk-top publishing, book-keeping, fund-raising and translation. Some shadow the jobs of the Director of Appeals, the Director of Programmes or the Volunteer Administrator. The tasks are varied and training, supervision and support will be given. The Fund holds frequent mail-out parties in which volunteers and staff stuff envelopes to Latin American music, and food and drink are provided. Fluency in Spanish is therefore useful; black and Latin American applicants are very welcome. Most volunteers stay for six months; this is reviewed after six months. Extra volunteers are needed during Central America Week at the end of March. The Fund will pay for volunteers' travel expenses to and from the office.

Those interested should contact Sonay Yusuf at the above address.

One Village

Charlbury, Oxford OX7 3SQ (tel/fax 0608-811811).

One Village works with craft producers' co-operatives in Africa, Asia, South America, and sells their products in the UK. There are opportunities for volunteers in One Village shops in the UK, particularly in Oxford; these take the form of both long-term commitments and temporary holiday-time jobs. Other posts can also sometimes be filled by volunteers. The length of time for which volunteers are recruited varies. Expenses are sometimes paid

Applicants, of any nationality, should contact Roy Scott at the above address.

OXFAM

Oxfam House, 274 Banbury Road, Oxford OX2 7DZ (tel 0865-56777).

OXFAM volunteers work in the UK and Republic of Ireland to help OXFAM carry out its objective of relieving poverty, distress and suffering in any part of the world. As well as raising funds, this involves campaigning and educating the public in order to help tackle the causes of poverty. OXFAM is committed to an Equal Opportunities Policy and welcomes offers of help from people of all backgrounds and abilities.

OXFAM does not send volunteers overseas but around many thousands of people are involved in OXFAM's work throughout the UK and Ireland. They run over 800 shops and work in area and district offices throughout the UK and Ireland.

Some help organize fundraising events, others are involved in campaigning and educational work. In the area offices, help with clerical and administrative work is often needed too. People with special skills such as book-keeping, design and typing can often put their talents to good use with OXFAM, but there are lots of opportunities for people without any particular qualifications.   In the Oxford headquarters over 100 volunteers work with 450 staff on a range of duties from routine packing and mailing through to research projects. Local OXFAM groups also exist in Rome, Bonn and Hong Kong. They do not provide accommodation or pocket money, but do reimburse travel expenses and meals, depending on the number of hours the volunteer works each day. Many areas offer a local one-day 'knowledge of Oxfam' course as an introduction to the organization. A Booklet, *Volunteer for a Fairer World*, gives more details about volunteering opportunities in OXFAM.

For further information, look up your local OXFAM office in the telephone book, or contact the National Volunteers Advisor at the above address.

PLAN International (UK)

5/6 Underhill Street, Camden, London NW1 7HS (tel 071-485 6612; fax 071-485 2107)

PLAN International operates in developing countries worldwide — Asia, the Far East, Africa and Central and South America. However, volunteers are only needed in the London office. On average, about ten volunteers are employed each week; they help with sending out letters from the children in the developing countries to their sponsors, some computer work and general office duties. Every effort is made to match the skills of the volunteer to the work which is available. Applicants of any nationality are welcome, and no special skills or qualifications are needed. The length of time for which volunteers are normally recruited varies considerably. Some volunteers come between jobs, others for a week or two at a time, many regularly each week. Travel expenses within London are paid, and desks and any other materials required are provided.

Those interested should contact Frances E. Pope at the above address at any time of the year.

Population Concern

231 Tottenham Court Road, London W1P 9AE (tel 071-637 9582 or 071-631 1546).

Population Concern raises funds for overseas population and development programmes, provides an information service and campaigns on population and related issues in schools and amongst the public. Projects are being undertaken in many developing countries in Africa, the Caribbean, Asia and the Pacific but volunteers are only required in the London office. Volunteers may work on a regular basis or just for short intensive periods, all year round. The work available depends on the applicant's interests and skills but includes such areas of work as information, education, fund raising and occasional project work.

Special skills such as typing, word processing and artwork skills are desirable but not essential. Students or recent graduates in Demography and related disciplines are very welcome. Payment of travelling expenses is negotiable but accommodation is not provided.

Those interested should apply to the Information Officer at the above address.

Psychiatry Research Trust
De Crespigny Park, Denmark Hill, London SE5 8AF (tel 071-703 6217; fax 071-703 5796).

The Trust raises funds for research into mental illness, brain disease and mental handicap at the Institute of Psychiatry. Approximately 50 volunteers per year are engaged by the Trust to assist with fund-raising and general office work. Volunteers may be of all nationalities; there are no restrictions on the type of volunteer required by the Trust.

For further information please contact Sandra Refault at the above address.

Ranfurly Library Service Ltd.
39-41 Coldharbour Lane, London SE5 9NR (tel 071-733 3577; fax 071-978 8006).

This organization sorts and processes books to be sent to libraries and institutions in the Third World. Between 15 and 20 volunteers of all nationalities per year help with the packing, sorting and stamping of books in the Warehouse in London. They also carry out secretarial and administrative duties in the office, as well as assisting with fundraising. The length of time for which volunteers are normally recruited varies, but they are required all year round. Expenses are paid.

Those interested should contact David Membrey at the above address.

Research Into Ageing
49 Queen Victoria Street, London EC4N 4SA (tel 071-236 4365; fax 071-489 0384).

This is a UK-based medical charity dedicated to improving the quality of life of the elderly through the initiation and funding of medical research. The funding relies on volunteer support groups, and volunteers are also needed in the Head Office in London.

Between 200 and 300 volunteers work for RIA every year. In Head Office volunteers are required to assist with general clerical work, including work on computers; volunteers are also needed to raise public awareness of the issues of ageing by organizing events and fund-raising. Applicants may be of all nationalities, and no special skills or qualifications are needed. Volunteers are recruited all the year round, and there is no restriction on the length of placement. Some expenses, mainly travel, will be paid.

Applications should be made to Julie Brierly, Appeals Co-ordinator, at the above address.

Royal National Lifeboat Institution
West Quay Road, Poole, Dorset BH15 1HZ (tel 0202-671133).

The operator of the lifeboat service throughout Britain and the Irish Republic, the RNLI is supported entirely by voluntary contributions. It is impossible to estimate the number of volunteers who assist the service; most of the crews of the life boats run from the 200 lifeboat stations are unpaid, and there are also some 2,000 fund raising branches around the UK.

There is an important distinction between these two forms of voluntary work; while anyone who is willing will be welcomed to assist with the raising of money, only those who are qualified seamen and live in the vicinity of a lifeboat station can be accepted as crew.

It is preferred that those interested should apply to their local branch of the RNLI, but if there is any difficulty about obtaining the relevant address, please contact the Public Relations Department at the above address.

St. James's House

108 Hampstead Road, London NW1 2LS (tel 071-388 2588; fax 071-388 1553).

St. James's House provides work and training for people with mental health problems in London. A drop-in service is planned, together with some structured activities which will benefit enormously from the support of volunteers. Volunteers do some supervisory work directly with clients, as well as administrative and secretarial work. Volunteers are required to assist with research and development and they could also become involved in outreach work, such as buddying. Projects open to volunteers might include feasibility studies and fundraising events, and longer-term volunteers might be needed for specific tasks. There are no restrictions on the type of volunteer required other than people living legally in the UK, able to communicate effectively in English. Volunteers are required all year round for an indefinite amount of time. Travelling expenses are paid.

Those interested should contact Helena Holt at the above address.

Soil Association

The Organic Food and Farming Centre, 86 Colston Street, Bristol B51 5BB (tel 0272-290661; fax 0272-252504).

The Soil Association is dedicated to the promotion of organic food and farming in the UK. The number of volunteers engaged annually varies enormously; there are usually two or three volunteers in the office at any one time, but some have been regular volunteers for years.

Volunteers assist with general office and administrative work, as well as being involved with special projects. Applicants of all nationalities are accepted as long as they have good written and spoken English. Office and keyboard skills would be useful. There is no age limit and volunteers must be in good health. The length of time for which they are recruited varies but it would help if volunteers can come to the office on a regular basis. Lunch and local travel expenses are paid.

Applications should be made to Francis Cooper at the above address.

SOS Childrens Villages UK

32 Bridge Street, Cambridge CB2 1UJ (tel 0223-65589).

SOS Childrens Villages is an international charity caring for orphaned and abandoned children all over the world, and SOS Childrens Villages UK was formed to help fund SOS projects. Volunteers are needed to staff two shops in Cambridge which sell top quality third world crafts. Around 50 volunteers act as shop assistants throughout the year. No special skills are required but volunteers should have common sense and be reasonably active. No accommodation is provided but local bus fares are refunded.

For further details contact the Trading Manager at the above address.

Survival International

310 Edgware Road, London W2 1DY (tel 071-723 5535).

Survival International is an organization working for and publicising the rights of threatened tribal peoples. Approximately ten volunteers are needed in London each year to help with routine clerical work and other duties in all departments of Survival International including press, publications, projects, membership and administration. Duties include filing, typing, photocopying and mailing. Volunteers are needed year round and must give a regular commitment of a certain number of days per week for at least three months. No special skills are needed but there is no access for people in wheelchairs. Up to £2 per day is provided for travel expenses.

Enquiries to the Administrative Assistant at the above address.

Teaching Aids At Low Cost (TALC)

PO Box 49, St Albans, Herts AL1 4AX (tel 0727-53869; fax 0727-46852).

This organization co-ordinates the distribution of health care teaching materials worldwide. One or two volunteers per year help with office work in St Albans for one or two days per week. Volunteers may be of any nationality, but they must speak fluent English and have a good knowledge of third world issues. They must also be fit enough to carry piles of books. There is no fixed length of time for which volunteers are normally be recruited, and volunteers are required all the year round. Travel and lunch expenses are paid.

Applications to Barbara Harvey at the above address.

The Tibetan Community in Britain/The Tibetan Refugee Charitable Trust

13 St Giles Court, Dane Road, Ealing, London W13 9AQ (tel 081-567 7882).

The Tibetan Community in Britain is the association of all Tibetans living in the United Kingdom, formed in 1970 to establish a formal organization to inform the people and government of Britain of the plight and suffering of the Tibetan people under the occupation of the Chinese Communists. Anyone interested in the struggle of Tibetans to regain their independence and preserve their unique culture is welcome to become involved. The Community organizes public events in the UK and sends donations to the Tibetan administration in India towards their various projects for Tibetan refugees and sponsoring Tibetan children's education.

There are over 200 supportive members who participate in the Community's functions and raise funds for its work for the Tibetan cause. Anyone who subscribes to the Community's objectives and pays an annual subscription of £5 is welcome to join as a supportive member. Most of these volunteers work to publicize monthly events but there is no fixed job description. Most of the Community's activities are related to fundraising and the promotion of a greater awareness of Tibetan issues. Any skills in publicity and fundraising are therefore very welcome, as would be anyone with a driving licence. There are no age limits.

Those interested should contact the above address.

Tidy Britain Group
The Pier, Wigan WN3 4EX (tel 0942-824620; fax 0942-824778).
This organization is a government agency dedicated to the control of litter and environmental improvement. Volunteers are needed all the year round to help with general office work in local offices throughout the UK. Expenses are sometimes paid.
For further information please contact Judith Wheeler at the above address.

War On Want
37 — 39 Great Guildford Street, London SE1 OES (tel 071-620 1111).
This organization undertakes development and relief work to alleviate famine in the Third World. A national network of groups throughout the United Kingdom raise funds and campaign in their local areas. Volunteers are needed to join these local groups and volunteers are required annually for office and administrative work in the head office in London. Work continues all year round and volunteers give whatever time they can.
Any special skills that volunteers have will be utilized but none are essential. All volunteers are welcome but there is no access for disabled people at the London office. London office volunteers have their travelling expenses within London paid and receive a £2 lunch allowance per day. Local groups make their own arrangements.
Those interested in obtaining a list of local groups or wishing to work in the London office should contact the Volunteer Co-ordinator at the above address.

WOMANKIND (Worldwide)
122 Whitechapel High Street, London E1 7PT (tel 071-247 6931/9431; fax 071-247 3436).
This is a small development charity dedicated to helping women in developing countries to help themselves to overcome poverty, ill-health and disadvantage. Volunteers are not recruited for overseas work. Five or six volunteers at any one time are needed in London to help with office work, fundraising, events and sometimes, research. What the volunteer actually does depends very much on what skills the applicant has and the time she or he can offer. Applicants of more than one nationality are accepted. Volunteers are needed all the year round, but the length of time for which they are recruited depends on the individual. Travel and lunch expenses are paid.
Those interested should contact Emanuela Brahamsa at the above address.

The Women's Environmental Network (WEN)
Aberdeen Studios, 22 Highbury Grove, London N5 2EA (tel 071-354 8823; fax 071-354 0464).
WEN is dedicated to informing and educating women who care about the environment. 20 volunteers are needed at any one time to assist with general office tasks and fundraising. Volunteers might find themselves involved in research, campaigning, PR, financial administration or dealing with the media. Applicants

of any nationality are welcome as long as they have commitment and motivation. The length of time for which volunteers are normally recruited varies but help is needed all year round. Travel expenses are paid and lunch is provided.

Those interested should contact Lin Collins at the above address.

Women's Therapy Centre

6-9 Manor Gardens, London N7 6LA (tel 071-263 6200; fax 071-281 7879).

The Centre was founded in 1976 to provide a psychotherapeutic service for women by women, and to develop and promote an understanding of women's psychology. Many regular volunteers work at the Centre so there is not a great deal of scope for new volunteers, but one might be able to help with administrative work in the office. There might also be an opportunity for a volunteer to become involved in giving out advice and information, as long as the volunteer can make a long-term regular commitment and has relevant experience. Applicants must be women only, but they may be of any nationality and the minimum age limit is 18 years. Depending on vacancies, it might be possible for a volunteer to work one day per week indefinitely. Fares will be reimbursed and lunch provided (if needed).

Those interested should contact Lynne Stenner at the above address.

World Wide Fund for Nature

Panda House, Weyside Park, Godalming, Surrey GU7 1XR (tel 0483-42644; fax 0483-426409).

WWF fundraises and campaigns through a network of around 300 voluntary supporters' groups in the UK. Scientific research could be carried out by volunteers who can finance themselves and with appropriate degrees. Volunteers can also assist with fundraising in the UK. Accommodation cannot be offered.

Volunteers within the UK should write to the above address to obtain a list of regional WWF Units; international volunteers can apply to WWF International, 1196 Gland, Switzerland.

Writers In Prison Committee of International PEN

9-10 Charterhouse Buildings, Goswell Road, London EC1M 7AT (tel 071-253 3226; fax 071-253 5711).

This organization researches and campaigns on behalf of writers, journalists, publishers, poets, editors, etc. who have been arrested, killed or attacked because of their views. It deals with all cases in all countries. Volunteers of all nationalities are needed to help with photocopying, filing and general correspondence. Other tasks might be open to volunteers according to their skills.

Volunteers should have typing skills, and knowledge of languages other than English, French or Spanish would be useful. The office is situated up eight flights of stairs and there is no lift which makes it unsuitable for disabled applicants. Volunteers should be able to make a commitment of one day per week for at least two months. Help is needed all year round. Local travel costs are paid.

Applications should be made to Sara Whyatt at the above address.

Hospitals

There is much that volunteers can do to help the hard-pressed professional staff of a hospital to make a patient's stay more comfortable. It must be stressed, however, that the range of activities a volunteer can do is strictly limited, as they must not encroach upon the professional's preserve, and in many cases the number of hours a volunteer can help will be limited.

For example, it is permitted to drive a patient's relatives to and from hospital, but driving an out-patient home would encroach on the work of the ambulance service so may not be permitted. Nearly all of the work involving hospitals is concerned with direct contact with the patients and their families. The range of services provided by volunteers includes running shops, canteens and libraries, manning telephones, befriending and escorting patients, and arranging outings, flower arranging hairdressing and writing letters for them. They may also be of use in preparing the homes of patients for their return.

The majority of hospitals either have their voluntary work organized by a League of Hospital Friends (see the entry for the National Association of Leagues of Hospital Friends below) or employ their own Voluntary Services Co-ordinator; the voluntary services of the remaining hospitals may be run by another organization such as the Red Cross or the WRVS. A simple telephone call to a local hospital should be inform you who to contact if you wish to offer your services there. The individual hospitals listed below are given only as examples of the needs of hospitals up and down the country.

Other work involving hospitals and hospital patients will be found in the sections on *Sick and Disabled People* , *Mental Health*, *Children and Youth* and *Elderly People*

Amandus Club
Atkinson Morley's Hospital, Copse Hill, Wimbledon SW20 ONE (tel 081- 946 7711, ext. 41048).

Volunteers are used to assist in a small workshop twice a week engaged in re-cycling greeting cards, printing, knitting, making toys, etc. and to provide a hot midday meal for those who attend the workshop and tea and coffee for visitors. Some secretarial help is also needed.

Anyone interested in helping should contact the Secretary at the above address; please note that the office is manned on Tuesdays and Thursdays only.

BLISS: Baby Life Support Systems
17-21 Emerald Street, London WC1N 3QL (tel 071-831 9393/8996; fax 071-404 0676)

This UK based organization needs approximately 2,000 volunteers throughout the UK every year to help raise funds for the purchase of neonatal life-saving equipment and for the training of nurses. Voluntary befrienders with personal experience of babies in special/intensive care are also sought to support parents who are going through the same trauma. Volunteers would also help with general administrative tasks at BLISS HQ. Applicants of any nationality are welcome to apply, but BLISS HQ does not have disabled access. It is preferable that volunteers should make a long-term commitment, providing on-going support where possible. Expenses will be re-imbursed by prior agreement.

Those interested should apply to Judy Kay, the Director, at the above address.

Ida Darwin Hospital

Fulbourn, Cambridge, CB1 5EE (tel 0223-248074).

The Ida Darwin Hospital is home for some 100 adults with profound learning disabilities, many of whom are also physically handicapped. Many volunteers, both short and long term, join with trained staff to improve the residents' quality of life, primarily in developing their leisure opportunities. No special qualifications are needed, but it would be helpful if applicants had some experience of working with people with a learning disability. Volunteers should be at least 18 years old.

Those interested should write to the Voluntary Services Organizer at the above address.

National Association of Leagues of Hospital Friends

2nd Floor, Fairfax House, Causton Road, Colchester CO1 1RJ (tel 0206- 761227).

The National Association acts as a support, resource and advice centre to some 1,214 Leagues of Friends in England, Scotland and Wales. Together these have 270,000 members and 50,000 volunteers who give about $6\frac{1}{2}$ million hours of voluntary time to their Leagues. About £31 million pounds is raised each year of which £26 million is spent on patient comforts and medical equipment needed by the hospitals.

The aim of the charity is to improve the life of patients and ex-patients from hospitals and health care establishments by offering service and support facilities. The work of the volunteer is very varied and can stretch from patient befriending, through help in canteens, shops or ward trolleys to chaperoning on patient outings, etc. The emphasis is now also changing to help within community care homes.

The work can be rewarding and interesting with as much variety as the individual volunteer wants. For more details ask at the local hospital for the League of Friends contact or write direct to the National Association at the above address.

Queen Mary's University Hospital

Roehampton Lane, London SW15 5PM (tel 081-789 6611; fax 081-780 9571).

The Hospital urgently needs people to help in its wards. Volunteers can improve the quality of the patients'stay in hospital by simply giving a few hours of their time every week. There are many ways in which volunteers can help, including visiting patients and chatting to them, reading or writing letters for patients, playing games with them, helping at meal times, tidying the ward gardens, providing occasional transport, greeting and directing out-patients in the hospital and helping in non-patient departments. In these ways volunteers help to brighten a patient's stay and provide additional support for staff giving them more time for their professional duties.

About 30 volunteers of all nationalities per year help in this way. Skills required depend on the post in question and the maximum age limit is 70 years. Volunteers are needed all the year round, and they usually work for half a day per week. Volunteers sometimes receive lunch vouchers and/or bus fares.

Those interested should contact Yvonne Wilson, Voluntary Services and Security Manager at the above address.

St Pancras Hospital Voluntary Help Department

4 St. Pancras Way, London NW1 (tel 071-387 4411 ext. 368).

The range of jobs for volunteers at St Pancras Hospital is very varied: chatting to patients, writing letters, helping with arts, crafts and pottery, doing the shopping for patients, accompanying wheelchair patients to parks or on other outings and other activities run by the Activities Organizer, helping with the trolley ship and entertainment afternoons.There is a well organized voluntary programme for the large number of helpers under the direction of a full time Voluntary Help Organiser. The patients at St. Pancras are primarily geriatrics, but there are also psychiatric and tropical diseases wards and two Day Hospitals (Psychiatric and Elderly). Volunteers are also needed from time to time in these areas to assist in groups. Many of the patients have been in hospital for a long time and are in particular need of contact with ordinary people leading ordinary lives. Personal attention to lonely patients, whether in the capacity of listener or entertainer, is invaluable.

Volunteers are provided with overalls and free meals, but no accommodation. All volunteers must commit themselves to three hours per week for at least eight weeks. Volunteers of any nationality over 18 years of age can bring pleasure to a person in hospital. The most important requirement is the possession of a cheerful and relaxed personality.

Applications may be submitted to the Voluntary Help Organizer at the Hospital.

University College Hospital Voluntary Help Department

Main Hall, Gower Street, London WC1 6AU (tel 071-388 6866).

The Department co-ordinates the voluntary services in the North Bloomsbury Hospitals unit. Around 200 volunteers give up their time to help patients, some for only a few months, others for years. There are no particular requirements beyond a willingness to make a regular commitment of time and effort, but any special qualities, such as the knowledge of a foreign language or an interest in craft work, are noted and used whenever the need arises. Volunteers serving for three or more hours a day are given a voucher for refreshments of up to £1.15 in value, and small travel expenses are paid in certain cases.

Enquiries should be made to the Voluntary Services Co-ordinator at the above address.

Whittingham Hospital Volunteer Scheme

Whittingham Hospital, Whittingham, Preston, Lancs. PR3 2JH (tel 0772- 865531).

This volunteer scheme operates within the Priority care Division in all areas relating to mental health problems within the Preston Health District. Volunteers may work in hospital or community settings in a number of varied tasks including direct assistance on wards, in nursing homes, day hospitals or domestic residences befriending patients, car driving, entertaining, library duties etc.

The minimum age is 15 with no upper age limit. Travelling expenses, luncheon vouchers and other out-of-pocket expenses are paid where appropriate.

For further information contact the Community Development Officer at the above address.

Pressure Groups

Most charities and voluntary organizations would like to change public knowledge of and interest in their chosen area, whether it is research into heart disease or care for the mentally handicapped. Pressure groups go further than this and are working for long term defined changes not just in public perception, but in real terms.

Those groups listed in this chapter have many different objectives, from abolishing blood sports to fighting for the human rights of prisoners of conscience abroad.Clearly, a prospective volunteer is required to share the views of the organisation he would like to help. Involvement with an organization such as Hunt Saboteurs Association may call for conviction deep enough to motivate someone to risk physical danger or arrest and so people should examine their motives carefully before becoming involved in the more controversial organisations. We have not included organizations that are protesting against specific local developments, such as the extension of a motorway or the closing of a village school, because such groups normally receive full coverage in the local media.

Alcohol Concern
275 Gray's Inn Road, London WC1X 8QF (tel 071-833 3471).

There are many local alcohol advice agencies which train and use volunteers as alcohol counsellors to give individual help to those who come to them with problems. Alcohol Concern operates a scheme called VACTS (Volunteer Alcohol Counsellors Training Scheme) which is a national initiative set up to ensure minimum standards in the training and on-going supervision of volunteer counsellors. Local alcohol agencies whose courses meet the agreed minimum standards are granted official recognition and any counsellors who undertake the recognized course of training and supervision are eligible for formal accreditation.

For further details on the scheme and information on which agencies train volunteers to the VACTS standard, contact the VACTS Training and Development Officer at the above address.

Amnesty International
British Section, 5, Roberts Place, off Bowling Green Lane, London EC1R OEJ (tel 071-251 8371).

Amnesty International won the Nobel Peace Prize in 1977. It works for the release of men and women imprisoned for their religious, political or other conscientiously held beliefs, their colour, language or ethnic origin. Only those prisoners who have either used or advocated violence are excluded from the cause. It actively opposes the death penalty as well as torture and cruel or degrading punishment for all prisoners. Between 50 and 100 volunteers are needed to do routine clerical work: stuffing envelopes, typing, wrapping parcels, etc. Travelling expenses are reimbursed for office helpers and luncheon vouchers are provided.

Enquiries should be sent to the Volunteer Organizer, Amnesty International, at the above address.

Animal Aid
7 Castle Street, Tonbridge, Kent TN9 1BH (tel 0732-364546; fax 0732-366533).

This UK based organization campaigns against all animal abuse (including vivsection, factory farming, the fur trade and circuses), and promotes living without cruelty as an alternative. 10 volunteers are needed for 1-4 weeks all the year round to assist with general office duties at Tonbridge. Applicants may be of any nationality.

Applications should be made to Gillian Egan at the above address.

ASH (Action on Smoking and Health)
109 Gloucester Place, London W1H 3PH (tel 071-935 3519)

ASH is an information campaign which aims to prevent the disability and death caused by smoking. It needs volunteers in its office to help service the thousands of requests for information received each year and to assist with projects on the many different aspects of smoking control, including smoking in public places, children and smoking, and passive smoking. Volunteers are paid travelling expenses and £1 to cover lunch.

Anyone interested should contact the Volunteer Co-ordinator at the above address.

Campaign for Nuclear Disarmament
22-24 Underwood Street, London N1 (tel 071-250 4010).

The aim of CND is to persuade the Government to abandon nuclear weapons, and all foreign policy based on their use. The membership of 250,000 is distributed among 1,500 local groups which collect signatures for petitions against nuclear warfare, hold meetings, and recruit people to join in nationally organized marches and demonstrations, and help organize them. Specific weapons recently campaigned against include Trident, the Cruise Missile, Polaris and the Neutron Bomb as well as Russian SS20s. Membership is optional: any supporter is welcome to join in the activities of the organization.

Those interested should apply to the organization at the above address to find out the address of their local group.

Child Poverty Action Group (CPAG)
1-5 Bath Street, London EC1V GPY (tel 071-253 3406)

CPAG works to draw attention to the problems of the impoverished and to provide these people with advice concerning their rights. They accomplish this by publishing research pamphlets, such as *The National Welfare Benefits Handbook* and *The Rights Guide to Non-Means-Tested Benefits*. Volunteers are needed to carry out the clerical work of sending out the literature. Travelling expenses are paid and an allowance is given for lunch.

Enquiries may be addressed to the Publications Distribution Worker at the above address.

Farmers' World Network

The Arthur Rank Centre, National Agriculture Centre, Stoneleigh Park, Warks CV8 2LZ (tel 0203-696969 ext. 338; fax 0203-696900).

The Farmers' World Network is a collection of farmers and people with agricultural connections which seeks to promote awareness within the United Kingdom farming community of the problems of developing countries and the relationship between European and Third World agriculture. Volunteers are needed to join local groups which have specific action committees, assist volunteers going to Third World countries and host farmers and students from overseas on their farms.

Volunteers need a knowledge of agriculture or food production but no other restrictions apply.

Those interested should contact the Co-ordinator at the above address.

Friends of the Earth

26-28 Underwood Street, London W1 1JQ (tel 071-490 1555).

Friends of the Earth (FoE) is one of the UK's leading environmental groups. It is currently campaigning on air pollution and climate change, energy, tropical rainforests, water pollution, waste and toxics, recycling and the coutryside, land use and transport. It has an active network of over 300 local groups and a youth and education section.

Those interested in volunteering at FoE's national office please write with a cv or personal details to Martin Jones at the above address.

The Green Alliance

49 Wellington Street, London WC2E 7BN (tel 071 836-0341; fax 071 240-9205)

The Green Alliance is a London based environmental policy organization. Its central aim is to raise the prominence of the environment on the agendas of the key policy-making institutions of the UK and in so doing to help improve their environmental performance across the board in Britain and throughout the world.

One or two volunteers are needed to assist with general duties in the London office. Applicants can be of any nationality but they must have a work permit and be able to speak English; specialist office skills would also be useful. Volunteers would only be needed intermittently all year round. Expenses will be paid.

Please apply to K. Crane at the above address.

Greenpeace

Canonbury Villas, Canonbury Villas, London N1 2PM (tel 071 354-5100; fax 071 696-0013).

The London based administrative office of the international environmental pressure group group engages approximately 100-200 volunteers to help with fund-raising and routine office work every year. Duties might include envelope stuffing, filing, photocopying, word-processing and helping in reception. Applicants of all nationalities are welcome, and no special skills are needed. Volunteers are required all the year round for a minimum period of two months. Travel expenses will be reimbursed and lunch is provided.

Those interested should contact Jacqui Collison, Personnel Assistant, at the above address.

Hunt Saboteurs Association
PO Box 1, Carlton, Nottingham NG4 2JY (tel 0602 59037).

This unique organization was formed in 1963 and is engaged in a continuing campaign on non-violent direct action style campaigning which both saves the lives of hunted animals and brings to the public's attention the atrocities inflicted upon wild animals in the name of sport. The HSA is an animal rights organisation and is opposed as much to angling and shooting as it is to hunting deer, hare, mink and fox with hounds.

The HSA has nearly 5,000 members of which nearly 1,000 are active on a once weekly basis, normally Saturdays, throughout the winter months. Less activity takes place during the summer months. The Association will advise on the tactics to be employed in the saving of lives and welcomes enquiries from interested people.

The HSA employs no staff and has a decentralized structure. Volunteers may offer their services for as long as they like; it is preferable that active members are over 16 years of age. The annual membership fee is £8 for the waged and £5 for unwaged.

Further details are obtainable from the above address.

International Broadcasting Trust
2 Ferdinand Place, London NW1 8EE (tel 071-482 2847).

International Broadcasting Trust is a television production organization which specializes in the making of programmes on Third World, development and environmental issues. The Trust's aim is to promote a wider understanding of these issues through the use of the media. Volunteers are occasionally needed to complete very basic office duties such as telephone answering and photocopying. Travelling expenses (London area only) and lunch allowance are paid.

Those interested should apply to the Volunteer Co-ordinator at the above address.

Japan Animal Welfare Society Limited
RMC House, Townmead Road, London SW6 2RZ (tel 071-736 9306).

JAWS was set up in Tokyo in 1954 to provide help and care for mistreated dogs, cats and other animals in Japan. Two years later a Society was established here to raise funds for their work and organize other assistance such as arranging for the training of Japanese Veterinary Inspectors in England. Voluntary help is always welcome in running the office. Volunteers who know Japan, or even better, Japanese are preferred.

Ring the Office Manager, Andrew Laird, for a chat.

Liberty (National Council for Civil Liberties)
21 Tabard Street, London SE1 4LA (tel 071-403 3888).

Liberty is a pressure group which works to defend and extend civil liberties throughout the UK. Volunteers at the London office help prepare publications, assist with research or perform routine administrative tasks/ Volunteer lawyers assist with legal casework. A luncheon allowance is provided for volunteers and travelling expenses are paid inside London.
nquiries should be sent to the General Secretary at the above address.

Minority Rights Group
379 Brixton Road, London SW9 7DE (tel 071-738 6265; fax 071-978 94898®).

MRG is concerned with the research and publication and advocacy of human rights about minority groups around the world. Although space restrictions mean that MRG is able to accept only a small number of volunteers, it is happy to consider applications from individuals who wish to apply. Members from ethnic minority communities and refugees are especially welcome. Work is likely to involve the following: information collecting and filing, general office work, assisting members of staff, helping with mailing, etc. Travelling expenses within London are paid.
    Enquiries to the above address.

National Peace Council
88 Islington High Street, London N1 8EG (tel 071-354 5200; fax 071-354 0033).

The National Peace Council is at the centre of a network of over 150 peace organizations and related movements, including trade unions and religious peace associations. The council's task is to provide an exchange of information between its member organizations to facilitate co-operation among them. It also acts as a pressure group on behalf of its affiliates. A small number of volunteers are needed to look after the correspondence and mailing services, and to do continuing research into current events which pertain to disarmament issues. Typing, some computer experience and general office experience would be an asset for those volunteers wishing to apply.
    Enquiries may be sent to Lib Peck, Co-ordinator, at the above address.

National Council for the Welfare of Prisoners Abroad
82 Rosebery Avenue, London EC1R 4RR (tel 071-833 3467).

This charity works for the welfare of British prisoners in foreign jails. The specific work done for individual prisoners varies enormously; dealing with foreign and British lawyers, and prison and other authorities, writing personally to prisoners and organizing penpals, providing funds for prisoners to buy essentials like blankets and medicines, etc. Around 20 volunteers are needed all year round to help with all office activities; typing and other clerical work, answering both telephone and postal queries, word processing and writing letters to prisoners. Volunteers normally help for three months or more on a regular basis, with full days of work being preferred to half days.
    Volunteers of all nationalities are welcome. Good communication skills are

important and languages are an advantage but not necessary. All other skills will be put to good use. As the office is located on the second floor of the building with no lift disabled people will find access difficult. Travelling expenses and a lunch allowance are paid.

Volunteers should apply to the Administrator at the above address. "One World Week

One World Week

PO Box 100, London SE1 7RT (tel 071-620 4444).

One World Week in October of each year is a chance for churches and other groups to get together, celebrate and learn about issues of justice, peace, the environment and development. Offices in London, Edinburgh and Cardiff provide support for this by supplying study materials and suggestions for activities and providing local contacts. Volunteers are needed to help existing groups celebrate the week or to organize their own activities. Fundraising is not encouraged.

Those interested should contact a Programme Worker at the above address for more information.

Railway Development Society

48 The Park, Great Bookham, Surrey KT23 3LS (tel 0372-452863).

The RDS was formed in 1978 by an amalgamation of earlier societies. It is a pressure group fighting for the retention and improvement of Britain's railway system as a vital environmental issue. It maintains contacts with British Rail, Ministers, MPs, Local Authorities and other bodies. It produces Railguides, other booklets and leaflets and publishes a quarterly journal and branch newsletters.

It needs almost 100 volunteers a year to help with its activities, and makes use of a wide range of experience. Involvement can be at national or branch level or with help in the organization of local rail users' groups to encourage local communities to take an active interest in their rail services. There are no restrictions on applicants and no special qualifications are required apart from an interest in the aims of the Society.

Enquiries should be sent to the Administrative Officer at the above address.

Survival International

310 Edgware Road, London W2 1DY (tel 071-723 5535; fax 071-723 4059).

Survival International is a world wide movement supporting tribal peoples, standing for their right to decide their own way of life. Survival works for threatened tribal peoples in the Americas, Africa, Asia and Australasia. Survival lobbies international organizations, governments and multi-national companies, works to raise awareness of the situation of tribal peoples and supports practical realistic field projects with the aim of assisting the survival and self-determination of tribal peoples.

Volunteers are required in the London office to assist with clerical and secretarial work, library duties, visual aid materials, translation and fundraising activities. A commitment of anything from half a day to five days per week for a minimum of three months is required. Those interested should contact the London office.

Tools for Self Reliance
Ringwood Road, Netley Marsh, Southampton SO4 2GY (tel 0703-869697).

Tools for Self Reliance is a charity which collects and refurbishes basic hand tools in Britain and then provides tool kits to co-operative work schemes in Africa and Central America. Volunteers are needed to help with all aspects of this work; office work, building maintenance, gardening and general site maintenance, refurbishing tools and preparing and packing tools. In addition to work undertaken by the various local groups around Britain. Tools for Self Reliance hold workcamps lasting for up to two weeks a their national headquarters in Netley Marsh. The workcamps cater for up to 12 volunteers at any one time and are designed for volunteers who cannot help regularly throughout the year. Contact the Workshop Supervisor at the above address for further information.

The Vegetarian Society
Parkdale, Dunham Road, Altringham, Cheshire WA14 4¿G (tel 061-928 079; fax 061-926 9182).

The Society's aim is to increase the numbers of vegetarians in the UK in order to save animals, benefit human health and protect the environment and world food resources. More than 15 volunteers are needed each year to help at their headquarters. Tasks include administrative duties, answering children's letters and helping with school talks, cooking demonstrations and stalls. Volunteers give whatever time they can. Those interested should contact the Campaigns Director at the above address.

World Development Movement
25 Beehive Place, Brixton SW9 7QR (tel 071-737 6215).

The World Development Movement campaigns for political changes in Britain's aid, trade and debt policies needed to help Third World countries. A small number of staff work on research and publications which together with the membership attempts to influence key decision makers. Volunteers are needed in the London office to help with general office work, all year round. No special skills are required and volunteers may be of any nationality. No accommodation is provided but travel expenses to and from the London office and a lunch allowance of £1.20 are paid. Those interested should apply to Jo Collinge, Groups Officer, at the above address.

World Disarmament Campaign
45-47 Blythe Street, London E2 6LX (tel 071-729 2523).

This UK based organization campaigns for nuclear and conventional disarmament, third world development and environmental protection on the basis of resolutions agreed by the UN. A few full-time volunteers assist with general office duties in London. Applicants of any nationality are welcome as long as they have knowledge of English. Volunteers are required all the year round apart from at the height of summer. Expenses will be paid. Those interested should contact Tony Farsky, Treasurer, at WDC HQ at the above address.

Prisons and Probation

There is a strong historical link between volunteers and prisons: indeed, the statutory Probation Service itself was begun when the authorities realised how successful voluntary involvement had been in re-integrating prisoners into society. The special value of volunteers in this work lies in the fact that they are not a formal part of 'the system', and so offenders respond more readily and openly to them than they would to paid and officially appointed officers.

By visiting a convicted prisoner, a volunteer can be of use either by simply providing companionship, or by maintaining a link with the prisoner's family, as a period of imprisonment can prove a strain on marriages. The need for the help of a volunteer does not end with the release of an offender; the support of a known and trusted volunteer can be of great help in finding a job and somewhere to live. This is especially valuable in time of high unemployment, as prisoners will experience more difficulty than most people in finding work. The organizations listed below show the many ways in which a volunteer can be of use to a prisoner bothe before and after release.

Apex Trust
2-4 Colchester Street, London E1 7PG (tel 071-481 4831).

The Apex Trust is a registered charity which aims to secure appropriate access to jobs and careers for people who have gained a criminal record. The Trust operates through the provision of a network of practical programmes such as occupational training schemes, Job Clubs, enterprise opportunities and specialist employment advice and support both in the community and in prisons. The Trust builds working partnerships with employers and other agencies as well as establishing a dialogue with other policy-makers towards the creation of equal oportunities for people seeking to turn away from crime.

Voluntary assistance will be appreciated in general areas such as industries and employer liaison, public relations and fundraising and assistance with pre-employment training and job search, clerical help, etc.

For further details please contact the above address.

The Bourne Trust
189a Old Brompton Road, London SW5 0AR (tel 071-370 6612)/St Mary's Lodge, St Mary's Yard, Friargate, Preston, Lancs PR1 2AT (tel 0772-821215).

The Trust assists prisoners and ex-prisoners, helping them to re-establish themselves in the community after release. It offers support to families of prisoners during sentence; from its London office, its welfare officers provide counselling and social services, visiting clients in prison and families at home. The Preston office and voluntary groups in Durham and Newcastle, West Yorkshire, North London and South Devon offer support to local clients. Volunteers are invited to assist in the local work undertaken by these groups. The Bourne Trust's work is based on Christian concern for prisoners, their families and society at large, regardless of race and creed.

Those interested should contact either of the above addresses.

Inner London Probation and After-Care Service
73 Great Peter Street, London SW1P 2BN (tel 071-222 5656).

The Service undertakes a wide range of activities with voluntary helpers within the 12 Inner London boroughs. These relate to most aspects of the Probation Service's work and would entail, for example, one-to-one contact with clients, group work, adventure activities, or practical help on a regular or single task basis.

Applicants should be at least 18 years old and under most circumstances it would be helpful if they could offer their services for at least 12 months. The personal qualities needed are sound common sense, tolerance and kindness. Applicants must also be prepared to work closely with supervising Probation Officers.

Those interested should, in the first instance, contact Ms L Daly, Senior Probation Officer, Camden House, 199 Arlington Road, NE1 (North of Thames) or Mr P Jefferies, Assistant Chief Probation Officer, 217 Balham High Road, SW17 7BP (South of Thames).

National Association for the Care and Resettlement of Offenders (NACRO)
169 Clapham Road, London SW9 OPU (tel 071-582 6500).

NACRO runs housing, employment, youth training, education and advice projects for offenders and others; provides research, information and training services for people concerned about crime and offenders; and contributes to the development of crime policy and the prevention of crime. Over 1,000 staff work in some 150 projects and other services throughout England and Wales.

Opportunities for voluntary work are limited to a small number of projects providing education for unemployed adults and activities for young people, which are organized on a local basis. NACRO aims to be an equal opportunities employer and to eliminate unfair descrimination against anyone in its selection process.

For further information, contact NACRO's Information Department at the above address.

National Association of Prison Visitors
46B Hartington Street, Bedford (tel 0234-359763).

In the UK prison visitors are officially appointed. Normally they make an appointment to see the govenor of the prison nearest them. If this interview passes satisfactorily they are accepted for a probationary period of three months. After this they must be appointed by the Home Office. It is important that people in prison (and in other penal institutions) should not lose contact with the outside world. Prison staff and visiting probation officers have a part to play, but the prison visitor has a unique contribution to offer, working alongside this team rather than as a member of it. Although appointed by the Home Office and subject to the regulations of the prisons, he or she is a volunteer, not an 'official' and this independent status has an appeal to the prisoner. The main role of the visitor is to establish a one-to-one , impartial, non-authoritarian relationship with the prisoner. There are 950-1000 visitors in the UK and 8-10% of prisoners have prison visitors. The Association wishes to expand its activities and new recruits will be welcome. Prison visitors should not be confused with Voluntary Associates, who work in co-operation with the Probation and After-care service.

Visitors must be at least 21 and not over 70, and are normally expected to retire at 75. To be of value, visits must be made at frequent intervals, normally weekly or fortnightly, early in the evening, and at weekends. Both men and women are taken on, and women visitors can visit men's prisons. Visitors usually visit their nearest prison.

Those interested should apply to the Governor at their nearest prison.

The New Bridge
Room A, 1 Thorpe Close, Ladbroke Grove, London W10 5XL (tel 081-969 9133).

The New Bridge operates two schemes: a nationwide befriending scheme for people who are in prison, and an employment service for those who have left prison in the greater London area. Some 150 volunteers lend their time to the organization, of whom the majority are involved in the befriending scheme. This means that the volunteer keeps in touch with a prisoner both by personal visits and by letters while he is in prison, and offers help and encouragement in starting a new life on his release.

The only specific requirement is that volunteers should be over 18; but anyone living in London with time to spare during the day would be welcomed to help with the employment service, which involves making contact between prospective employers and released prisoners. Expenses in London may be reclaimed.

Those interested should write to the Befriending Scheme Organizer at the above address for further details.

Problems, Emergencies and Housing

If the stereotypical image of the last decade was that of the yuppie wheeling and dealing city, that of the current decade is the now familar sight of a homeless person bedding down for the night in a cardboard box on a city street. There are many people trapped in a vicious circle of unemployment and homelessness, and the social services find it hard to cope. The following organizations illustrate how the individual can help to alleviate homelessness and other housing-related problems.

Many of the organizations listed below deal with individuals who are facing a rapid succession of linked problems, such as bereavement, poverty, homelessness, unemployment and poverty, and are unable to cope with the pressure. Without some assistance many such cases may end up with suicide or crime. Often all that is needed is a friendly voice for someone to speak to: it is significant that the suicide rate has dropped since the Samaritans began operating. In other cases skilled help is needed, to liaise with council housing departments, for example.

Some of the organizations listed under *Sick and Disabled People* , *Children and Youth*, *Elderly People* and *Prisons and Probation* also contain provisions for dealing with crises within their respective areas of activity.

Catholic Housing Aid Society (CHAS)

189a Old Brompton Road, London SW5 OAR (tel 081-373 4961).

The Society has 10 branches throughout the country. It helps anyone with a housing problem. The branches advize on landlord-tenant questions, council housing arrangements and problems with purchasing. The time at which advisory services are open varies from branch to branch, although most operate in the evenings. Volunteers are needed to work in the advice centres, to do administrative office work and to help with research work; Those working in the advisory centres need to offer a couple of evenings a month and the Society runs a number of in-service training programmes.   Those interested should apply to the above address or to their local branch.

Centrepoint Off The Streets

54 Dean Street, London W1 (tel 071-434 2861).

This is an emergency night shelter for up to 12 homeless people who are living on and around the streets of London or are felt to be at risk in the West End. Volunteers work as part of a team of about six, one night a week under the supervision of a full-time worker. Their main function is to provide a welcoming atmosphere for clients and a sympathetic ear when required, as well as helping with practical chores such as cooking and washing.   All nationalities are welcome but applicants should be able to speak English, and preferably be aged over 18. It is preferred also if volunteers can make a long term commitment, i.e. at least six months.

For further information and application forms contact the Volunteer Administrator.

Salvation Army

105-109 Judd Street, King's Cross, London WC1H 9TS (tel 071-383 4230).

The Salvation Army performs a greater variety and volume of social service than any other voluntary organization in the world. It has 25,000 Officers in 84 countries who have dedicated their lives to the service of God in the Army; but their work is made even more effective by the support of individuals who give voluntary help in hostels, homes and centres. In Britain alone the Army has nearly 1,000 centres of worship, evangelism, and community activity, as well as 125 social centres, all of which operate varying programmes for helping others.   There now exists in Britain a nationwide network of homes, hostels and other centres caring for people in physical and moral need. Although much of the work is done by Officers, volunteers can provide valuable ancillary services.   For further details contact the Personnel Secretary, Social Services, at the above address.

Samaritans

10 The Grove, Slough SL1 1QP (tel 0753-532713; fax 0753-819004).

The Samaritans exist to befriend the suicidal and despairing, by means of telephone, letter, or face to face meetings. There are 185 branches throughout the UK which make use of over 22,000 volunteers, and at each branch there are at least two volunteers manning the phones at any one time. The organization is frequently the last straw at which a troubled person can grasp for assistance, so the recruitment system for volunteers is very selective to ensure that the applicant is suitable. The initial procedure of interviews and classes may take three to five months; thereafter, volunteers are expected to work three or four shifts per month.   Applicants should be 17 or over, and possess good hearing. They need not own a phone, and expenses will be paid to cover travel, other than ordinary commuting to and from the centres.

It is preferred that the applicants write to their local branch (the address is in the phone book). Similar organizations outside the British Isles are affiliated to Befrienders International, 228 Bishopsgate, London EC2M 4QD.

SHELTER, National Campaign for the Homeless
88 Old Street, London EC1V 9HU (tel 071-253 0202; fax 071-608 3325).

Shelter helps provide a housing aid service and aims to improve housing conditions all over the country, as well as offering telephone advice direct to London's homeless people. Volunteers work in the national headquarters and in the regional offices around the country. The type of work that they do depends on their personal skills; for example, some may be able to type, which is always useful, while others may have a specialized knowledge of housing or campaigning. But enthusiasm and conscientiousness can make a volunteer equally useful. In addition, many people help to finance the organization with fund raising events. All are welcome to join local groups or become members of the campaign.   The amount of help which is given to Shelter depends on the volunteer her/himself. Some people have helped for years, while others only do so for a week or two. Travel expenses are reimbursed.   Applicants should contact the Personnel Assistant at the above address for further information.

Womens Aid Ltd
P.O.Box 791, Dublin 6, Eire (tel 01-723122).

Women's Aid is an organization which provides advice, support and accommodation to women suffering physical, mental and sexual abuse in their own homes. Volunteers can assist with the work in many areas such as helping with the children, helping in our crisis refuge, staffing the crisis helpline, helping women with practical tasks and befriending women and their children in the comunity who have separated from violent partners.

There are no special requirements but personality traits such as the ability to show empathy, concern and a non-judgemental attitude are essential for all voluntary work with Women's Aid. There are no restrictions to age, nationality and race.   Those interested should apply to the above address.

Sick and Disabled People

In these cost-conscious times The National Health Service is unable to provide full support for all those who have chronic illnesses or permanent disabilities. The organizations in this section are able to help fill this gap because they have specialized knowledge of the condition and can provide appropriate support. Volunteers can help these organizations in a wide variety of ways, whether directly, perhaps by helping with swimming therapy, or indirectly, such as by walking puppies for future training as guide dogs for the blind. In cases such as Arthritis Care (below) there is a particular need for volunteers with the relevant disabilities or injuries. In other cases, able-bodied volunteers prove more useful.

Other sections dealing specifically with the sick and disabled include *Hospitals*, *Children and Youth* and *The Elderly*.

Anorexic Aid
The Priory Centre, 11 Priory Road, High Wycombe, Bucks HP13 6SL.

This organization has 40 self-help groups throughout the country which offer help and advice for people suffering from Anorexia and Bulimia Nervosa. Volunteers are needed to help with office duties, counselling, befriending new members, organizing group meetings and manning the telephone.

Anyone interested in offering their help should contact the Secretary.

Arthritis Care
18 Stephenson Way, London NW1 2HD (tel 071-916 1500).

Arthritis Care was founded in 1948 by a young person with arthritis who wished to help and encourage others. There are at present about 550 branches around the country (all the branch officers and helpers are volunteers) and around 60,000 members. Active branch members render indispensable help in running the branch meetings, which may be a housebound member's only contact with the outside world. Any assistance which can be given with transport is much appreciated. Volunteers are needed to visit the housebound on a regular basis.

Those interested in joining should contact the Secretary at the above address to be put in touch with their local branch.

The Association of Swimming Therapy
4 Oak Street, Shrewsbury, Salop SY3 7RH (tel 0743-4393).

The Association encourages handicapped people to take part in swimming and water recreation and the formation of swimming clubs and swimming competitions for them. Instructors and helpers are trained within their clubs and at regional training courses. The AST works through regional associations to which local clubs can affiliate and on whose experience, advice and instructor training they can call. Many of the clubs engage in other activities besides swimming.

Between 600 and 700 volunteers are used annually as instructors, bathside keepers, safety helpers, dressers for males and females, time-keepers, social officers, doctors, administration officers, committee members and drivers for transporting handicapped members to and from the baths. Volunteers are selected after a period of attending swimming sessions to ascertain whether they are suitable for dealing with handicapped people. Volunteers should be in good health.

Further information can be obtained from the Honorary Secretary at the above address.

Birmingham Tapes for the Handicapped Association

20 Middleton Hall Road, Kings Norton, Birmingham B30 1BY (tel 021-628 3656).

The Association sends a monthly tape recorded sound magazine to handicapped people around the country. It also has a tape library which is free to members.

Those interested in helping should contact Mr Derek L Hunt, Honorary Secretary, at the above address.

Body Positive (London)

51B Philbeach Gardens, Earls Court, London SW5 9EB (tel 071-835 1045; fax 071-373 5237).

This is a drop-in centre based in London for people affected by HIV/AIDS, offering external support groups for such people. Between 50 and 100 volunteers help at Body Positive each year. In the Centre itself practical help is needed such as laying tables, washing up and welcoming its users. Volunteers are also required to visit people in hospitals in the London area, write to people in prison and drive people to and from the Centre and other groups. Applicants of any nationality are welcome. Each applicant must complete an induction/training program. The length of placement depends on the volunteer; volunteers are needed all the year round. Expenses are paid for public transport on Body Positive business only.

Those interested should contact Mike Campling at the above address.

Bristol Cancer Help Centre

Grove House, Cornwallis Grove, Clifton, Bristol BS8 4PG (tel 0272-743 216).

Opened in 1980, the Centre offers programmes which complement orthodox medical treatment for cancer patients. The patient receives medical supervision and counselling on nutrition, lifestyle and relaxation and meditation methods, as treatment is based on the principle that the whole person rather than just the disease should be treated. Approximately 20 volunteers are needed all year round to assist with postal queries (often the first contact patients have with the Centre), gardening, fund raising and clerical duties. Ideally volunteers work for a half or full day per week on an on-going basis.

Volunteers should be reliable, over 17 years old, and have a caring but humorous personality. A driving licence is an advantage but not essential. Only in special circumstances will travelling expenses be paid.

Those interested should contact the General Administrator at the above address.

British Limbless Ex-Servicemen's Association (BLESMA)

185-187 High Road, Chadwell Heath, Romford, Essex RM6 6NA (tel 081-590 1124).

BLESMA operates two residential homes and a welfare service to make sure that limbless ex-servicemen and women (including widows) do not suffer hardship. The Association operates a regular Welfare Visiting Service through its branches across the country. Organized social activities are arranged and a general information and advice service is provided.

The Association is now in need of some 200 volunteers to help branches with committee work, welfare visits and fundraising. Individuals may undertake any or all of these tasks. The amount of time given is at the discretion of the individuals concerned. Possession of a driving licence would be advantageous and a motor mileage allowance can be paid.

For further details contact the General Secretary at the above address.

British Wheelchair Sports Society
Gutman Sports Centre, Harvey Road, Stoke Mandeville, Bucks HP21 9PP (tel 0296-84848).

BWSF is involved with the promotion and encouragement of active sports among paraplegics and tetraplegics. Volunteers are needed to offer assistance at National and International Sports meetings. They may be needed for any period from one to ten days: accommodation is sometimes available.

Applicants should write to the Chief Executive at the above address.

The British Retinitis Pigmentosa Society
Pond House, Lillingstone Dayrell, Bucks MK18 5AS (tel 02806-363).

The Society was formed in 1975 and it aims to give relief to sufferers of RP in any way which may help them to live with, or overcome, their handicap, and to pursue measures towards finding the cause of RP and means of its treatment and cure.

For further details of how volunteers can help with this please contact the Honorary Secretary at the above address.

The Central Remedial Clinic
Penny Ansley Memorial Building, Vernon Avenue, Clontarf, Dublin 3, Eire (tel 01-332206).

The work of the Clinic is in the area of assessment, treatment, education, employment and general social care of people who have physical disabilities. The volunteer section is integral to the efficient functioning of the Clinic. The 140 volunteers who work there are involved in most departments within the Clinic and are a competent, highly motivated group of people.

Areas of voluntary work include helping out in the special school, swimming programme, dining hall, pre-school, therapy departments, child minding programme, summer activity programme, day activity centre, adult training workshop, fundraising department, nursing unit and microelectronics resource centre. The volunteer section consists of people from all walks of life including retired people, housewives, students on work experience programmes and unemployed people. All are bound by a shared desire to give freely of their time for the benfit of others and all are mature, caring individuals. Help is needed at most times of the year and appropriate training is provided where necessary.

For further information please contact the Development Officer at the above address.

The Chalfont Centre for Epilepsy
Chalfont St Peter, Gerrards Cross, Bucks SL9 ORJ(tel 0494-873991).

The Centre, run by the National Society for Epilepsy, welcomes volunteers to assist their work with the care and rehabilitation of people with epilepsy. Volunteers are needed to provide caring assistance, raise funds, provide transport and act as escorts for outings, teach craft, help at social events, help with sporting activities and teach mentally handicapped residents, etc. At present about 15 volunteers help the Society but any others are welcome. Help is useful at any time, but especially during holiday periods. Volunteers may stay for any length of time. No qualifications are necessary. Travelling expenses to and from the Centre are not paid, but outings and holidays are paid for.

Applications to Colonel D. W. Eking, Chief Executive, at the above address.

Cope Foundation
Bonnington, Montenotte, Cork, Eire (tel 021-507131).

The Association operates a number of services for the mentally handicapped in Cork city and County, including care units, schools, training centres, hostels and a sheltered workshop. Voluntary help is needed in all of these areas, especially during the school holidays.

For further details contact the Personnel Officer at the above address.

Cystic Fibrosis Research Trust
Alexandra House, 5 Blyth Road, Bromley, Kent BR1 3RS (tel 081-464 7211; fax 081-313 0472).

The Trust has branches throughout Britain which give support to patients and their families. Volunteers are generally already familiar with cystic fibrosis and its problems, due to prior experience of the disease; however, outside volunteers within the local community may be of service.

Enquiries may be sent to the Director, at the above address.

Eating Disorders Association
Sackville Place, 44 Magdalen Street, Norwich, Norfolk NR3 1JE.

This organization has 40 self-help groups throughout the country which offer help and advice for people suffering from Anorexia and Bulimia Nervosa. Volunteers are needed to help with office duties, lead self-help groups and telephone counselling. The Association also has a part-time office in High Wycombe.

Anyone instructed in offering their help should contact the Secretary.

Guide Dogs for the Blind Association
Hillfields, Burghfield Common, Reading RG7 3YG (tel 0734-835555; fax 0734-835433).

Help is needed by the Association in rearing its puppies until they are ready to be taken back for training. Anyone interested in becoming a puppy-walker should live near Bolton, Exeter, Forfar, Leamington, Middlesbrough, Redbridge or Wokingham. The Association pays a feeding allowance, meets vet's bills and offers regular support and advice from puppy-walking supervisors. Most of the Association's brood bitches also live with families and there are occasional opportunities to help in this way.

Fundraising for the Association is organized through over 400 local branches that have been formed by volunteer supporters. Those who would like to help in these activities should contact the offices in Windsor.

Home Farm Trust

Merchants House North, Wapping Road, Bristol B54 2RB (tel 0272-273746; fax 0272-225938).

HFT is a registered charity dedicated to providing an environment in which people with a learning disability (mental handicap) can find the support they need to live a full and fulfilled life. The Trust was founded in 1962 by a group of parents of children with a mental handicap who were about to leave a special school. The lack of suitable alternatives which gave rise to their action then, continues to apply today. The Trust fills this gap. It provides the lifelong security and the quality of care needed to develop individual potential and to lead satisfying and worthwhile lives. HFT now runs schemes in many parts of the country.

As many volunteers as possible are needed to work as full-time basic care staff in these homes. Staff are expected to form a strong team of dedicated people, and will be given the support and training they need to conform with internationally accepted standards. The atmosphere in Trust homes is warm, cheerful and supportive, but not intrusive. The expression of emotion is valued and the need for privacy respected.

Applicants of any nationality may apply as long as they have a good command of English and both qualifications and experience in social work. It is also important that volunteers should be in good health as the work can sometimes be physically demanding. Volunteers are needed all the year round. Wages are paid to care staff, although HFT is happy to take workers from abroad as temporarily waged or unwaged staff. Applications should be sent to John Rotherham at the above address.

International Disability Education and Awareness (IDEA)

William House, 101 Eden Vale Road, Westbury, Wiltshire BA13 3QF (tel 0373-827635; fax 0375-858815).

IDEA is a UK based training organization and as such does not have any overseas projects. IDEA organizes study tours in this country for disabled people from developing countries. People with experience of working in developing countries with disabled people may be asked if they are willing to assist on a training course. Between one and three volunteers are needed to help with work in the office in Westbury and also to provide accessible accommodation for visitors from developing countries. Other tasks might include taking them out sight-seeing etc., and assisting with various courses and workshops. Applicants of all nationalities will be considered, although assistance on a course covers many areas of experience such as teaching skills, overseas/disability experience, sign language, braille production and translation etc.

The courses have a duration of 5 days and occur three times per year. IDEA also runs 2-day workshops six times per year. Part-time office help is ongoing throughout the year. Most expenses will be covered. IDEA also provides information on working overseas, training for relevant work and can give relevant

contacts.
Those interested should contact Madeline Greenhalgh at the above address.

Kith and Kids
404 Camden Road, London N7 0SJ (tel 071 700-2755).

Kith and Kids is a London based organization that holds '2:1 Social Training Schemes' for learning disabled children and young adults at Christmas, Easter and during the summer, as well as organizing weekend and evening activities throughout the year. About 60 volunteers for each '2:1 Project' are engaged annually as well as a pool of approximately 80 volunteers for ongoing events. Volunteers are needed to help with all the above activities and also with the Kith and Kids summer camp and weekend outings. Applicants may be of any nationality; no special skills, qualifications or experience are needed, but they must be over 16 years of age.

Volunteers are needed all year round to help with ongoing events; the '2:1 Projects' last for 1-2 weeks. Expenses are paid. Applications should be sent to Sharon Schaffer.

MIND (National Association for Mental Health)
22 Harley Street, London W1 (tel 071-637 0741).

MIND has over 200 affiliated local mental health associations in England and Wales which work for improvements in the care of people with mental health problems. They organize day centres, employment projects, social clubs, sheltered accommodation and facilitate self-help groups, all of which rely to a large extent upon voluntary help. Making friends with people in the community is often the most important step to rehabilitation for people with mental health problems. Volunteers are also needed in MIND groups' 'Nearly New' clothing shops around the country, the proceeds of which are used to continue the work.

Although most of the tasks for volunteers require a long term commitment, occasionally short term projects are arranged. Depending on the resources of the local association, travelling expenses may be reimbursed. There are no restrictions on those wishing to volunteers. People who have experienced problems of mental distress in their own lives can bring particularly valuable insights to their voluntary work. Professional mental health workers, supporting and advising in a voluntary capacity also have an important role.

Inquiries may be sent to the Information Officer at the above address. There are also regional offices: WALES MIND, 23 St Mary Street, Cardiff CF 1 2AA; NORTHERN MIND, 158 Durham Road, Gateshead, Tyne and Wear NE8 4EL; NORTH WEST MIND, 21 Ribblesdale Place, Preston, Lancs PR1 3NA; TRENT AND YORKSHIRE MIND, First Floor Suite, The White Building, Fitzalan Square, Sheffield, S1 2AY; WEST MIDLANDS MIND, Princess Chambers, (3rd floor), (3rd floor), 52/54 Lichfield Street, Wolverhampton WV1 1DG; SOUTH WEST MIND, Bluecoat House, Saw Close, Bath, Avon BA1 1EY; SOUTH EAST MIND, 4th Floor, 24-32 Stephenson Way, London NW1 2HD.

Mobility Trust
4 Hughes Mews, 143A Chatham Road, London SW11 6HJ (tel 071 924-3597; fax 071 924-3938).

Mobility Trust is run on an entirely voluntary basis. It purchases, then offers on loan, specific pieces of equipment aiding mobility for the disabled such as powered wheelchairs, scooters and so forth. Anyone wishing to volunteer their services is welcome to apply, irrespective of age, race, colour and creed. Between seven and ten volunteers per year help in all facets of voluntary work with disabled people, including offering advice and counselling. A driving licence is an advantage, but is not essential. Most volunteers work for 2-3 months and sometimes longer. Expenses are paid.

Applications should be sent all the year round to Peter Mahon, the Director, at the above address.

Multiple Sclerosis Society of Great Britain and Northern Ireland
25 Effie Road, London SW6 1EE (tel 071-736 6267).

The Society operates over 360 local branches throughout the UK to provide a welfare service to suffering members and to raise funds both for welfare and for research into the causes and cure of multiple sclerosis. Volunteers can be of service in raising the morale of MS sufferers and providing friendship by visiting them and by arranging and funding excursions.

Enquiries to the General Secretary at the above address will be forwarded to the appropriate branch office.

Muscular Dystrophy Group of Great Britain and Northern Ireland
7-11 Prescott Place, London SW4 6BS (tel 071-720 8055; fax 071-498 0670).

The Muscular Dystrophy Group raises funds for medical research into these neuro-muscular conditions and offers practical advice and support to those people (and those families) affected by it. There are over 450 branches and representatives throughout the UK and Northern Ireland, all of whom are anxious for local helpers to assist in their fundraising and other activities.

Write to the Branch Services Manager at the above address for the details of local branches.

National Deaf-Blind Helpers' League
18 Rainbow Court, Paston Ridings, Peterborough PE4 6UP (tel 0733- 73511; fax 0733-325353).

The National Deaf-Blind League offers hope and support to deaf-blind people by working to improve social conditions, encouraging a spirit of confidence and providing counselling, guides and interpreters, particularly during sickness and hospitalization. The League has also built and manages accommodation for deaf-blind people and publishes a bi-weekly newspaper and a quarterly magazine. It also finances investigation into technical equipment and reading systems to enable the deaf-blind to communicate with each other and their sighted and hearing friends.

Anyone with a genuine concern for people with the double handicap of deafness and blindness, and time and energy to spare to help promote these activities, should contact the Chief Executive at the above address.

National Eczema Society
4, Tavistock Place, London WC1H 9RA (tel 071-388 4097).

This Society aims to promote mutual support for individuals and families coping with eczema. Volunteers are required to assist with the day to day running of the National Office and they may find themselves working within any of the Society's departments. Help is required all the year round. Both travel and lunch expenses are paid.

Those interested should contact Jackie Wynne, Office Administrator at the above address.

National Library for the Blind
Cromwell Road, Bradbury, Stockport, Cheshire SK6 2SG (tel 061-494 0217; fax 061-406 6728).

The Library is the only large general library lending books in braille free to the visually handicapped throughout the UK and abroad. In order to meet readers' needs, the Library welcomes volunteers who are welcome to learn the braille code and help in building up the Library's stock of current books. Good copy typists are also needed to transcribe from print onto magnetic disc for automatic brailling (experience with a word processor would be useful). Training and equipment is provided at no cost to the volunteer who should be able to devote a minimum of ten hours work per week to this demanding but rewarding work.

Those interested should contact the Director General at the above address.

Phab
12-14 London Road, Croydon CRO 2TA (tel 081-667 9443).

Phab works through social clubs and activities in which physically disabled and able bodies people work together on an equal basis in membership, management and programme issues. Phab also provides holidays and courses in which physically disabled and able bodied people live, work and play together. Volunteers can help with all aspects of these programmes by joining a local club.

For further information and details of local clubs contact the secretary of the Chief Executive at the above address.

Parkinson's Disease Society of the United Kingdon Ltd
22 Upper Woburn Place, London WC1H 0RA (tel 071-383 3513; fax 071-383 5754).
The aims of the society are threefold: to help patients and their relatives with the problems arising from Parkinson's Disease; to collect and disseminate information on the disease; and to encourage and provide funds for research into it. Voluntary workers provide vital assistance in the achievement of these aims; they assist at the national headquarters and run over 200 local branches. Helpers are especially desirable if they can assist in the setting up of new branches, as at present many voluntary workers are relatives of sufferers from the disease who already have many demands on their time. Drivers are always welcome at local branches, and

fuel costs are reimbursed where appropriate.

Enquiries should either be directed to the Office Manager at the above address, or to the Honorary Secretary of the local branch of the applicant.

Phoenix House
47-49 Borough High Street, London SE1 1NB (tel 071-407 2789; fax 071-407 6007).

Phoenix House is opening a new project called Fountain in April 1993 for illegal drug users who wish to become drug-free and who also have HIV or AIDS. The newly built project will have room for 36 beds, including 8 nursing home beds. Prior to opening, volunteers will be needed to help to see in new furniture and equipment when delivered.

When Fountain has opened, between five and ten volunteers would be needed at any one time to drive residents to and from hospital or clinic appointments, to talk to clients and to help with any activities. There is also a need for instructors in sport, literacy, alternative medicine and recreational pursuits such as art, drama or music. Applicants of any nationality will be welcome, but all applicants must have the ability to converse openly on issues such as bereavement, safer sex and drugs use. Training in counselling could be offered at a later date. Volunteers must be also be in excellent health and have no infections that could be passed on to clients whose immune systems are defeated. The minimum age limit is 18 years. Travel expenses will be paid.

Those interested should contact Annette Barratt at the above address.

Riding for the Disabled Association
Avenue 'R', National Agricultural Centre, Kenilworth, Warwickshire CV8 2LY (tel 0203-696510).

The aim of the Association is to provide the opportunity of riding to disabled people who might benefit in their general health and well-being. There are Member groups throughout the UK, whose voluntary helpers are drawn from many sources: Pony Clubs, Riding Clubs, the British Red Cross Society, Rotary Clubs, the Police Force, older school children, or simply responsible members of the community.

Prospective volunteers should contact a local Member Group directly. The list of Member Groups and a leaflet about the activities of the Association are available from the Director at the above address.

The Royal Association for Disability and Rehabilitation
25 Mortimer Street, London W1N 8AB (tel 071-637 5400).

The Association does not recruit volunteers directly, but can assist with information. Among its activities is the publication of a list of organizations which seek volunteers to help with holidays for disabled people.

Those interested should write to RADAR at the above address for the *Holiday Fact Sheet* enclosing a large stamped addressed envelope.

Royal Association in Aid of Deaf People (RAD)
27 Old Oak Road, Acton, London W3 7HN (tel 081-743 6187).

This association operates in the Greater London region, Essex, Kent and Surrey to promote the social, general and spiritual welfare of those who are deaf or both deaf and blind. RAD tries to enlarge their world by communicating ideas and knowledge to them which hearing people take for granted. Special work is also carried out for the deaf in psychiatric and handicapped hospitals. Social club meetings are held mainly in centres and clubs where special events such as bingo, billiards and drama evenings are organised. Volunteers help with special one-day excursion and longer holidays. Volunteers need to be in good health and willing to undertake the process of becoming fluent in sign language.

Enquiries may be sent to the Fundraising Co-ordinator at the above address.

Royal National Institute for the Blind (RNIB)

224 Great Portland Street, London WIN 6AA (tel 071-388 1266).

RNIB is Britain's largest organization helping blind and partially sighted people, and needs volunteers in many different areas of its work. For instance, in fundraising, by organizing or helping at local events in co-operation with your local appeals organizer. The schools need qualified or experienced help with swimming, riding, outings, etc. The cassette library needs volunteer readers to record books at home or in the RNIB studios. Volunteers are also needed to read books to students at university or at home. The Braille Department needs volunteers to transcribe a variety of books into braille. Volunteers must pass an exam in braille proficiency, and will need to spend a fair amount of time transcribing each book. Talking books are recorded by professional readers, but volunteers are needed to service the playback machines loaned to members. No great technical knowledge is necessary. Volunteers are recruited for an indefinite period of time. Expenses are paid.

Applications should be sent to the Director General at the above address.

Royal National Institute for the Deaf

105 Gower Street, London WClE 6AH (tel 071-387 8033).

The RNID is the major service providing organization for deaf people in the UK. Most of its work is highly specialized. However, approaches by volunteers with administrative or office skills are welcomed in national and local offices in London, Bath, Birmingham, Salford, Sunderland, Belfast and Glasgow. Offers of voluntary fundraising support are always appreciated. Volunteers hoping to work directly with deaf people should contact their local deaf club, details of which can be obtained from the RNID.

St John Ambulance

1 Grosvenor Crescent, London SW1 7EF (tel 071-235 5231).

The St John Ambulance Brigade is a body of 250,000 volunteers worldwide who give millions of hours of unpaid service every year providing first aid cover at public events and undertaking a variety of welfare work in the local community. Recruits are always welcome; the UK membership now numbers over 80,000. Children aged between 6 and 10 can join St John Ambulance as Badgers, and become Cadets from the age of 10 to 16 and thereafter adult members.

For further information about the Brigade, contact the local county office (details in local telephone directory) or the address above.

SCODA — The Standing Conference on Drug Abuse
1-4 Hatton Place, Hatton Garden, London EC1N 8ND (tel 071-430 2341).
SCODA is the national co-ordinating body for the drug abuse treatment field. As such it has information on local agencies which may use volunteers, and is able to pass this information on to interested parties.

For information on these local agencies please contact the above address.

Scottish Society for the Mentally Handicapped
13 Elmbark Street, Glasgow G2 4QA (tel 041-226 4541).
The Society concerns itself with all aspects of the welfare of people with learning disabilities. The main thrust of the Society's voluntary work is the organization of social and recreational activities through its local branches, of which there are at present 80 in Scotland. Most branches run clubs and similar activities and welcome volunteers able to give up some time on a fairly regular basis.

Opportunities for other forms of voluntary work are limited, and there are few opportunities to participate in holiday camps; these are organized through local branches.

Those interested in the care of people with learning disabilities in Scotland are welcome to contact the Director at the above address for further information.

The Stroke Association Volunteer Stroke Service
Manor Farm House, Appleton, Abingdon, Oxon OX13 5JR (tel 0865-862954).
The Volunteer Stroke Scheme is designed to help people who suffer from communication and associated problems as the result of a stroke. Volunteers are recruited to establish personal relationships with patients with the objective of helping them work towards improving their disabilities. This is done by using shared interests, games, puzzles and other simple methods to stimulate them and help the difficulties they have with language, memory and tasks such as the handling of numbers and money, telling the time, etc.

Volunteers are well directed and advised and need no special qualifications apart from a wish to help and a willingness to make a commitment.

There are schemes in over 120 Health Districts in the United Kingdom, each run by a paid part-time organizer and co-ordinated by Regional Organizers. All schemes are under the Direction of the National Administrator at the above address, from whom further information can be obtained.

Terence Higgins Trust
52-54 Gray's Inn Road, London WC12 8JU (tel 071-831 0330; fax 071-242 0121).
The Trust is the UK's largest AIDS charity and continues to expand to meet the many demands which AIDS and HIV infection present to all. It currently involves over 1,300 people, nearly half of whom are volunteers. They provide help, advice, information, support and training not only to people with AIDS and HIV infection but to anyone concerned about this health crisis. The Trust provides direct services in Greater London as well as sharing information and its expertise throughout the UK and Europe.

Approximately 50 new volunteers are engaged per month to help with a wide range of services. Volunteers are needed in London to work in areas of advice, counselling and administration. Volunteers may also work with the Drugs and Prisons services, the Helpline, or participate in the befiending scheme as a Buddy. Special skills amy be needed, but training is provided. Volunteers must be over 18 years and London-based. Lengths of placement vary; the training process can take a long time. The Trust pays travel expenses and office-based volunteers will receive luncheon vouchers.

Those interested should contact Peter Fraser at the above address.

Umbrella

St James House, 108 Hampstead Road, London NW1 2LS (tel 071-387 2026).

Umbrella is a special needs housing project which provides a variety of accommodation with different levels of care and support to people with long-term mental health problems. All its projects are a short distance from the head office at the above address and, as a specific community care organization, it operates only in that particular locality.

About 40 volunteers help at Umbrella at any one time with each having their own allocated supervizor from amongst the paid staff. Volunteers can get involved in direct client work in many different ways; as befrienders, social facilitators, teachers of daily living skills, providers, facilitators of access to community facilities, etc. There are also volunteer opportunities in the finance department and in the administration of the organization as a whole, with opportunities to learn computer skills. This type of work can cover anything from photocopying, filing, typing and wordprocessing to spreadsheets and super calc, depending on the volunteer's ability, willingness to learn and particular interests. Work with clients is possible in three different areas distinguished by the particular needs of clients; housing and social care, nursing care and residential care.

Applicants may be of any nationality, but a reasonable command of the English language is essential. Any previous criminal convictions must be disclosed and the organization rejects the right to reject candidates with particular convictions. Minimum period of work is at least a few months; this is not necessarily on a full-time basis. Volunteers are needed all the year round. All expenses incurred while on Umbrella business will be paid. Volunteers who can commit themselves to a minimum of 35 hours work per week also qualify for one day or £50 worth of training to be decided in consultation with their supervisor.

For further details, or for a copy of a Volunteer Information Pack, contact Beate Schumacher at the above address.

Unity Centre of South London

64 Ravenswood Road, Balham, London SW12 9PJ (tel 071-673 0793).

The Centre runs a telephone Helpline for those suffering from, or at risk of developing, mental illness. It also provides hostel accommodation and rehabilitation for those recovering from mental ill-health. Volunteers are required to supervise residents in the hostels, and to organize rehabilitative and recreational activities. Applicants of any nationality are welcome. All volunteers will receive appropriate training. Volunteers are needed all the year round, and the length of placement is flexible. Expenses are paid.

Those interested should contact Rev. Harry Kudiabor at the above address.

Other Non Residential Opportunities

The following organizations have been included in the Short Term Residential chapter but they also welcome non residential support.

Conservation Volunteers
— Northern Ireland
Festiniog Railway Company
National Autistic Society
National Trust — Northern Ireland
Otto Schiff Housing Association
Upper Nene Archaeological
Society

Queen Elizabeth's Foundation
for the Disabled
Ritchie Russell House Young
Disabled Unit
The Scottish Conservation
Projects Trust
The Simon Community(UK)
Stallcombe House

The Volunteer and Unemployment Benefit

One of the basic principles behind the payment of unemployment benefit in Great Britain is that it must only be given to those who are free to take up a job if one becomes available. The official line used to be that if someone was doing voluntary work then they were not available for work, and so should not receive any benefit. The official attitude has changed in recent years, as it has been realized that in times of high unemployment it does not achieve anything to bar those who have little chance of finding work from making constructive use of their time. Ultimately, what is permitted is at the discretion of the individual's Benefit Office, so people are advised to consult the sheet listed below for full details of their entitlement.

The situation now is that volunteers can claim unemployment benefit, provided they meet a few basic conditions. They must remain available either for a job interview or to begin work at 24 hours notice, and be actively seeking work. They are allowed to receive reasonable expenses, such as the payment of bus fares to wherever they will be helping. They can also receive pocket money of up to £2 per day.

People who are unemployed can also continue to receive benefit if they take part in a voluntary workcamp lasting for 14 days or less in Great Britain as long as they give their Benefit Office advance warning and the camp is run by either a charity or a local authority. The situation is less clear for those wanting to join a work camp abroad, as it is at the discretion of their Benefit Officer whether or not they will be allowed to continue claiming. The same basic principles as those listed above apply for people claiming income support except that they can only receive up to £4 per week in pocket money. Further information on how volunteers can claim a range of benefits is contained in *Information Sheet 4: Welfare Benefits*, which is available for £1.00 to people who send a stamped addressed envelope to the Volunteer Centre UK Advisory Team, 29 Lower Kings Road, Berkhamsted, Hertfordshire HP4 2AB.

Further Reading

Please note that many of the organizations featured in this book also produce their own literature: do not hesitate to contact them if you would like further information about their activities.

Archaeology Abroad: 31-34 Gordon Square, London WC1H OPY. produces three information bulletins a year on archaeological opportunities abroad for its members: send a stamped addressed envelope for details of membership.

Central Bureau for Educational Visits and Exchanges: Seymour Mews House, Seymour Mews, London W1H 9PE. Publish *Volunteer Work*, a guidebook to organizations recruiting for medium and long-term voluntary service in Britain abroad. Available in bookshops, price £7.99, or by post from the above address (add £1 for postage).

Christians Abroad: 1 Stockwell Green, London SW9 9HP.. Produce a series of leaflets about work abroad, especially voluntary work and openings through NGOs: send a stamped addressed envelope for details.

Christian Service Centre: Holloway Street West, Lower Gornal, Dudley, West Midlands DY3 2DZ. (tel 0902-882836). Publishes a book entitled *Jobs Abroad* twice a year that contains details of current long-term opportunities abroad of interest to Christians. Send £3.30 sterling for a year's subscription. Also publishes a book entitled *Time to Give* once every two years that contains details of current short-term opportunities (from two weeks to two years) of interest to Christians. Send £1.50 sterling for a copy of the current issue.

Co-ordinating Committee for International Voluntary Service: 1, Rue Miollis, 75015 Paris, France. Produce a leaflet giving brief details of organizations arranging voluntary workcamps around the world: available in exchange for 4 international reply coupons.

Council for British Archaeology: 112 Kennington Road, London SE11 6RE. Publishes *British Archaeological News* which carries advertisements for volunteer help on archaeological sites in Britain. This publication commences in January each year and comes out every two months thereafter. The annual subscription for 1992 was £10.50 for the UK; £11.50 for Europe; £12.00 for surfacemail outside Europe; £20.00 for airmail outside Europe. US$ also acceptable; send International Postal Reply Coupon for details.

Council on International Educational Exchange: 205 East 42nd Street, New York, NY 10017, USA. Publish a paperback entitled *Volunteer!* that gives details of short and medium term voluntary projects in the US and around the world. Published every two years, the edition for 1992-1993 costs $8.95.

Israel Antiquities Authority: P.O.Box 586, Rockefeller Museum, Jerusalem 91004, Israel. Publishes an annual guide to archaeological digs in Israel requiring help from volunteers: send an international reply coupon to the above address.

The National Youth Agency: 17-23 Albion Street, Leicester LE1 6GD. Publishes a list of voluntary work placements which gives details of residential voluntary work for young people in England and Wales. Price 50p, available from the above address.

Returned Volunteer Action: 1 Amwell Street, London EC1R 1UL. Publish a pamphlet entitled *Thinking about Volunteering*: send £1 plus a large SAE.

The Royal Association for Disability and Rehabilitation (Radar): 25 Mortimer Street, London W1N 8AB. Publishes a factsheet on organizations which seek volunteers to help with holidays for disabled people. Send an A5 SAE to the above address.

Vacation Work Publications: 9 Park End Street, Oxford OX1 1HJ. Publish a range of books covering both voluntary and paid work in Britain and around the world, including: *The Directory of Jobs and Careers Abroad*, *The Directory of Work and Study in Developing Countries*, *Kibbutz Volunteer*, *The Directory of Summer Jobs Abroad*, *The Directory of Summer Jobs in Britain* and *Work Your Way Around the World*. Send a stamped addressed envelope to the above address for a list of books and an order form.

The Volunteer Centre: 29 Lower King's Road, Berkhamsted, Herts. HP4 2AB. Produces a range of information sheets containing advice and information for both volunteers and voluntary organizations in Britain: Send a stamped addressed envelope for a list of these sheets.

Index of Organizations

260

261

Vacation Work also publish:

The Directory of Summer Jobs Abroad...£12.95
The Directory of Summer Jobs in Britain..............................£12.95
Adventure Holidays..£10.95
The Teenager's Vacation Guide to Work, Study & Adventure.............£9.95
Teaching English Abroad...£14.95
Work Your Way Around The World..£15.95
The Au Pair & Nanny's Guide to Working Abroad.........................£12.95
Working in Ski Resorts — Europe...£7.95
Kibbutz Volunteer..£8.95
The Directory of Jobs & Careers Abroad.......................................£15.95
The Directory of Work & Study in Developing Countries.................£10.95
Live & Work in France...£9.95
Live & Work in Germany..£11.95
Live & Work in Belgium, The Netherlands & Luxembourg...............£11.95
Live & Work in Spain & Portugal...£11.95
Live & Work in Italy..£10.95

Travel Titles (all softback)

Travellers Survival Kit: South America..£12.95
Travellers Survival Kit: Central America.......................................£8.95
Travellers Survival Kit: Cuba..£9.95
Travellers Survival Kit: USA & Canada...£9.95
Travellers Survival Kit: Europe..£6.95
Travellers Survival Kit: Soviet Union & Eastern Europe....................£8.95
Travellers Survival Kit to the East..£6.95
Travellers Survival Kit: Australia & New Zealand...........................£8.95
Hitch-hikers' Manual Britain..£3.95
Europe — a Manual for Hitch-hikers...£3.95
The Traveller's Picture Phrase-Book..£1.95

Distributors of (all softback):

Summer Jobs USA...£9.95
Internships (On-the-Job Training Opportunities in the USA)..............£15.95
The Directory of College Accommodations.....................................£5.95
Emplois d'Ete en France...£7.95
Jobs in Japan..£9.95
Teaching English in Asia...£8.95

Vacation Work Publications, 9 Park End Street, Oxford OX1 1HJ
(Tel 0865-241978. Fax 0865-790885)